E. Lütjen-Drecoll
Basic Aspects of Glaucoma Research III

34-00

Schriftenreihe der

# Akademie der Wissenschaften und der Literatur, Mainz

Mathematisch-naturwissenschaftliche Klasse
Kommission für Humanforschung
und Kommission für Alternsforschung

Herausgegeben von
**E. Lütjen-Drecoll**
und
**J. W. Rohen**

**Mainz 1993**

# Basic Aspects
# of Glaucoma Research III

International Symposium held at the Department of Anatomy
University of Erlangen-Nürnberg, FRG,
September 23-25, 1991

Edited by
**E. Lütjen-Drecoll**

With 128 Figures and 29 Tables

 **Schattauer**

Stuttgart –
New York 1993

This book was supported by the Bundesministerium für Forschung und Technologie, Bonn, and the Bayerische Staatsministerium für Wissenschaft und Kunst, München, and generously sponsored by Alcon Laboratories Inc., Fort Worth, Texas, USA.

Die Deutsche Bibliothek — CIP-Einheitsaufnahme

**Basic aspects of glaucoma research** : international symposium held at the Department of Anatomy, University of Erlangen-Nürnberg, FRG, ... — Stuttgart ; New York : Schattauer.
(Schriftenreihe der Akademie der Wissenschaften und der Literatur, Mainz, Mathematisch-Naturwissenschaftliche Klasse, Kommission für Humanforschung und Kommission für Alternsforschung)
NE: Anatomisches Institut &lt;Erlangen&gt;

3. September 23 — 25, 1991. — 1993
ISBN 3-7945-1571-4

© 1993 by Akademie der Wissenschaften und der Literatur, Mainz. Printed in Germany
Satz: Ahorn GmbH Satz + Bild, 6837 St. Leon-Rot 1;
Druck: Rheinhessische Druckwerkstätte GmbH, 6508 Alzey

Gedruckt auf säurefreiem, chlorfrei gebleichtem Papier

ISBN 3-7945-1571-4

# Contents

## II Ciliary epithelium

## III Trabecular Meshwork

*Physiology*

*Biochemistry*

## IV Clinical Aspects

# List of contributors

ALVARADO, JORGE A.
  Cellular Pharmacology Laboratory, Department of Ophthalmology, University of California, Medical Center, 10 Kirkham Street, San Francisco, CA 94143, USA
BILL, ANDERS
  Department of Physiology and Medical Biophysics, Uppsala Universitet, Biomedicum, Box 572, S-751 23 Uppsala, Sweden
BLOOM, ERNEST
  Cellular Pharmacology Laboratories, Department of Ophthalmology, University of California Medical Center, 10 Kirkkam Street, San Francisco, CA 94143, USA
BUDDECKE, ECKART
  Institut für Physiologische Chemie, Westfälische Wilhelms-Universität, Waldeyerstr. 15, 4400 Münster, West Germany
DE KATER, ANNELIES W.
  Southwestern Medical Center, Department of Ophthalmology, University of Texas, 5323 Harry Hines Blvd., Dallas, TX 75235, USA
EPSTEIN, DAVID D.
  Department of Ophthalmology, Duke University Eye Center, Durham, NC 27710, USA
ERICKSON-LAMY, KRISTINE A.
  Howe Laboratory of Ophthalmology, Harvard Medical School, Massachusetts Eye & Ear Infirmary, 243 Charles Street, Boston, MA 02114, USA
FAUSS, DONALD J.
  Cellular Pharmacology Laboratories, Department of Ophthalmology, University of California Medical Center, 10 Kirkham Street, San Francisco, CA 94143, USA
FAY, FREDRIC S.
  Bio. Imaging Group, University of Massachusetts, Medical School, Worcester, MA, USA
GABELT, B'ANN T.
  Department of Ophthalmology, F4/338 Clinical Science Center, University of Wisconsin, Medical School, 600 Highland Avenue, Madison, WI 53792, USA
GAO, HUA
  Cullen Eye Institute, Baylor College of Medicine, One Baylor Plaza, Houston, Texas 77030, USA
GIPSON, ILENE K.
  Eye Research Institute of Retina Foundation, 20 Staniford Street, Boston, MA 02114, USA
HELBIG, H.
  Freie Universität Berlin, Universitätsklinikum Steglitz, Institut für Klinische Physiologie, Hindenburgdamm 30, 1000 Berlin 45, West Germany
HERNANDEZ, ROSARIO M.
  The Eye Research Institute, Harvard Medical School, 20 Staniford Street, Boston, MA 02114, USA
HOLLYFIELD, JOE G.
  Cullen Eye Institute, Baylor College of Medicine, One Baylor Plaza, Houston, Texas 77030, USA
HOOSHMAND, LEILA
  Howe Laboratory of Ophthalmology, Harvard Medical School, Massachusetts Eye & Ear Infirmary, 243 Charles Street, Boston, MA 02114, USA
HUANG, WEIDONG
  Cellular Pharmacology Laboratory, Department of Ophthalmology, University of California Medical Center, 10 Kirkham Street, San Francisco, CA 94143, USA
JIKIHARA, SHIUCHI
  Department of Ophthalmology, Gifu University, School of Medicine, Tsukasa-Machi 40, Gifu 500, Japan

KATZ, MARTIN L.
Department of Ophthalmology, School of Medicine, University of Missouri-Columbia, Mason Institute of Ophthalmology, One Hospital Drive, Columbia, MO 65212, USA

KAUFMAN, PAUL L.
Department of Ophthalmology, F4/338 Science Center, University of Wisconsin, Medical School, 600 Highland Avenue, Madison, WI 53792, USA

KLEIMAN, NORMAN J.
College of Physicians & Surgeons, Columbia University, Department of Ophthalmology, 630 West 168th Street, New York, NY 10032, USA

KITAZAWA, YOSHIAKI
Department of Ophthalmology, Gifu University, School of Medicine, Tsukasa-Machi 40, Gifu 500, Japan

KORBMACHER, C.
Freie Universität Berlin, Universitätsklinikum Steglitz, Institut für Klinische Physiologie, Hindenburgdamm 30, 1000 Berlin 45, West Germany

KURTZ, RON M.
Cellular Pharmacology Laboratories, Department of Ophthalmology, University of California Medical Center, 10 Kirkham Street, San Francisco, CA 94143, USA

LEPPLE-WIENHUES, A.
Freie Universität Berlin, Universitätsklinikum Steglitz, Institut für Klinische Physiologie, Hindenburgdamm 30, 1000 Berlin 45, West Germany

LÜTJEN-DRECOLL, ELKE
Anatomisches Institut II, Universität Erlangen-Nürnberg, Universitätsstr. 19, 8520 Erlangen, West Germany

LUI, GE MING
Cellular Pharmacology Laboratories, Department of Ophthalmology, University of California Medical Center, 10 Kirkham Street, San Francisco, CA 94143, USA

NGUYEN, THAI D.
Cellular Pharmacology Laboratory, Department of Ophthalmology, University of California Medical Center, 10 Kirkham Street, San Francisco, CA 94143, USA

POLANSKY, JON R.
Cellular Pharmacology Laboratory, Department of Ophthalmology, University of California, Medical Center, 10 Kirkham Street, San Francisco, CA 94143, USA

PREHM, PETER
Institut für Physiologische Chemie, Westfälische Wilhelms-Universität, Waldeyerstr. 15, 4400 Münster, West Germany

REDDY, VENKANT N.
Eye Research Institute, Oakland University, 422 Dodge Hall, Rochester, Michigan 48309-4401, USA

ROBINSON, JAMES C.
Department of Ophthalmology, F4/338 Clinical Science Center, Universtity of Wisconsin, Medical School, 600 Highland Avenue, Madison, WI 53792, USA

ROHEN, JOHANNES W.
Anatomisches Institut II, Universität Erlangen-Nürnberg, Universitätsstr. 19, 8520 Erlangen, West Germany

SCHROEDER, ALISON
Howe Laboratory of Ophthalmology, Harvard Medical School, Massachusetts Eye & Ear Infirmary, 243 Charles Street, Boston, MA 02114, USA

SPECTOR, ABRAHAM
College of Physicians & Surgeons, Columbia University, Department of Ophthalmology, 630 West 168th Street, New York, NY 10032, USA

SPERBER, GÖRAN O.
Department of Physiology and Medical Biophysics, Uppsala Universitet, Biomedicum, Box 572, S-75123 Uppsala, Sweden

STAHL, F.
Freie Universität Berlin, Universitätsklinikum Steglitz, Institut für Klinische Physiologie, Hindenburgdamm 30, 1000 Berlin 45, West Germany

STREETEN, BARBARA W.
Department of Pathology, State University of New York, Health Science Center, College of Medicine, 750 East Adams Street, Syracuse, NY 13210, USA

VON DER MARK, KARL
Institut für Experimentelle Medizin, Universität Erlangen-Nürnberg, Schwabachanlage 10, 8520 Erlangen, West Germany

WANG, LIN
Department of Physiology and Medical Biophysics, Uppsala Universitet, Biomedicum, Box 572, S-751 23 Uppsala, Sweden

WIEDERHOLT, MICHAEL
Freie Universität Berlin, Universitätsklinikum Steglitz, Institut für Klinische Physiologie, Hindenburgdamm 30, 1000 Berlin 45, West Germany

WOLLENSAK, JOSEF
Universitäts-Augenklinik, Spandauer Damm 130, 1000 Berlin 19, West Germany

YAMAMOTO, TETSUYA
Department of Ophthalmology, Gifu University, School of Medicine, Tsukasa-Machi 40, Gifu 500, Japan

# Introductory remarks

This symposium was organized to celebrate the 70th birthday of Prof. Johannes Rohen. We are particularly thankful that so many outstanding scientists have come to Erlangen in order to honor my revered teacher who had made so many basic contributions to the subjects discussed in this symposium.

The main intention of the present symposium was to discuss the age-related changes within the *entire* eye, bringing together specialists working either on age-related changes of connective tissue in general or on changes in the different ocular regions. In this way, we hoped that we could produce a broad survey of what is known today about ageing processes in *all* ocular tissues. In Helsinki, at the occasion of the IXth ISER-Congress we had already discussed some of these problems in a symposium on "ageing and non-ageing-processes". The concept emerging from that meeting was that age-related changes within the eye vary greatly from tissue to tissue and that the time-course for the ageing processes seems to depend more on the functional significance than on the absolute age of the individual tissue. The present symposium also follows this line. The papers presented here, show that the ageing processes "follow different rules" in different regions of the eye, so that the picture as a whole is heterogeneous and variable.

It is well established that *chronic simple glaucoma* is a disease of older age. The relationship between normal ageing processes and glaucomatous changes is still not sufficiently clarified, particularly whether glaucoma represents solely a pronounced ageing process or a true disease that is only enhanced by the normal age-related tissue changes. This question applies to the posterior as well as to the anterior segment of the eye and certain aspects of glaucoma pathophysiology. Nevertheless, resolution of these questions requires that the structural and functional changes of the tissues in the *entire* eyeball with increasing age be thoroughly studied, before the specific changes occuring with the development of the glaucoma disease can be recognized as such.

E. Lütjen-Drecoll

*Department of Ophthalmology, Free University of Berlin*

# Structure, metabolism and function of proteoglycans of the eye

E. BUDDECKE and J. WOLLENSAK

## 1. General composition and structure of proteoglycans

Proteoglycans are a rapidly expanding and heterogenous family of macromolecules which play a multitude of key roles in the normal physiology of cells and tissues. Disturbances in the metabolism can produce a variety of pathological changes. In animal tissues the near ubiquitous distribution of proteoglycans both on plasma membranes of cells and in the extracellular matrix means that they are strategically positioned to regulate the interactions between cells and their microenvironment. The progress in our understanding of the structure and function of proteoglycans has been recently reviewed (HASSELL et al. 1986; WIGHT and MECHAM 1987; EVERED and WHELAN 1986; POOLE 1986).

In spite of their heterogeneity proteoglycans share a common structural characteristic: they contain a protein backbone, to which a various number of glycosaminoglycan side chains and N- and O-linked oligosaccharides are covalently attached. Where the chemical composition of the glycosaminoglycan side chains is well known for a long time, the core protein of proteoglycans is a less well studied component of these macromolecules. The complete core protein sequence has so far been established for only a few proteoglycans (RUOSLAHTI 1989).

Classification of proteoglycans according of the type of the glycosaminoglycan side chains shows that there is a great variety in the type and the number of glycosaminoglycan chains attached to the protein core. Chondroitin sulfate, dermatan sulfate, heparan sulfate, keratan sulfate and heparin have been identified as glycosaminoglycan moiety of proteoglycans (POOLE 1986). The chemical composition of glycosaminoglycans and their linkage to the core protein are schematically shown in Table 1. The number of glycosaminoglycan side chains is ranging from 1–2 chains in the dermatan sulfate containing proteoglycan of skin (DAMLE et al. 1982; GLÖSSL et al. 1984) up to 100 glycosaminoglycan side chains in the large chondroitin sulfate and keratan sulfate containing proteoglycan of cartilage (HEINEGÅRD and AXELSSON 1977). While the relative molecular mass of the glycosaminoglycan side chains is in the order of 15 to 60 kD, the molecular weight of the protein core exhibits differences between about 40 and 400 kD (POOLE 1986). This heterogeneity is exemplified in Table 2.

Table 1: Schematic structure of proteoglycans and hyaluronate. CS, chondroitin sulfate; DS, dermatan sulfate; HS, heparan sulfate; KS (I), keratan sulfate (cornea); KS (II), keratan sulfate (cartilage); HA, hyaluronate; 2/4/6-SO$_3^-$, 2–, 4–, 6-sulfate ester groups; ( ), not regulary present substituents.

| GAG Type | Glycosaminoglycan (GAG) | Carbohydrate – Protein Linkage Region | Protein |
|---|---|---|---|
| CS | — GlcA β1,3 GalNAc β1,4 [GlcA β1,3 GalNAc β1,4]$_n$ , 4/6SO$_3^-$ | β1,4 GlcA β1,3 Gal β1,3 Gal β1,4 Xyl β | Ser |
| DS | — IdoA α1,3 GalNAc β1,4 [GlcA β1,3 GalNAc β1,4]$_n$ , (2SO$_3^-$) 4/6SO$_3^-$ | β1,4 GlcA β1,3 Gal β1,3 Gal β1,4 Xyl β | Ser |
| HS | — GlcA / IdoA β1,4 GlcN α1,4 [GlcA β1,4 GlcNAc α1,4]$_n$ , 6SO$_3^-$ (2SO$_3^-$) SO$_3^-$/Ac | α1,4 GlcA β1,3 Gal β1,3 Gal β1,4 Xyl β | Ser |
| KS (I) | — Gal β1,4 GlcNAc [(6SO$_3^-$) Gal β1,3 GlcNAc β1,4]$_n$ , 6SO$_3^-$ | β1,2 Man α1,6 \ Man β1,4 GlcNAc β1,4 GlcNAc β ; β1,2 Man α1,3 / | Asn |
| KS (II) | — Gal β1,4 GlcNAc [(6SO$_3^-$) Gal β1,3 GlcNAc β1,4]$_n$ , 6SO$_3^-$ | β1,3 Gal β1,4 GlcNAc β1,6 GalNAc α ; NeuAc α2,3 Gal 1β1,3 Gal | Ser (Thr) |
| HA | — GlcNAc β1,4 GlcUA [GlcNAc β1,4 GlcUA β1,3]$_n$ | ? | |

Table 2: Macromolecular properties of proteoglycans from various sources (compiled from ref. 1–4). (HASSELL et al. 1986; WIGHT and MECHAM 1987; EVERED and WHELAN 1986; POOLE 1986)

| Source | Molecular weight (kDa) | Type and Number of GAG chains | | Molecular weight Protein core (kDa) |
|---|---|---|---|---|
| Pig laryngeal cartilage | $2-3 \times 10^3$ | CS<br>KS | > 100<br>30–60 | 400 |
| Bovine skin | ~ 170 | DS | 1 | 38 |
| Bovine aorta | ~ 190 | DS/CS | 3–4 | 38 |
| Bovine cornea | 100 – 150 | DS/CS | 1 | 40 |
| Basement membrane | 130 – 256 | HS | 4–5 | 90–170 |
| Hum. skin fibroblasts | ~ 170 | DS | 3 | 38 |
| Arterial smooth muscle cells | ~ 200 | HS | 3–4 | 48 |

## 2. Proteoglycan biosynthesis

The biosynthesis of proteoglycans involve the coordination of protein synthesis with co- and posttranslational modifications which take place in different intracellular compartments and in a specific chronological sequence (for review see HASSELL et al. 1986; WIGHT and MECHAM 1987; POOLE 1986).

The major stages of biosynthesis are as follows: the core protein of proteoglycan is assembled in the rough endoplasmatic reticulum, where co-translationally N-linked high mannose containing oligosaccharides were transferred via dolicholdiphosphate intermediates to asparagine residues of the core protein. The assembly of O-linked oligosaccharides, the processing of N-linked oligosaccharides and the addition of chondroitin sulfate, heparan sulfate, heparin and keratan sulfate chains, take place in the Golgi apparatus. The key intermediates for the chain elongation of glycosaminoglycans are UDP-N-acetylglucosamine, UDP-N-acetylgalactosamine, UDP-galactose, UDP-glucuronic acid and phophoadenelylsulfate which are transferred to the growing glycosaminoglycan chains by specific glycosyltransferases and sulfotransferases. Late posttranslational modifications during the proteoglycan biosynthesis in the medial/trans Golgi apparatus are the epimerization of glucuronic acid to iduronic acid which converts chondroitin sulfate into dermatan sulfate, the sulfation of glycosaminoglycan chains and trimming and extention of oligosaccharides.

After intracellular synthesis and sorting the proteoglycans are packaged into secretory vesicles and sectreted into the extracellular matrix. Other proteoglycans remain associated or are integrated into the cell membrane. Table 3 gives an overview on the major stages of proteoglycan biosynthesis and their compartimentalization.

Table 3: Major stages in the biosynthesis of non-aggregating proteoglycans.

| Intracellular Site | Event |
| --- | --- |
| • Rough endoplasmic reticulum (Pre-Golgi compartment) ↓ | • Translation of protein core<br>• Co-translational attachment of N-linked oligosaccharides<br>• Attachment of xylose (?)<br>• Phosphorylation of Ser (and˙ Xyl) residues |
| • Cis-Golgi cisternae ↓ | • Glycosaminoglycan chain (chondroitin) polymerisation<br>• 6-sulfation |
| • Medial/Trans Golgi cisternae ↓ | • Epimerisation of GlcA —> IdoA<br>• 4-sulfation<br>• Trimming and extension of oligosaccharides<br>• Sulfation of tyrosine residues |
| • Secretory vesicles | • Packaging and sorting |

## 3. Proteoglycans of the eye

Proteoglycans has been found in all ocular tissues. They are located either at the cell surface or are constituents of the extracellular matrix or basement membranes but data on the macromolecular and biochemical characteristics and functions of proteoglycans are available preferably from experimental animals. However, many findings on the properties of proteoglycans and the known or suspected functions of proteoglycans may be generalized and probably apply also to the human visual

organ. Table 4 gives some examples for the localization and function of proteoglycans of the eye.

Table 4: Localization of glycosaminoglycans and function of proteoglycans of ocular tissues.

| Localisation | Type of glycosaminoglycan | Function |
|---|---|---|
| Corneal Stroma | Dermatan sulfate Chondroitin sulfate Keratan sulfate | Interaction with collagen fibrils |
| Corneal Endo- thelial Cells | Heparan sulfate Chondroitin sulfate | Cell-matrix interaction Inhibition of proliferation |
| Descemet Membrane | Heparan sulfate | Interaction with membrane proteins |
| Trabecular Meshwork | Chondroitin sulfate Dermatan sulfate Keratan sulfate Heparan sulfate | Aqueous humour outflow resistance barrier (?) |
| Vitrous Body | Hyaluronate | Water binding |
| Retinal Photo- receptor Cells | Chondroitin sulfate Dermatan sulfate Heparan sulfate | Cell-matrix interaction, Retinal development, Synaptogenesis (?) |
| Retinal Pigment Epithelium | Chondroitin sulfate Heparan sulfate | Cell adhesion, Interphotoreceptor matrix |

## 4. Corneal stroma

Corneal stroma proteoglycans have been isolated from oxen (AXELSSON and
HEINEGÅRD 1980; GREILING and STUHLSATZ 1966), rabbit (FUNDERBURGH and
CHANDLER 1989; GREGORY et al. 1982), embryonic chicken (MIDURA et al. 1989;
MIDURA and HASCALL 1989), and rhesus monkey (HASSELL et al. 1979; NAKAZAWA
et al. 1983) and are partially characterized with respect to the macromolecular and
biochemical properties.

In mammalian cornea two major proteoglycan populations of small molecular
size were identified (HASSELL et al. 1979): a proteoglycan with hybrid chondroitin
sulfate/dermatan sulfate chains which are O-glycosidically linked to a protein core
with a molecular weight of 100-150 kD and one chondroitin sulfate/dermatan sulfate side chain. The other proteoglycan contained two keratan sulfate side chains
with an overall size of 100 kD.

From normal human cornea two predominant proteoglycans were obtained.
One proteoglycan had an overall mass of 150 kD, 2 dermatan sulfate chains (Mr ~

50000) with an iduronic acid content of 24 % – 28 % and a core protein of 48 kD. The other proteoglycan had an overall size of 110 kD, one keratan sulfate chain of ~ 60 kD and a core protein of 46 kD. Each proteoglycan population was further fractionated into two subpopulations by chromatography on Concanavaline A Sepharose (WOLLENSAK and BUDDECKE 1990).

The hydrodynamic size of the corneal proteoglycans permit them to fit well within the space between the regular lattice of defined domains of collagen fibrils. An interaction of proteglycans with specific domains of collagen maintains and stabilizes the orderly packing of collagen fibrils and guarantees optical transparency and mechanical properties. The dermatan sulfate containing proteoglycan interacts preferably with the d- and e-band of collagen fibrils while the keratan sulfate containing proteoglycan is located predominantly at the a- and c-band of collagen (SCOTT 1988). The self-aggregation of dermatan sulfate chains may increase the stabilizing function of proteoglycans on the collagen fibril network.

Alteration of the structure or in the metabolism of corneal proteoglycans leads to an impaired function of the cornea. Biochemically characterized examples are the macular corneal dystrophy, the mucopolysaccharidoses and the keratoconus.

### Macular corneal dystrophy

Macular corneal dystrophy is an inherited disorder that is clinically characterized, in part ,by the accumulation of opaque deposits in the corneal stroma. The basic defect is an error in the synthesis of keratan sulfate that results from a metabolic failure to process the precursor molecule into the mature proteokeratan sulfate (NAKAZAWA et al. 1984). An unsulfated glycoconjugate with polysaccharide chains similar in size to the normal keratan sulfate chains is formed. This indicates that a specific sulfotransferase involved in the sulfation of the lactosaminoglycan backbone of the chains is missing (Fig.1). The unusual unsulfated macromolecule is not able to interact with collagen fibrils and leads to an opaqueness composed predominantly of fine needle-shaped polychromatic crystals.

### Mucopolysaccharidoses

Corneal macular dystrophy is distinctly different from the mucopolysaccharidoses. Abnormalities in patients with macular dystrophy are limited to the cornea while in patients with mucopolysaccharidoses a large number of tissues are affected. The mucopolysaccharidoses are clinically progressive heriditary disorders characterized by the accumulation of incompletely degraded glycosaminoglycans in the lysosomes of various tissues including cornea. The mucopolysaccharidoses are

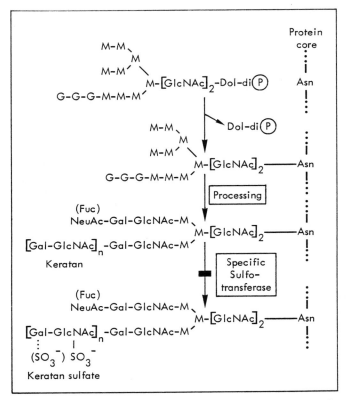

Fig. 1. Processing of proteokeratan sulfate precursor to the mature proteokeratan sulfate. Bar indicates the possible block of biosynthesis in macular corneal dystrophy.

lysosomal storage diseases in which specific glycosidases or sulfatases essential to degradation of glycosaminoglycans are deficient (for review see STANBURY et al. 1983). The accumulation of undegraded glycosaminoglycans in lysosomal bodies leads to a clouding of cornea especially in the mucopolysaccharidoses types where the catabolism of dermatan sulfate (type I H, I S, and VI) or keratan sulfate (type IV) is disturbed (KRESSE et al. 1987).

## Keratoconus

Keratoconus is an ocular disease of unknown etiology characterized by progressive alterations of the corneal shape accompanied by a thinning of the corneal tissue. In the development of keratoconus decreased resilience and low mechanically strength of corneal tissues seems to be important pathogenetic factors, but the basic molecular defect is unknown. The biochemical alterations of corneal stroma components in keratoconus are compiled in Table 5. Comparative studies in collagen types I, III, IV, V in normal and keratoconic cornea revealed neither differences in amino acid composition and type and number of crosslinks nor changes in the distribution and specific immunostaining of the various collagen types. BUDDECKE and WOLLENSAK 1966 found an increased hexosamine and decreased sulfate content in keratoconic cornea. Further comparative studies on the proteoglycans of normal and keratoconic cornea revealed that the dermatan sulfate and keratan sulfate containing proteoglycans isolated form keratoconus cornea and from healthy cornea had comparable molecular weight values and core proteins with identical molecular weights (WOLLENSAK and BUDDECKE 1990). However, the ratio of dermatan sulfate/keratan sulfate proteoglycans was increased in keratoconus cornea and the keratan sulfate chains of keratoconus keratan sulfate proteoglycans were considerably shorter (Mr 54kD, 33kD) than those of normal corneas (Mr 58 kD and 60 kD). FUNDERBURGH et al. 1989 extracted normal and keratoconus human corneas and assayed the extract for keratan sulfate and for the protein core of corneal keratan sulfate proteoglycan using a solid-phase immunoassay. There was no significant difference in the amount of keratan sulfate core protein antigens in keratoconus and normal corneal extracts but the keratan sulfate chains from keratoconus cornea contained only an average of 48 % as much keratan sulfate antigen as normal corneal extracts when assayed with anti-keratan sulfate monoclonal antibodies. These results suggest that corneas with keratoconus contain a form of proteokeratan sulfate that contains fewer keratan sulfate chains or in which the keratan sulfate has a modified structure.

## 5. Endothelial cells

Corneal endothelial cells are known ro regulate permeability and transport processes of electrolytes, water and metabolites and to maintain normal corneal hydratation and transparency by a constant removal of fluid from the corneal stroma. Although the mechanism of the transporting ion pump system has been the subject of several reports (for review see RILEY 1982), little is known about the biosynthesis and the chemical composition of Descemet's membrane which is formed by the endothelial cells and separates them from the underlaying corneal stroma. Normal morphology and thickness of the Descemet's membrane is dependent on a continuous monolayer of metabolically active endothelial cells.

Immunohistological studies have indicated that proteoheparan sulfate, laminin, type IV collagen, fibronectin and entactin (HASSELL et al. 1980; NEWSOME et al. 1981; PISTSOV et al. 1988) are integral components of Descemet's membrane, but their biochemical characterization is still incomplete. The proteoheparan sulfate

Table 5: Biochemical alterations of cornea stroma components in keratoconus.

| Structural component | Alteration in keratoconus | References |
|---|---|---|
| Proteoglycans | Increased hexosamine and decreased sulfate content | Buddecke & Wollensak, 1966 |
| | Fewer keratan sulfate (KS) chains or modified structure of KS (altered KS epitopes) | Funderbourgh et al., 1989 |
| | Shorter keratan sulfate chains, increased ratio DSPG/KSPG | Buddecke & Wollensak, 1990 |
| Collagen | Normal distribution of collagen types I, III, IV, V, VI, and VII (including cells and membrans) | Zimmerman et al., 1988 |
| | No change in the crosslinking pattern of collagen, no differences in amino acid composition | Oxlund & Simonsen, 1985 |
| Glycoproteins, Proteins | Two abnormal bands (54 and 26 kDa) in electrophoresis Some normal bands in higher or reduced amount | Pangwani et al., 1989 |
| | Elevated amounts of cell membrane associated glycoconjugates with Glc/Man residues and terminal Gal and GalNAc residues | Yue et al., 1988 |
| | Increased level of protein, uronic acid and neutral hexose, one abnormal non-collagenous component (75 kDa) | Critchfield et al., 1988 |

has received special attention since it was found to be an ubiquitous constituent of mammalian cell surfaces (HÖÖK et al. 1984) and an integral component of cell and basement membranes in a variety of tissues including eye (HASSELL et al. 1980). Cell surface proteoheparan sulfate is thought to be involved in cell-cell and cell-matrix adhesion and regulation of cell growth (GALLAGHER 1986).

A study on cultured bovine corneal endothelial cells revealed that they synthesize two proteoheparan sulfate species. One is found associated with the cells while the other is secreted into the culture medium. The proteoheparan sulfate secreted into the medium has a molecular weight of about 300 kD and a molecular weight of its protein core of 64 kD, while the native cell-associated proteoheparan sulfate has a lower molecular weight ($<$ 150 kD) and a molecular weight of its protein core of 33 kD.

There are also differences in the molecular weight of the heparan sulfate side chains. The heparan sulfate moiety released from the proteoheparan sulfate of the culture medium has a molecular weight of about 60 kD that of the cell-associated proteoheparan sulfate a molecular weight of about 30 kD (WOLLENSAK et al. 1990).

The growth of human corneal endothelial cells in tissuse culture is severely limited compared with that of bovine or rabbit corneal endothelial cells (BAUM et al. 1979; VAN HORN and HYNDIUK 1973; VAN HORN et al. 1978). Although culturing of human corneal endothelial cells has been achieved (YUE et al. 1989), long term serial cultivations has generally been limited only to the endothelial cells from human donors 20 years and younger (NAYAK and BINDER 1984). This could be due to an age-dependent increase in the production of an endogenuous antiproliferatively active proteoheparan sulfate by human endothelial cells which effectively binds and immobilizes endogenuous growth factors and mitogenes (GOSPODARO-WICZ et al. 1977; BASHKIN et al. 1989; SCHWEIGERER et al. 1987). The growth promoting effect on cultured endothelial cells of high concentrations of chondroitin sulfate (13.5 – 25 µg/ml) must be considered to be an unspecific effect (BOURNE 1988).

## 6. Trabecular meshwork

The trabecular meshwork in the anterior chamber is the major site for the regulation of aqueous humour outflow (YUE et al. 1988; SEILER and WOLLENSAK 1985). This specialized connective tissue is composed of sheets of trabecular meshwork beams. Lining the beams are trabecular meshwork cells that can produce extracellular matrix material including proteoglycans (ROHEN and LÜTJEN-DRECOLL 1982; TAWARA et al. 1989; ACOTT et al. 1988; SCHACHTSCHABEL et al. 1982; ROBEY et al. 1988; ACOTT et al. 1985). The distribution of proteoglycans in trabecular tissue of human and animal eyes was evaluated by histochemical and biochemical methods.

Human corneal-scleral explants may be maintained for several weeks under organ culture conditions in a metabolically active form (ACOTT et al. 1988). In the presence of [$^{35}$S]sulfate or [$^3$H]glucosamine the glycosaminoglycans of trabecular meshwork can be obtained in radiolabelled form and quantified by sequential enzymatic degradation. Hyaluronate, chondroitin sulfate, dermatan sulfate and heparan sulfate have been identified as glycosaminoglycan components (SCHACHT-SCHABEL et al. 1982).

After staining the proteoglycans with cupromeronic blue at critical electrolyte concentration the proteoglycans can be visualized under electron microscopy allowing for their precise localization at the ultrastructural level (TAWARA et al. 1989). From these studies it was concluded that the sulfated proteoglycans present in human trabecular meshwork tissue consist principally of heparan sulfate, dermatan sulfate and chondroitin sulfate containing proteoglycans (Table 6). In the extra-

Table 6: Distribution of proteoglycans in the human trabecular tissue (TAWARA et al. 1989).

| Compartment | Proteoglycan type | | |
| --- | --- | --- | --- |
| | Chondroitin sulfate | Dermatan sulfate | Heparan sulfate |
| Collagen fibrils | + | + | − |
| Basal Lamina[a] | − | − | + |
| Fine fibrillar-like material | + | + | + |

[a] and basal lamina-like material

cellular matrix of the trabecular tissue chondroitin sulfate and dermatan sulfate proteoglycans are associated with collagen fibrils. Chondroitin sulfate proteoglycans are randomly arrayed around the collagen fibrils while dermatan sulfate proteoglycans are usually associated with the d- or e-band of collagen fibrils. Heparan sulfate proteoglycan is present in associaton with the basal lamina and displaced basal lamina-like material. Chondroitin sulfate, dermatan sulfate and heparan sulfate, all are present in the fine fibrillar-like material. Basal lamina, basal lamina-like material and fine fibrillar-like material may play an important role in establishing aqueous outflow resistance with juxtacanicular connective tissue.

Although the identity of the components in the trabecular meshwork responsible for resistance to aqueous outflow are not known, the glycosaminoglycans have been discussed to be implicated by the report that outflow resistance was reduced by hyaluronidase (VAN BUSKIRK and BRETT 1978; KNEPPER et al. 1984). This effect, however, was observed only in bovine (BÁRÁNY and SCOTCHBROOK 1954) and rabbit (VAN BUSKIRK and BRETT 1978; KNEPPER et al. 1984) trabecular meshwork, but not in higher primates (GRIERSON, LEE and ABRAHAM 1979) and may be explained by the fact, that the action of testicular hyaluronidase is restricted to the hydrolysis of β 1 – 4 glycosidic linkages between N-acteylglucosamine and glucuronic acid in hyaluronate and chondroitin 4- and 6-sulfate, while iduronic acid containing dermatan sulfate and 1 – 4 glycosidic linkages in heparan sulfate are resistant to hyaluronidase.

## 7. Vitreous body and aqueous humour

The vitreous body is a specialized connective tissue which has two basic functions: (a) to serve as a transparent medium which occupies the major volume of the globe, (b) to absorb and redistribute forces applied to surrounding ocular tissues.

These properties are established by a highly viscous gel which is composed of a collagen framework interspersed with hydrated hyaluronate molecules (BERMAN and VODEN 1970).

Hyaluronate resembles the other glycosaminoglycans in so far that it is a linear polymer which consists of repeating disaccharide units (see Table 1), but it differs from the proteoglycans by two characteristics (a) it is a protein-free polysaccharide that has not been shown to be covalently linked to protein and (b) it is synthesized at the cell membrane (PREHM 1983) by a mechanism which is completely different from that of proteoglycans. Hyaluronate is synthesized from UDP-glucuronic acid and UDP-N-acetyl-glycosamine by a membrane integrated hyaluronate synthase. The chain elongation takes place by addition of sugar to the reducing end (PREHM 1984).

Studies on eye tissue have shown that hyaluronate disappears from the vitreous body by diffusion and from the anterior chamber by the regular flow of the aqueous humour. In spite of the low concentrations of hyaluronate in the aqueous humour (LAURENT 1983) the total amount of hyaluronate that is turned over in the anterior chamber is larger than that in the vitreous body, indicating a significant synthesis of hyaluronate in the anterior segment (LAURENT and FRASER 1983; LAURENT and GRANATH 1983).

The function of the hyaluronate entrapped in the collagen scaffold can be described as a mechanical coupling of the load-supporting collagen fibrils with an energy storing and energy dissipating hyaluronate (BALAZS and GIBBS 1970). The primary mechanical stress is supported by the collagen fibrils but then a large part of energy is transferred to the visco-elastic macromolecules for storage and dissipation through the frictional coupling of these two network elements.

## 8. Neural retinal cells

Photoreceptor cells, interneurons and ganglion cells are cellular elements of the retina. As part of the nerve system they all are permanent cells and unable to divide. There is, however, a steady turnover and a continuous renewing of their constituents. The neural retina cells form a functional unit. Establishing of connections betweeen the photoreceptor and the other retina cells occurs during embryogenesis and depends on a variety of cell recognition processes which include cell-cell and cell-matrix interactions. In these processes cell adhesion molecules and proteoglycans are involved. One of the best studied examples are the embryonic chick neural retina cells which synthesize proteoglycans and secrete them partially into the interphotoreceptor matrix or integrate them into the plasma

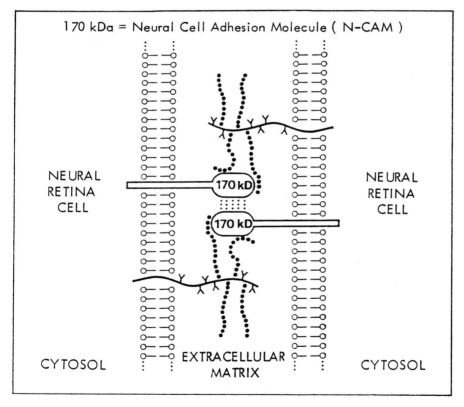

Fig. 2. Cell – cell interaction of neural retina cells. Interaction of cell-associated heparan sulfate with neural cell adhesion molecules (170 kD) facilitates homophilic binding between neural cell adhesion molecules (modified from COLE et al. 1986, Nature *230*: 445 – 447).

membrane (HEWITT 1986). While chondroitin sulfate containing proteoglycans were found almost entirely within the extracellular matrix, most of proteoheparan sulfate was associated with either the plasma membrane or the basal lamina (MORRIS et al. 1987; THRELKELD et al. 1989). The retina cells interact with another by the neural cell adhesion molecules (SCHUBERT and LA CORBIERE 1985; COLE et al. 1985) and proteoheparan sulfate (COLE and GLASER 1986; COLE et al. 1986). The neural cell adhesion molecule (N-CAM) is a multifunctional glycoprotein with a molecular weight of 170 kD (Fig. 2). It is anchored in the lipid bilayer of the retina cells and contains several binding domains: the heparan sulfate binding domain of N-CAM (Mr about 25 kD) may interact with the cell membrane integrated proteoheparan sulfate. This binding to the proteoheparan sulfate results in a conformational change of the N-CAM molecule which then leads to a homophilic binding between two N-CAM molecules (COLE et al. 1986; BURG and COLE 1990). A heparan sulfate proteoglycan that copurifies with the N-CAM molecule has been partially characterized (COLE and BURG 1989).

The N-CAM is a component of adherons which are particles of 15 nm diameter in electron microscopy. Another component of adherons is the purpurin (SCHUBERT and LA CORBIERE 1986) which is secreted by embryonic chick neural retinal cells and promotes the cell-adheron adhesion by interacting with the cell surface proteoheparan sulfate. In addition purpurin has the ability to bind retinol and has 50% sequence homology with human serum retinol binding protein.

The visual process is characterized by an intermitted influx of $Na^+$ ions from the extracellular space into the outer segment of the rod cells via sodium channels (dark) and a photon-induced closing of the $Na^+$ channels (light). The intracellular $Na^+$ flows out again into the extracellular compartment from the inner segments of the rod cells. The recycling of sodium ions requires a sufficient $Na^+$ pool and a permanent extracellular sodium transport from the inner to the outer segment. The highly charged rod cell membrane associated proteoheparan sulfate could fulfill this function and would facilitate the extracellular transport of sodium ions from the inner to the outer segment.

## 9. Pigment epithelium cells

In the course of the turnover of cell constituents the photoreceptor membrane disc proteins are synthesized at a rate of 3-4/h. The older discs are diplaced toward the pigment epithelium cells which endocytose and degrade debris of the photoreceptor cells. This explains the close connection and cooperation between photoreceptor and pigment epithelial cells. Human retina pigment epithelial cells synthesize proteoglycans containing chondroitin sulfate and heparan sulfate. In culture these cells exhibit a polarity with regard to the size and types of proteoglycans secreted apically into the medium and deposited basically onto the substratum. Retina pigment epithel cells from donors with dominant retinitis pigmentosa show alterations in deposition of proteoglycans particulary with regard to those that are associated to the cell surface (HEWITT and NEWSOME 1988).

## Conclusions

The proteoglycans of the ocular tissue share the general characteristics of proteoglycans from other sources. They contribute not only to the organization of the extracellular matrix but are also present at the cell surface. A number of functions can be proposed for the extracellular and the cell membrane associated proteoglycans of the eyes including: (a) interaction with extracellular matrix molecules, formation of basement membrane and control of extracellular transport processes, (b) regulation of cell proliferation, (c) participation in cell-cell interactions and regulation of cell substrate adhesions. All functions appear to be essential for maintaining the high degree of order and transparency of ocular tissues, for regulation of the intraocular pressure and for the physiological process of light perception. Further studies will provide a more detailed picture of the structure and function of proteoglycans of the eye.

## References

ACOTT, T. S., P. D. KINGSLEY, J. R. SAMPLES, E. M. VAN BUSKIRK, E. M. (1988): Human trabecular meshwork organ culture: Morphology and glycosaminoglycan synthesis. Invest. Ophthalmol. Vis. Sci. 29, 90 – 100.

ACOTT, T. S., M. WESTCOTT, M. S. PASSO, E. M. VAN BUSKIRK (1985): Trabecular meshwork glycosaminoglycans in human and cynomolgus monkey eye. Invest. Ophthalmol. Vis. Sci. 26, 1320 – 1329.

AXELSSON, I. and D. HEINEGÅRD (1980): Characterization of chondroitin sulfate-rich proteoglycans from bovine corneal stroma. Exp. Eye Res. 31, 57 – 66.

BALAZS, E. A. and D. A. GIBBS (1970): The rheological properties and biological function of hyaluronic acid. In: BALAZS, E. A. (Ed.): Chemistry and molecular biology of the intercellular matrix, Vol. 3 pp. 1241 – 1253, Academic Press, London and New York.

BÁRÁNY, E. H., S. SCOTCHBROOK (1954): Influence of testicular hyaluronidase on the resistance to flow through the angle of the anterior chamber. Acta Physiol. Scand. 30, 240 – 248.

BASHKIN, P., S., DOCTROW, M. KLAGSBRUN, C. M. SVAHN, J. FOLKMAN, I. VLODAVSKY (1989): Basic fibroblast growth factor binds to subendothelial extracellular matrix and is released by heparitinase and heparin-like molecules. Biochemistry 28: 1737 – 1743.

BAUM, J. L., R. NIEDRA, C. DAVIS, B. Y. J. T. YUE (1979): Mass culture of human corneal endothelial cells. Arch. Ophthalmol. 97: 1136.

BERMAN, E. R., M. VODEN (1970): The vitreous body, In: C. N. GRAYMORE (Ed.): Biochemistry of the eye, pp. 373 – 472, Academic Press, London, New York.

BOURNE, W. M. (1988): The endothelial cell assay method for the evaluation of corneal preservation. In: The cornea: Transactions of the world congress on the cornea III, edited by H. D. CAVANAGH. Raven Press, Ltd., New York.

BUDDECKE, E., J. WOLLENSAK (1966): Saure Mucopolysaccharide und Glykoproteine der menschlichen Cornea in Abhängigkeit vom Lebensalter und bei Keratoconus. Graefe's Arch. klin. exp. Ophthal. *171*: 105–120.

BURG, M., G. J. COLE (1990): Characterization of cell-associated proteoglycans synthesized by embryonic neural retinal cells. Arch. Biochem. Biophys. *276*: 396–404.

COLE, G. J., M. BURG (1989): Characterization of the heparan sulfate proteoglycan that copurifies with the neural cell adhesion molecule. Exp. Cell Res. *182*: 44–60.

COLE, G. J., L. GLASER (1986): A heparin-binding domain from N-CAM is involved in neural cell-substratum adhesion. J. Cell Biol. *102*: 403–412.

COLE, G. J., A. LOEWY, L. GLASER (1986): Neuronal cell-cell adhesion depends on interactions of N-CAM with heparin-like molecules. Nature *320*: 445–447.

COLE, G. J., D. SCHUBERT, L. GLASER (1985): Cell-substratum adhesion in chick neural retina depends upon protein-heparan sulfate interactions. J. Cell Biol. *100*: 1192–1199.

DAMLE S. P., L. CÖSTER, J. D. GREGORY (1982): Proteodermatan sulfate isolated from pig skin. J. Biol. Chem. *257*: 5523–5527.

EVERED, D., J. WHELAN (Eds.) (1986): Function of the proteoglycans. John Wiley & Sons.

FUNDERBURGH, J. L., J. W. CHANDLER (1989): Proteoglycans of rabbit corneas with nonperforating wounds. Invest, Ophthalmol. & visul Sci. *30*: 435–441.

FUNDERBURGH J. L., N. PANJWANI, G. W. CONRAD, J. BAUM (1989): Altered keratan sulfate epitopes in keratoconus. Invest. Ophthalmol. Vis. Sci. *30*: 2278–2281.

GALLAGHER, J. T. (1986): Structure and function of heparan sulfate proteoglycans. Bioch. J. *236*: 313–325.

GLÖSSL, J., M. BECK,H. KRESSE (1984): Biosynthesis of proteodermatan sulfate in cultred human fibroblasts. J. Biol. Chem. *259*: 14144–14150.

GOSPODAROWICZ, D., A. L. MESCHER, C. R. BIRDWELL (1977): Stimulation of corneal endothelial cell proliferation in vitro by fibroblast and epidermal growth factors. Exp. Eye Res. *25*: 75–89.

GREGORY, J. D., L. CÖSTER, S. P. DAMLE (1982): Proteoglycans of rabbit corneal stroma. J. Biol. Chem. *257*: 6965–6970.

GREILING, H., H. W. STUHLSATZ (1966): Struktur und Stoffwechsel von Glykosaminoglykan-Proteinen, I: Die Keratansulfat-Peptide der Rinder Cornea. Hoppe-Seylers' Z. Physiol. Chem. *345*: 236–248.

GRIERSON, I., W. R. LEE, S. ABRAHAM (1979): A light microscopic study of the effects of testicular hyaluronidase on the outflow system of the baboon (papio cynocephalus). Invest. Ophthalmol. Vis. Sci. 18: 356–360.

HASSELL, J. R., J. H. KIMURA, V. C. HASCALL (1986): Proteoglycan core protein families. Annu. Rev. Biochemistry *55*:, 539–554.

HASSELL, J. R., D. A. NEWSOME, V. C. HASCALL (1979): Characterization and biosynthesis of proteoglycans of corneal stroma from rhesus monkey. J. Biol. Chem. *254*: 12346–12354.

HASSELL J. R., P. G. ROWEY, H. J. BARRACH, J. WILCZEK, S. I. RENNARD, G. R. MARTIN (1980): Isolation of a heparan sulfate-containing proteoglycan from basement membrane. Proc. Natl. Acad. Sci. 77: 4494–4498.

HEINEGÅRD, D. K., I. AXELSSON (1977): Distribution of keratan sulfate in cartilage proteoglycans. J. Biol. Chem. *252*: 1971–1979.

HEWITT, A. T. (1986): Extracellular matrix molecules: Their importance in the structure and function of the retina. In: R. ADLER , D. FARBER (Eds.): The retina: A model for cell biology, pp. 169–214, Academic Press, Orlando.

HEWITT, A. T., D. A. NEWSOME (1988): Altered proteoglycans in cultured human retinitis pigmentosa retinal pigment epithelium. Invest. Ophthalmol. Vis. Sci. 29: 720–724.

HÖÖK, M., L. KJELLEN, S. JOHANSSON, J. ROBINSON (1984): Cell surface glycosamoniglycans. Annu. Rev. Biochem. *53:* 847–869.

KNEPPER, P. A., A. I. FARBMAN, A. G. TELSER (1984): Exogenous hyaluronidases and degradation of hyaluronic acid in rabbit eye. Invest. Ophthalmol. Vis. *Sci.* 25: 286.

KRESSE, H., M. CANTZ, K. V. v. FIGURA, J. GLÖSSL, E. PASCHKE (1987): The mucopolysaccharidoses: Biochemistry and clinical symptoms. Klin. Wschr. *59:* 867.

LAURENT, U. B. G. (1983): Hyaluronate in human aqueous humour. Arch. Ophthalmol. *101:* 129 – 130.

LAURENT, U. B. G., J. R. E. FRASER (1983): Turnover of hyaluronate in the aqueous humour and vitreous body of the rabbit. Exp. Eye Res. *36:* 493 – 504.

LAURENT, U. B. G., K. A. GRANATH (1983): The molecular weight of hyaluronate in the aqueous humour and vitreous body of rabbit and cattle eye. Exp. Eye Res. *36:* 481 – 492.

MIDURA, R. J., HASCALL, V. C. (1989): Analysis of the proteoglycans synthesized by corneal explants from embryonic chicken II. J. Biol. Chem. *264;* 1423 – 1430.

MIDURA, R. J., O. M. S. TOLEDO, M. YANAGISHITA, V. C. HASCALL (1989): Analysis of the proteoglycans synthesized by corneal explants from embryonic chicken I. J. Biol. Chem. *264:* 1414 – 1422.

MIOZZO, M. C., E. R. LACOSTE, J. A. CURTINO (1989): Characterization of the proteoglycan fraction non-extractable from retina by trichloroacetic acid. Biochem. J. *260:* 287 – 289.

MORRIS, J. E., M. YANAGISHITA, V. C. HASCALL (1987): Proteoglycans synthesized by embryonic chicken retina in culture: Composition and Compartmentalization. Arch. Biochem. Biophys. *258:* 206 – 218.

NAKAZAWA, K., J. R. HASSELL, V. C. HASCALL, L. S. LOHMANDER, D. A. NEWSOME, J. KRACHMER (1984): Defective processing of keratan sulfate in macular corneal dystrophy. J. Biol. Chem. *259:* 13751 – 13757.

NAKAZAWA, K., J. R. HASSELL, V. C. HASCALL, D. A. NEWSOME (1983): Heterogeneity of proteoglycans in monkey corneal stroma. Arch. Biochem. & Biophys. *222:* 105 – 116.

NAYAK, S. K., P. S. BINDER (1984): The growth of endothelium from human cornea in tissue culture. Invest. Ophthalmol. Vis. Sci. *25:* 1213 – 1219.

NEWSOME, D. A., J. M. FOIDART, J. R. HASSELL (1981): Detection of specific collagen types in normal and keratoconus cornea. Invest. Ophthalmol. Vis. Sci. *20:* 738.

PISTSOV, M. Y., E. Y. SADOVNIKOVA, S. M. DANILOV (1988): Human corneal endothelial cells: Isolation, characterization and longterm cultivation. Exp. Eye Res. *47:* 403 – 414.

POOLE, A. R. (1986): Proteoglycans in health and disease: structure and functions Biochem. J. *236:* 1 – 14.

PORRELLO, K., D. YASUMURA, M. M. LaVAIL (1989): Immunogold localization of chondroitin 6-sulfate in the interphotoreceptor matrix of normal and RCS rats. Invest. Ophthalmol. Vis. Sci. *30:* 638 – 651.

PREHM, P. (1983): Synthesis of hyaluronate in differentiated keratocarcinoma cells. Characterization of the synthetase. Mechanism of chain growth. Biochem. J. *211:* 181 – 198.

PREHM, P. (1984): Hyaluronate is synthesized at plasma membranes. Biochem. J. *220:* 597 – 600.

RILEY, M. (1982): Transport of ions and metabolites across the endothelium. In: Cell Biology of the Eye, edited by D. MCDEWITT, pp. 53 – 95, Academic Press, New York.

ROBEY, P. G., J. A. KIRSHNER, C. E. CUMMINS III, E. J. BALLINTINE, M. M. RODRIGUES, D. E. GAASTERLAND (1988): Synthesis of glycoconjugates by trabecular meshwork of glaucomatous corneoscleral explants. Exp. Eye Res. *46:* 111 – 115.

ROHEN, J. W., E. LÜTJEN-DRECOLL (1982): Biology of the trabecular meshwork. In: LÜTJEN-DRECOLL, E. (Ed.): Basis aspects of glaucoma research, Schattauer-Verlag, Stuttgart.

RUOSLAHTI, E. (1989): Proteoglycans in cell regulation. J. Biol. Chem. *264:* 13369 – 13372.

SCHACHTSCHABEL, D. O., K. WILKE, R. WEHRMANN (1982): In vitro cultures of human and monkey trabecular meshwork. In: E. LÜTJEN-DRECOLL (Ed.): Basic aspects of glaucoma research, F. K. Schattauer Verlag, Stuttgart-New York.

SCHUBERT, D., M. LaCORBIERE (1985): Isolation of a cell-surface receptor for chick neural retina adherons. J. Cell Biol. *100:* 56 – 63.

SCHUBERT, D., M. LaCORBIERE, F. ESCH (1986): A chick neural retina adhesion and survival molecule is a retinol-binding protein. J. Cell Biol. *102:* 2295 – 2301.

SCHWEIGERER, L., N. FERRARA, T. HAAPARANTA, G. NEUFELD , D. GOSPODAROWICZ (1987): Basic fibroblast growth factor: Expression in cultured cells derived from corneal endothelium and lens epithelium. Exp. Eye Res. *46:* 71 – 80.

SCOTT, J. E. (1988): Proteoglycan-fibrillar collagen interactions Biochem. J. *252:* 313 – 323.

SEILER, T., J. WOLLENSAK (1985): The resistance of the trabecular meshwork to aqueous humour outflow . Graefe's Arch. Clin. Exp. Ophthalmol. *223:* 88 – 91.

STANBURY, J. B., J. B. WYNGAARDEN, D. S. FREDERICKSON, J. L. GOLDSTEIN, M. S. BROWN (Eds.) (1983): The metabolic basis of inherited disease. Mc Graw-Hill, New York.

TAWARA, A., H. H. VARNER, J. G. HOLLYFIELD (1989): Distribution and characterization of sulfate proteoglycans in the human trabecular tissue. Invest. Ophthalmol. Vis. Sci. *30:* 2215 – 2231.

THRELKELD, A., R. ADLER, A. T. HEWITT (1989): Proteoglycan biosynthesis by chick embryo retina glial-like cells. Developmental Biology *132:* 559 – 568.

VAN BUSKIRK, E. M., J. BRETT (1978): The canine eye: In vitro dissolution of the barriers to aqueous outflow. Invest. Ophthalmol. Vis. Sci. *17:* 258.

VAN HORN, D., R. A. HYNDIUK(1973): Endothelial wound repair in primate cornea. Exp. Eye Res. *21:* 113 – 124.

VAN HORN, D., R. A. HYNDIUK, S. SEIDEMAN, P. J. BUCO, J. DE BRUIN (1978): Endothelial regeneration in cornea: a comparative study in rabbit and cat. In: Proceedings of Scanning Electron Microscopy, part *5:* 285 – 290.

WIGHT, T. N. and R. P. MECHAM (Eds.) (1987): Biology of proteoglycans. Academic Press, New York, London.

WOLLENSAK, J., E. BUDDECKE (1990): Graefe's Arch. Ophthalmology *228,* 517 – 523.

WOLLENSAK, J., A. SCHMIDT, E. BUDDECKE (1990): Two different proteoheparan sulfate species are synthesized by bovine corneal endothelial cells. Exp. Eye Res. *51,* 287 – 293.

YUE, B.Y. J.T., J. SUGAR, J. E. GILBOY, J. L. ELVART (1989): Growth of human corneal endothelial cells in culture. Invest. Ophthalmol. Vis. Sci. *30:* 248 – 253.

YUE, B.Y. J.T., A. KUROSAWA, J. L. ELVART, V. M. ELNER, M. O. M. TSO (1988): Monkey trabecular meshwork cells in culture: growth, morphologic, and biochemical characteristics. Graefe's Arch. Clin. Exp. Ophthalmol. *226:* 262 – 268.

*Institut für Physiologische Chemie und Pathobiochemie, Münster*

# Cellular functions of hyaluronate

P. Prehm

## Introduction

Until recently, hyaluronate was thought to serve as a relatively inert scaffolding that stabilizes the physical structure of tissues. But now it is clear that it plays a far more active role in regulating the behaviour of cells that contact it – influencing their development, migration, proliferation, shape, and metabolic functions. It is widely distributed in the matrix and secreted by local cells, especially fibroblasts.

Karl Meyer isolated hyaluronate from vitreous humor in 1934 (MEYER and PALMER 1934) and found it in many other connective tissues such as synovial fluid, umbilical cord, skin and rooster comb (MEYER 1947). Streptococci are also able to produce the polysaccharide (KENDALL et al. 1937). Hyaluronate has unique physio-chemical properties among the extracellular macromolecules. The linear polymer exhibits high shear – dependent viscosity and reaches a molecular mass of several millions. The molecular diameter of an expanded random core is larger than 500 nm (LAURENT 1970). In the connective tissue it regulates flow resistance and water balace, interacts with other proteins to stabilize the structures and acts as a lubric-ant (COMPER and LAURENT 1978).

Hyaluronate influences many physiological processes including angiogenesis (WEST et al. 1985); phagocytosis (DARZYNKIEWICZ and BALAZS 1971; FORRESTER and BALAZS 1971; FORRESTER and BALAZS 1980); chondrogenesis (TOOLE et al. 1972), wound healing (WEIGEL et al. 1986) and myogenesis (KUJAWA et al. 1986). Extracellular hyaluronate can modify cell growth (GOLDBERG and TOOLE 1987; WEST and KUMAR 1989 b), aggregation (UNDERHILL 1982) and migration (PRATT et al. 1975; Hakansson & Venge 1985; Partsch et al. 1989). It inhibits its own synthesis (SMITH and GHOSH 1987) and the synthesis of proteoglycans (HANDLY and LOWTHER 1976; BANSAL et al. 1986; SOLURSH et al. 1974; WIEBKIN and MUIR 1977).

These effects depend greatly on three factors: the size, the concentration and the cell type. The way by which hyaluronate affects cell behaviour is via interaction with proteins in the extracellular matrix or with cell surface receptors.

In order to understand these functions it is necessary to analyze the cellular com-ponents which synthesize, retain and release hyaluronate and the factors which modulate these processes.

## Hyaluronate synthesis

Hyaluronate synthesis is altered during morphogenesis, differentiation, transformation and the cell cycle.

Morphogenesis was extensively studied in the chick embryo which develops in a programmed manner. In the early stages mesodermal cells proliferate producing large amounts of hyaluronate. In the subsequent stages of mesodermal condensation the cells differentiate into chondrocytes and myocytes carrying hyaluronate receptors on the cell surface. These receptors mediate endocytosis of hyaluronate which is then degraded (Toole et al. 1989).

Differentiation of F9 teratocarcinoma cells into endodermal cells is accompanied by hyaluronate induction (Prehm 1980) and collagen type IV and laminin stimulation (Prehm et al. 1982). During fusion of myoblasts hyaluronate synthesis and hyaluronate is lost from the cell surface (Angello and Hauschka 1979; Orkin et al. 1985).

Transformation of fibroblasts or chondrocytes usually enhances hyaluronate production dramatically. This was already recognized by Kabat (1939) who isolated hyaluronate from tumors of sarcosis and leukosis. Viral transformation by RSV stimulates hyaluronate production in chondrocytes (Mikuni-Takagaki and Toole 1979), in chick fibroblasts (Hamerman et al. 1965; Ishimoto et al. 1966) and myoblasts (Yoshimura 1985). SV40 transformation induces a similar increase in 3T3 fibroblasts (Hopwood and Dorfman 1977; Goldberg et al. 1984). In fact hyaluronate production correlates with the invasiveness and metastatic potential of tumors (Toole et al. 1979).

However, in most tumors the transformed cell itself does not produce hyaluronate but induces the surrounding stroma (Knudson et al. 1984; 1989). The responsible factors are still unknown. Tumor cells can also stimulate hyaluronate synthesis in coculture with smooth muscle cells (Iozzo et al. 1989) or fibroblasts (Knudson et al. 1984). Similarly, leukocytes stimulate synovial fibroblasts (Yaron and Castor 1969).

Many factors have been shown to stimulate hyaluronate synthesis (Table 1). They are either growth or differentiation factors acting on a specific target cell. Although the precise mechanism of activation is not known, growth factors may exert the effects through general activation of the cell cycle. Proliferating cells produce more hyaluronate than resting cells (Hronowski and Anastassiades 1980;Tomida et al. 1975). But there are also other routes which influence hyaluronate synthesis. Treatment of fibroblasts with hyaluronidase activated the synthase (Philipson et al. 1985). Whether this signal is transduced by intracellular messengers, is debatable. We observed that the synthase was even stimulated on isolated membranes, when nascent chains were dissociated by salt treatment (Prehm, unpublished ). Since thermodynamics do not allow indefinite chain growth of a polymer, nascent hyaluronate could also feed back on its own elongation just by virtue of its chain length.

Synchronized fibroblasts show highest hyaluronate production during mitosis, because hyaluronate synthesis is required for detachment and mitosis of fibroblasts. This was shown by blocking the synthesis in synchronized cells just before mitosis (BRECHT et al. 1986). These experiments were made possible after a new class of inhibitors, periodate oxidized nucleotide sugars, has been designed and introduced into living cells (PREHM 1985). Hyaluronate synthesis has also been correlated with cell migration (TOOLE 1972) and was found in large amounts together with fibronectin in substratum adhesion plaques of migrating cells (LARK and CULP 1982).

Hyaluronate could serve similar functions in all these cellular processes, namely disruption of adhesive plaques or cell contacts. A basal level of synthesis during the $G_1$, S and $G_2$ phases could enable cell migration, if it were synthesized at the trailing edge of a migrating cell. During mitosis the synthesis could be activated at all cellular contact areas and result in cell detachment and rounding. Hyaluronate synthesis could be a general detachment mechanism of dividing and migrating cells. This hypothesis is supported by detachment variants of chinese hamster cells which produce more or less hyaluronate (BARNHART et al. 1979; KRAEMER and BARNHART 1978).

## Mechanism of synthesis

Hyaluronate was the first polysaccharide to be synthesized from the precursors UDP-GlcNac and UDP-GlcA in a cell extract (GLASER and BROWN 1955). However, it took some 30 years – longer than for most other polysaccharides – to propose a mechanism for the synthesis.

A soluble and particulate form of the enzyme was found in the vitreous (OESTERLIN and JACOBSON 1968 a, b; OESTERLIN 1968 1969; JACOBSON 1978 a, b). The synthase was also characterized in particulate fractions of fibroblasts (APPEL et al. 1979). A promising approach was the analysis of streptococcal protoplast membranes (MARCOWITZ and DORFMAN 1962; STOOLMILLER and DORFMAN 1969; SUGAHARA et al. 1979), but a satisfying model for chain assembly could not be established from these investigastions.

It was experimentally difficult to prove that hyaluronate did not contain covalently bound protein (MASON et al. 1982). Previous claims were based on metabolic spillover or radioactive leucine-label into the glycocyamine moiety (FRASER and BAXTER 1984). We were able to disprove a secret assumption that hyaluronate is synthesized like other proteoglycans. First, hyaluronate is not a proteoglycan. It deserves however the decoration "honorary proteoglycan" after several decades of unification. Second, its synthesis differs from other polysaccharides in many aspects. We have shown that membranes of differentiated teratocarcinoma cells synthesized hyaluronate by alternate transfer of UDP-hyaluronate to the substrates UDP-GlcNac and UDP-GlcA. The hyaluronate chain is glycosylated at the reducing end substituting its UDP-moiety by one of the substrates (Fig. 1) (PREHM 1983 a, b).

The unconventional mechanism of synthesis made another secret dogma questionable: that all extracellular polysaccharides are assembled in the Golgi apparatus. Initial doubts have been raised by streptococci which managed to produce hyaluronate without any intracellular organelles.

Indeed, PHILIPSON and SCHWARTZ (1984) demonstrated that the synthase resided in plasma membranes of a chondrosarcoma cell line. At the same time I demonstrated that nascent hyaluronate is susceptible to extracellular degradation by hyaluronidase (PREHM, 1984). Therefore, hyaluronate is synthesized through the plasma membrane (Fig. 2). Whether there are holes conducting the chains into the matrix, is unknown. Gap junctional proteins could possibly serve this function.

These results raised a new scenario for the dynamics of the extracellular matrix. The membrane intercalated synthase elongates hyaluronate which in turn can be bound by many other matrix components such as cartilage proteoglycans (HARDINGHAM and MUIR 1972 1973 1974), fibronectin (ISEMURA et al. 1982) or fibrinogen (LeBOEUF et al. 1986).

## The synthase

The identification and isolation of the synthase was again hindered by many experimental fences. It is not abundant in plasma membranes and inactivated upon disintegration of membranes with many detergents. MIAN (1986 a, b) tried to dissolve plasma membranes with NP-40 and obtained an enzymatically active extract which was further purified chromatographically to yield a complex of proteins with molecular weights of 116, 84, 66 and 55 kD. This complex was identified by its binding activity for the labelled precursors and not by its enzymatic activity. We have shown that nucleotide sugars bind to many membrane proteins and concluded that this approach was not appropriate to isolate an enzyme which has lost its activity (PREHM 1989).

NG and SCHWARZ (1989) dissolved plasma membranes with digitonin which preserved the activity. After several steps of chromatographic fractionation a single protein of $M_r = 58$ Kd was isolated. We took another approach, because we found it too cumbersome to obtain sufficient material from eukaryotic membranes. Streptococci contain a synthase activity in their protoplast membranes with 100-fold higher activity than plasma membranes. The synthase could be solubilized in active form by digitonin or cholate (TRISCOTT and VAN DE RIJN 1986).

The streptococcal synthase was identified by binding to radioactive affinity labels as a 52 kD protein (PREHM and MAUSOLF 1986). The synthase was active in a cholate extract and was inhibited by antibodies against the 52 kD protein. Growing streptococci shed the synthase together with hyaluronate into the culture media (MAUSOLF et al. 1990). This may have important implications for streptococcal infections. Streptococci may cause rheumatic fever, an autoimmune disease elicited by cross-reactive antigens, because the antibodies against the 52 kD protein cross-reacts with a plasma membrane protein (PREHM 1989).

The synthase activity appears to be regulated at multiple levels (PREHM 1989). It is activated after viral transformation by phosphorylation at tyrosine residues. In addition the enzyme is induced at the transcriptional level. Furthermore its activity can be regulated by the substrate concentrations and the competitive inhibitor ATP. In chondrosarcoma cells the synthase is rapidly turned over with a half life of two hours (BANSAL and MASON 1986). Finally elongation is inhibited by nascent chains (PHILIPSON et al. 1985).

## Hyaluronate binding proteins

Two major classes of hyaluronate binding proteins have been described. The first class is composed of hyaluronate-binding proteoglycans and link proteins that aggregate with hyaluronate to form cartilage (HASCALL 1977). Related proteins have also been detected in brain (CRAWFORD 1988; RIPELLINO et al. 1988; MARKS et al. 1990; BIGNAMI et al. 1989) and on glial cells (PERIDES et al. 1989). Immunological methods have identified another hyaluronate binding protein on brain, hyaluronectin, which is also related to proteoglycan (DELPECH and HALAVENT 1981; DELPECH et al. 1989). Even lymphoid cell lines express a binding protein which has been identified as CD44 or Pgp-1 (MIYAKI et al. 1990; LESLEY et al. 1990). This protein was known to be involved in leukocyte adherence and T-cell activation (HYANES et al. 1989).

A second class of hyaluronate binding proteins occurs in plasma membranes of serveral cell types. Two unrelated proteins have been detected on 3T3 and SV3T3 cells, a 85 kD plasma membrane-bound glycoprotein (UNDERHILL et al. 1985 1987) and a 60 kD protein (TURLEY et al. 1987). The 85 kD protein transverses the membrane and binds to actin filaments (LACY and UNDERHILL 1987). It is preferentially expressed on proliferating cells (ALHO and UNDERHILL 1989). A serum binding protein of the same molecular weight has recently been detected which is not identical with the cell surface protein (YONEDA et al. 1990). The 60 kD protein is concentrat-

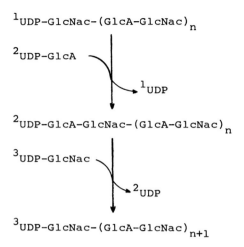

$^1$UDP-GlcNac-(GlcA-GlcNac)$_n$

$^2$UDP-GlcA

$^1$UDP

$^2$UDP-GlcA-GlcNac-(GlcA-GlcNac)$_n$

$^3$UDP-GlcNac

$^2$UDP

$^3$UDP-GlcNac-(GlcA-GlcNac)$_{n+1}$

Fig. 1. Mechanism of hyaluronate synthesis. Hyaluronate chains are elongated by alternate addition of UDP-hyaluronate to the substrates UDP-GlcNac and UDP-GlcA with liberation of UDP. Chains can be started by the substrates.

ed in membrane ruffles of migrating cells, codistributes with $p21^{k-ras}$ and is associated with a protein kinase activity (TURLEY et al. 1985; TURLEY and TORRENCE 1985; TURLEY and AUERSPERG 1989; TURLEY 1989 a, b). A hyaluronate binding protein on liver endothelial cells is probably involved in clearance of hyaluronate from plasma (LAURENT et al. 1986a; RAJA et al. 1988). A hyaluronate binding protein has also been isolated from chondrosarcoma cell membrane (MCCARTY and TOOLE 1989; MASON et al. 1989; CROSSMAN and MASON 1990). This protein is not related to cartilage proteins and its function is still not known.

Two other binding proteins appear to fulfil special functions: Binding of hyaluronate to fibrin has been proposed to occur during the early events of inflammation and wound healing (FROST and WEIGEL 1990; WEIGEL et al. 1989). Hyaluronate accelerates the clotting and fibrin polymer formation leading to larger fibrin clots (LEBOEUF et al. 1986).

Hyaluronate interacts with fibronectin and inhibits aggregation of fibronectin with heparan sulfate and collagen (HÖRMANN and JELINIC 1981; JILEK and HÖRMANN 1979; ISEMURA et al. 1982). Hyaluronate has a higher affinity to cell surface fibronectin than to plasma-derived firbonectin which lack a C-terminal peptide. This binding may influence aggregation and detachment of fibroblasts (LATERRA and CULP 1982).

## Degradation

Hyaluronate is shed from connective tissue and carried to lymph nodes, the main site of degradation in the body (FRASER et al. 1988). From the blood stream it is scavenged by liver endothelial cells. Metabolic degradation is principally intracel-

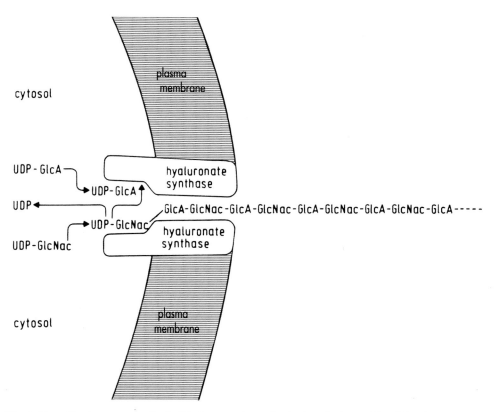

Fig. 2. Site of hyaluronate synthesis. Hyaluronate is synthesized at the inner side of the plasma membrane and the chains are extruded to the extracellular matrix.

lular and relies on the uptake by a receptor which also binds chondroitin sulfate, in contrast to other hyluronate binding proteins (ERIKSSON et al. 1983; FRASER and LAURENT 1989; SMEDSROD et al. 1984; FRASER et al. 1981, 1983, 1984, 1985; LAURENT et al. 1986b; TZAICOS et al. 1989). The receptor delivers hyaluronate to lysosomes and recycles back to the surface (McGARY et al. 1989). Lysosomal hyaluronidases produce fragments down to tetrasaccharides which are subsequently hydrolyzed by β-D-glucuronidase and β-N-acetyl-D-hexosaminidase (RODEN et al. 1989). These

Table 1: Effect of hormones, growth factors and drug on cellular hyaluronate synthesis

S = stimulation
I = inhibition

| Cell type, tissue | factor | S/I | Reference |
|---|---|---|---|
| chondrocytes | tunicamycin | i | Bansal & Mason (1987) |
| | cyclofenil – diphenol | i | Mason et al. (1984) |
| | monensin | i | Mitchel & Hardingham (1982) |
| | cartilage derived growth factor | s | Hamerman et al. (1986) |
| fibroblasts | serumfactor | s | Tomida et al. (1977 a) |
| | cAMP | s | Tomida et al. (1977 b) |
| | serum | s | Tomida et al. (1975) |
| skin fibroblasts | IL-I | s | Bronson et al. (1987) |
| | dexametason | i | Mapleson & Buchwald (1981) |
| lung fibroblasts | TGF-β | s | Westergren-Thornsson et al. (1990) |
| human fibroblasts | EGF | s | Lembach (1976) |
| | PDGF-ββ | s | Heldin et al. (1989) |
| | EGF | s | |
| | GFGF | s | |
| | n-butyrate | i | Smith (1987) |
| chick fibroblast | Phorbol myristate | s | Ullrich & Hawkes (1983) |
| retrobulbar fibroblasts | glucosamin | s | Sisson (1977) |
| | dibutyryl | s | |
| | c-AMP | s | |
| synovial fibroblasts | Monocyte factor | s | Bocquet et al. (1985) |
| | Diflunisal | i | Yaron & Yaron (1986) |
| | Interferon | i | Yaron et al. (1978) |
| | Poly IC | i | |
| | IL-I | s | Hamerman & Wood (1984) |
| | aurothiomalate | i | Vuorio et al. (1979) |
| | Diclofenac | i | Meyer et al. (1989) |
| | indomethacin | i | |
| | hydrocortison | i | |
| | antiinflammatory steroids | i | Saari & Hopsu-Havu (1978) |
| | cortisol | i | Saari et al. (1977) |
| | hydrocortisol | i | Castor et al. (1968) |
| | cortisol | i | Saari et al. (1977) |
| | hydrocortisol | i | Castor et al. (1968) |

|  |  |  |  |
|---|---|---|---|
|  | glycosaminogycan-polysulfate | s | Nishikawa et al. (1988) |
|  | IL-I | s | Pulkki (1986) |
| fibrosarcoma cells | sera from bovine fetus or cancer patients | s | Decker et al. (1989) |
|  | Monensin | i | Goldberg & Toole (1983) |
| chondrosacroma | Insulin, Serum | s s | D'Arville & Mason (1983) |
|  | hyaluronidase | s | Philipson & Schwartz (1985) |
| oocyte-cumulus cells | follicle stimulat. hormone, PGE$_2$ | s s | Eppig (1979) Eppig (1981) |
| mesothelial cells | vanadate | s | Ohaski et al. (1988) |
| bronchia lepithelical cells | retinoids | s | Wu & Wu (1986) |
| teratocarcinoma cells | trypsin | s | Prehm (1983a) |
| rat liver fat storing cells | TGFd,β1 | s | Bachem et al. (1989) |
| synovial organ culture | corticosteroids | i | Myers (1985) |
| bone organ culture | parathyroid hormone | s | Luben et al. (1974) |
| oocyte cumulus | follicle stimulat. hormone | s | Salustri et al. (1989) |
| bone organ culture | colchicine | s | Severson (1979) |
| cartilage | dibutyryl-cAMP | s | Stack & Brandt (1980) |
| skin | retinoic acid | s | Tammi & Tammi (1986) |
| osteocytes | parathormon | s | Wong et al. (1978) |
| Cartilage | H$_2$O$_2$ | i | Bates et al. (1985) |
| embryonic chick skin | Insulin | s | Bashey & Fleischmajer (1974) |

enzymes can be secreted from endothelial, smooth muscle and fibroblasts cell cultures, but they are inactive in the media, because they require an acidic environment (McGuire et al. 1987; Orkin et al. 1982). Thus fibroblasts are unable to degrade extracellular hyaluronate (Arbogast et al. 1975; Klein and von Figura 1980).

Hyaluronidases appear in tissues which differentiate during morphogenesis and metamorphosis (Toole 1972) and during wound healing (Alexander and Donoff 1979). They seem to prepare the tissue for final differentiation and have been found in chicken cardiac cushion and myocardial cells (Bernanke and Orkin 1984; Orkin & Toole 1978; 1980), rabbit eye (Knepper et al. 1984), chick embryo kidney (Belsky and Toole 1983), chick limb (Toole 1972; Toole and Gross 1971), and

chick cornea (TOOLE and TRELSTAD 1971). During the final stage of limb mesoderm differentiation the mesodermal cells stop the production of hyaluronate,
express receptors on their surface and endocytose hyaluronate to degrade it intracellularly (TOOLE et al. 1989). At this condensation stage the cells are aggregating
and differentiate into chondrocytes which produce cartilage proteoglycans.

Another degradation reaction is radical cleavage. This reaction has been alleged
to reduce the viscosity of synovial fluid in patients with rheumatoid arthritis
(McCORD 1974; DAHL et al. 1985), but direct degradation in the synovia has not
been proven (BALAZS et al. 1967b). However, activated granulocytes are able to
reduce the molecular weight of hyaluronate in vitro (McNEIL et al. 1985; GREEN-
WALD and MOAK 1986). In vitro radical degradation can be inhibited by superoxide
dismutase and catalase indicating that hydroxyl radical is the reactive species
(KENNEDY and TUN 1972; MOTOHASHI and MORI 1985; WONG et al. 1981; CLELAND
et al. 1969). Hyaluronate can also be degraded by hypochlorite which is produced
by $H_2O_2$ and myeloperoxidase (BAKER et al. 1989). Radical degradation yields transient intermediates of the unfragmented chains, before they break into strands containing reactive aldehydes, 4.5-unsaturated glucuronic acid and arabopentauronic
acid at the ends (BALAZS et al. 1967a; CLELAND et al. 1969; MYINT et al. 1987;
UCHIYANA et al. 1990).

Fibroblasts in cell culture produce a massive hyaluronate coat which is deposited
at the surface. It can be visualized by light microscopy, when particles such as erythrocytes sediment onto the cells in an appropriate concentration (CLARRIS and
FRASER 1968). This coat is lost upon transformation (UNDERHILL and TOOLE 1982;
MIKUNI-TAKAGAKI and TOOLE 1979) or during myoblasts fusion (ORKIN et al.
1985). Theoretically, hyaluronate can be released from the cell surface by dissociation as intact macromolecule or by intrachain degradation. We have shown that
both mechanisms operate in cell culture (PREHM 1990). B6 cells lost hyaluronate
only by dissociation. In contrast , transformed SV3T3 cells were able to degrade
their own hyaluronate by radical cleavage. Degradation could partially be inhibited
by salicylate.

If degraded hyaluronate stimulated cell growth, as discussed above, the endolytic degradation fragments could act as autocrine and paracrine growth factors. The
enzymes responsible for radical generation have not yet been identified in fibroblasts. It is known that many transformed cells have diminished activities of superoxide dismutase (OBERLEY and BUETTNER 1979). But also a cell surface NADPH-
oxidase which has recently been discovered on fibroblasts could be blamed (MEIER
et al. 1989).

## A unifying concept

This review described several paradoxical observations regarding the cellular functions of hyaluronate. The contradictory effect of hyaluronate on cell aggregation and detachment is not understood. Hyaluronate mediates cell aggragation (UNDERHILL 1982), but also cell detachment during mitosis (BRECHT et al. 1986) and migration (LARK and CULP 1982). It binds to fibronectin (LATERA and CULP 1982), an adhesive molecule, yet it also inhibits the aggregation of fibronectin with collagen and heparin (JILEK and HÖRMANN 1979). A clue to the solution could be the unique mechanism of synthesis and release from the cell surface. Both functions could operate on a single migrating cell, as demonstrated hypothetically in Fig. 3. Hyaluronate is synthesized through the cell membrane and retained by

### Hyaluronate as detachment and adhesion factor

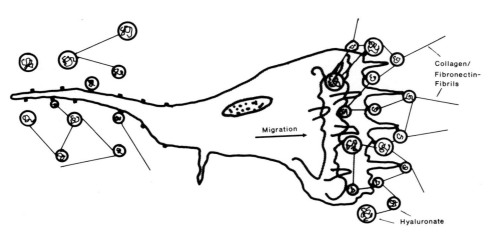

Fig. 3. Hypothetical model of cell attachment and detachment. At the leading edge of a migrating cell hyaluronate is retained by receptors and anchors extracellular matrix components via binding of fibronectin. At the trailing edge hyaluronate dissociates from the surface. Hydration of nascent hyaluronate displaces adhesive matrix components.

receptors. The cell could modulate the affinity or the number of receptors – an assumption which is probable but not yet proven. In the adhesive mode – at the leading edge of a migrating cell – the receptors may have a high affinity to hyaluronate. Large hyaluronate chains are retained on the cell surface which inhibit further chain elongation. This hyaluronate could serve as an additional anchor of other matrix proteins such as fibronectin. In the detachment mode – at the trailing edge of a migrating cell of at all contact sites during mitosis – the receptors could be absent or have low affinity releasing hyaluronate from the cell surface together with attached matrix proteins. The synthase is free to start new chains and release them into the extracellular space where hyaluronate chains fold, hydrate and swell to displace adhesive molecules.

A second paradox was the function of hyaluronate as a growth stimulating and inhibiting factor depending on its molecular weight. These observations become plausible, if we make again an unproven assumption that the hyaluronate receptors may function as signal transducer, (Fig. 4). High molecular weight hyaluronate may

## Hyaluronate as growth inhibiting and stimulating factor

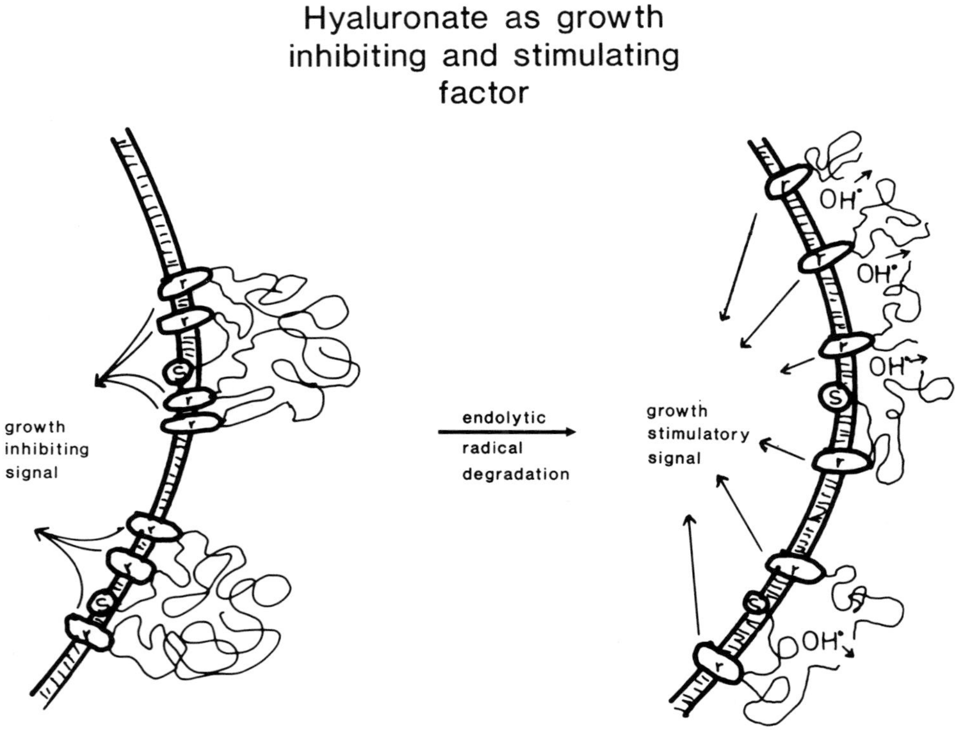

Fig. 4. Hypothetical model of growth stimulating and inhibiting action. Large hyaluronate chains cluster several receptors which could be a growth inhibiting signal. Smaller chains disperse the receptors which could be a growth stimulating signal. Many transformed cells produce radicals which degrade hyaluronate to sizes which could induce autocrine and paracrine growth stimulation.

cluster receptors on the surface which could be a growth inhibiting signal. Low molecular weight hyaluronate may keep the receptor dispersed on the surface which could be a growth stimulating signal. The assumptions could explain that endolytic radical degradation of surface hyaluronate leads to autocrine and paracrine growth stimulation (PREHM 1990).

## Acknowledgement

The work of the author was supported by the Deutsche Forschungsgemeinschaft.

## References

ALEXANDER, S. A., R. B. DONOFF (1979): Identification and localization of wound hyaluronidase. J. Surg. Res. *27:* 163 – 167.

ALHO, A. M., C. B. UNDERHILL (1989): The hyaluronate receptor is preferentially expressed on proliferating epithelial cells. J. Cell. Biol. *108:* 1557 – 65.

ANGELLO J. C., S. D. HAUSCHKA (1979): Hyaluronic acid synthesis and turnover by myotubes in culture. Dev. Biol. *73:* 322 – 37.

APPEL, A., A. L. HORWITZ, A. DORFMAN (1979): Cell-free synthesis of hyaluronic acid in Marfan syndrome. J. Biol. Chem. *254:* 12199 – 203.

ARBOGAST, B., J. J. HOPWOOD, A. DORFMAN (1975): Absence of hyaluronidase in cultured human skin fibroblasts. Biochem. Biophys. Res. Comm. *67:* 376 – 382.

BACHEM, M. S., U. RIESS, R. MELCHIOR, K. M. SELL, A. M. GRESSNER (1989): Transforming growth factors (TGF alpha and TGF beta 1) stimulate chondroitin sulfate and hyaluronate synthesis in cultured rat liver fat storing cells. FEBS Lett. *257:* 134 – 7.

BAKER, M. S., S. P. GREEN, D. A. LOWTHER (1989): Changes in the viscosity of hyaluronic acid after exposure to a myeloperoxidase-derived oxidant. Arthritis Rheum. *32:* 461 – 7.

BALAZS, E. A, J. V. DAVIES, G. O. PHILLIPS, M. D. YOUNG (1967a): Transient intermediates in the radiolysis of hyaluronic acid. Radiation Res. *31:* 243 – 255.

BALACZS, E. A., D. WATSON, I. F. DUFF, S. ROSEMAN (1967b): Hyaluronic acid in synovial fluid. I Molecular parameters of hyaluronic acid in normal and arthritic human fluids. Arthritis Rheum. *10:* 357 – 76.

BANSAL, M. K., R. M. MASON (1986): Evidence for rapid metabolic turnover of hyaluronate synthetase in Swarm rat chondrosarcoma chondrocytes. Biochem. J. *236:* 515 – 519.

BANSAL, M. K., H. WARD, R. M. MASON (1986): Proteoglycan synthesis in suspension cultures of Swarm rat chondrosarcoma chondrocytes and inhibition by exogenous hyaluronate. Arch. Biochem. Biophys. *246:* 602 – 10.

BANSAL, M. K., R. M. MASON (1987): Tunicamycin partially delays release of newly synthesized hyaluronate from Swarm rat chondrosarcoma chondrocytes. Biochem. Biophys. Acta *928:* 152 – 9.

BARNHART, B. J., S. H. COX, P. M. KRAEMER (1979): Detachment variants of Chinese hamster cells Hyaluronic acid as a modular of cell detachment. Exp. Cell. Res. *119:* 327 – 32.

BASHEY, R. I, R. FLEISCHMAJER (1974): Increased synthesis of hyaluronic acid by insulin in embryonic chick skin. Proc. Soc. Exp. Biol. Med. *145:* 18 – 20.

BATES, E. J., D. A. LOWTHER, C. C. JOHNSON (1985): Hyaluronic acid synthesis in articular cartilage an inhibition by hydrogen peroxide. Biochem. Biophys. Res. Commun. *132:* 714 – 20.

BELSKY, E., B. P. TOOLE (1983): Hyaluronate and hyaluronidase in the developing chick embryo kidney. Cell. Differ. *12:* 61 – 6.

BERNANKE, D. H., R. W. ORKIN (1984): Hyaluronate binding and degradation by cultured embryonic chick cardiac cush ion and myocardial cells. Dev. Biol. *106:* 360 – 7.

BIGNAMI, A., W. LANE, D. ANDREWS, D. DAHL (1989): Structural similarity of hyaluronate binding proteins in brain and cartilage. Brain Res. Bull. *22:* 67–70.

BOCQUET, J., M. LANGRIS, M. DAIREAUX, JOUIS, J. P. PUJOL, R. BELIARD, G. LOYAU (1985): Mononuclear cell-mediated modulation of synovial cell metabolism II Increased hyaluronic acid synthesis by a monocyte cell factor (MCF). Exp. Cell. Res. *160:* 9–18.

BRECHT, M., U. MAYER, E. SCHLOSSER, P. PREHM (1986): Increased hyaluronate synthesis is required for fibroblast detachment and mitosis. Biochem. J. *239:* 445–50.

BRONSON, R. E., C. N. BERTOLAMI, E. P. SIEBERT (1987): Modulation of fibroblast growth and glucosaminoglycan synthesis by interleukin 1. Collagen Relat. Res. *7:* 323–332.

CASTOR, C.W., E. L. DORSTEWITZ, K. ROWE, J. C. RITCHIE (1971): Abnormalities of connective tissue cells cultured from patients with rheumatoid arthritis. II. Defective regulation of hyaluronate and collagen formation. J. Lab. Clin. Med. *77:* 65–75.

CLARRIS, B. J., J. R.E. FRASER (1968): On the pericellular zone of some mammalian cells in vitro. Exp. Cell. Res. *49:* 181–193.

CLELAND, R. L., A. C. STOOLMILLER, L. RODEN, T. C. LAURENT (1969): Partial characterization of reaction products formed by the degradation of hyaluronic acid with ascorbic acid. Biochim. Biophys. Acta *192:* 385–394.

COMPER, W. D., T. C. LAURENT (1978): Physiological function of connective tissue polysaccharides. Physiol. Rev. *58:* 255–315.

CRAWFORD, T. (1988): Distribution in cesium chloride gradients of proteoglycans of chick embryo brain and characterization of a large aggregating proteoglycan. Biochim. Biophys. Acta *964:* 183–92.

CROSSMAN, M.V., R. M. MASON (1990): Purification and characterization of a hyaluronan-binding protein from rat brain. Biochem. J. *266:* 299–406.

D'ARVILLE, C., R. M. MASON (1983): Effects of serum and insulin on hyaluronate synthesis by cultures of chondrocytes from the swarm rat chondrosarcoma. Biochim. Biophys. Acta *760:* 53–60.

DAHL, L. B., I. M. DAHL, A. ENGSTROEM-LAURENT, K. GRANATH (1985): Concentration and molecular weight of sodium hyaluronate in synovial fluid from patients with rheumatoid arthritis and other arthropathies. Ann. Rheum. Dis. *44:* 817–822.

DARZYNKIEWICZ, Z., E. A. BALAZS (1971): Effects of connective tissue intercellular matrix on lymphocyte stimulation. Exp. Cell. Res. *66:* 113–23.

DECKER, M., E. S. CHIU, C. DOLLBAUM, A. MOIIN, J. HALL, R. SPENDLOVE, M. T. LONGAKER, STERN, R. (1989): Hyaluronic acid-stimulation activity in sera from the bovine fetus and from breast cancer patients. Cancer Res. *49:* 3499–505.

DELPECH, B., C. HALAVENT (1981): Characterization and purification from human brain of a hyaluronic acid-binding glycoprotein, hyaluronectin. J. Neurochem. *36:* 855–9.

DELPECH, B., A. DELPECH, G. BRUCKNER, N. GIRARD, C. MAINGONNAT (1989): Hyaluronan and hyaluronectin in the nervous system. Ciba Found. Symp. *143:* 208–20.

EPPIG, J. J. (1979): FSH stimulates hyaluronic acid synthesis by oocyte-cumulus cell complexes from mouse preovulatory follicles. Nature *281:* 483–4.

EPPIG, J. J. (1981): Prostaglandin E2 stimulates cumulus expansion and hyaluronic acid synthesis by cumuli oophori isolated from mice. Biol. Reprod. *25:* 191–195.

ERIKSSON, S., J. R. FRASER, T. C. LAURENT, H. PERTOFT, SMEDSROD, B. (1983): Endothelial cells are a site of uptake and degradation of hyaluronic acid in the liver. Exp. Cell. Res. *144:* 223–8.

FORRESTER, J.V., E. A. BALAZS (1980): Inhibition of phagocytosis by high molecular weight hyaluronate. Immunology *40:* 435–46.

FRASER, J. R., T. C. LAURENT, H. PERTOFT, E. BAXTER (1981): Plasma clearance, tissue distribution and metabolism of hyaluronic acid injected intravenously in the rabbit. Biochem. J. *200:* 415–424.

FRASER, J. R., L. E. APPELGREN, T. C. LAURENT (1983): Tissue uptake of circulating hyaluronic acid. A whole body autoradiographic study. Cell Tissue Res. *233:* 285–93.

FRASER, J. R., E. BAXTER (1984): Leucine metabolism as a source of acetate in the synthesis of hyaluronic acid. Connect. Tissue Res. *12:* 287–96.

FRASER, J. R., T. C. LAURENT, A. ENGSTROEM-LAURENT, U. G. LAURENT (1984): Elimination of hyaluronic acid from the blood stream in the human. Clin. Exp. Pharmacol. Physiol. *11:* 17–25.

FRASER, J. R., D. ALCORN, T. C. LAURENT, A. D. ROBINSON, G. B. RYAN (1985): Uptake of circulating hyaluronic acid by the rat liver. Cellular localization in situ. Cell Tissue Res. *242:* 505 – 10.

FRASER, J. R. E., W. G. KIMPTON, T. C. LAURENT, R. N. P. CAHILL, N. VAKAKIS (1988): Uptake and degradation of hyaluronan in lymphatic tissue. Biochem. J. *256:* 153 – 158.

FRASER, J. R., T. C. LAURENT (1989): Turnover and metabolism of hyaluronan. Ciba Found. Symp. *143:* 1 – 53.

FROST, S. J., P. H. WEIGEL (1990): Binding of hyaluronic acid to mammalian fibrinogens. Biochim. Biophys. Acta Gen. Subj. *1034:* 39 – 45.

GLASER, L., D. H. BROWN (1955): The enzymatic synthesis in vitro of hyaluronic acid chains. Proc. Natl. Acad. Sci. *41:* 253 – 260.

GOLDBERG, R. L., B. P. TOOLE (1983): Monesin inhibition of hyaluronate synthesis in rat fibrosarcoma cells. J. Biol. Chem. *258:* 7041 – 6.

GOLDBERG, R. L., J. D. SEIDEMAN, G. CHI-ROSSO, B. P. TOOLE (1984): Endogenous hyaluronate-cell surface interactions in 3T3 and simian virus-transformed 3T3 cells. J. Biol. Chem. *259:* 9440 – 6.

GOLDBERG, R. L., B. P. TOOLE (1987): Hyaluronate inhibition of cell proliferation. Arthritis. Rheum. *30:* 769 – 78.

GREENWALD, R. A., S. A. MOAK (1986): Degradation of hyaluronic acid by polymorphonuclear leukocytes. Inflammation *10:* 15 – 30.

HAKANSSON, L., P. VENGE (1985): The combined action of hyaluronic acid and fibronectin stimulates neutrophil migration. J. Immunol. *135:* 2735 – 9.

HAMERMAN, D., G. J. TODARO, H. GREEN (1965): The production of hyaluronate by spontaneously established cell lines and viral transformed lines of fibroblastic origin. Biochim. Biophys. Acta *101:* 343 – 51.

HAMERMAN, D., D. D. WOOD (1984): Interleukin 1 enhances synovial cell hyaluronate synthesis. Proc. Soc. Exp. Biol. Med. *177:* 205 – 10.

HAMERMAN, D., J. SASSE, M. KLAGSBRUN (1986): A cartilage-derived growth factor enhances hyaluronate synthesis and diminishes sulfate glycosaminoglycan synthesis in chondrocytes. J. Cell Physiol. *127:* 317 – 22.

HANDLEY, C. J., D. A. LOWTHER (1976): Inhibition of proteoglycan biosynthesis by hyaluronic acid in chondrocytes in cell culture. Biochim. Biophys. Acta *444:* 69 – 74.

HARDINGHAM, T. E., H. MUIR (1972): The specific interaction of hyaluronic acid with cartillage proteoglycans. Biochim. Biophys. Acta *279:* 401 – 5.

HARDINGHAM, T. E., H. MUIR (1973): Binding of oligosaccharides of hyaluronic acid to proteoglycans. Biochem. J. *135:* 905 – 8.

HARDINGHAM, T. E., H. MUIR (1974): Hyaluronic acid in cartilage and proteoglycan aggregation . Biochem. J. *139:* 565 – 81.

HASCALL, V. C. (1977): Interaction of cartilage proteoglycans with hyaluronic acid. J. Supramol. Struct. *7:* 101 – 120.

HYANES, B. F., M. J. TELEN, L. P. HALE, S. M. DENNING (1989): CD44, a molecule involved in leukocyte adherence and T-cell activiation. Immunol. Today *10:* 423.

HELDIN, P., T. C. LAURENT, C. H. HELDIN (1989): Effect of growth factors on hyaluronan synthesis in cultured human fibroblasts. Biochem. J. *258:* 919 – 22.

HOPWOOD, J. J., A. DORFMAN (1977): Glycosaminoglycan synthesis by cultured human skin fibroblasts after transformation with Simian virus 40. J. Biol. Chem. *252:* 4777 – 4785.

HÖRMANN, H., V. JELINIC (1981): Regulation by heparin and hyaluronic acid of the fibronectin-dependent association of collagen, Type III, with macrophages. Hoppe Seylers Z. Physiol. Chem. *362:* 87 – 94.

HRONOWSKI, L., T. P. ANASTASSIADES (1980): Rates of glycosaminoglycan synthesis and rates of incorporation of radioactive precursors into newly synthesized glycosaminoglycan by confluent rat muscle fibroblasts. J. Biol. Chem. *255:* 9210 – 9217.

IOZZO, R. V., P. M. SAMPSON, G. K. SCHMITT (1989): Neoplastic modulation of extracellular matrix, stimulation of chondroitin sulfate proteoglycan and hyaluronic acid synthesis in co-cultures of human colon carcinoma and smooth muscle cells. J. Cell. Biochem. *39:* 355 – 78.

ISEMURA, U., Z. YOSIZAWA, T. KOIDE, T. ONO (1982): Interaction of fibronectin and its proteolytic fragments with hyaluronic acid. J. Biochem. (Tokyo) *91:* 731–4.

ISHIMOTO, N., H. M. TEMIN, J. L. STROMINGER (1966): Studies of carcinogenesis by avian sarcoma virus II virus induced increase in hyaluronic acid synthetase in chicken fibreoblasts. J. Biol. Chem. *241:* 2052–2057.

JACOBSEN, B. (1978 a): Biosynthesis of hyaluronic acid in the vitreous. VI. Isolation of a complex containing hyaluronic acid and glycosyl transferase activity and studies on the activity of a soluble glycosyl transferase. Exp. Eye Res. *27:* 259–73.

JACOBSEN, B. (1978 b): Biosynthesis of hyaluronic acid in the vitreous. V. Studies on a particulate hyalocyte glycosyl transferase. Exp. Eye Res. *27:* 247–58.

JILEK, F., H. HÖRMANN (1979): Fibronectin (cold-insoluble globulin), VI Influence of heparin and hyaluronic acid on the binding of native collagen. Hoppe Seylers Z. Physiol. Chem. *360:* 597–603.

KABAT, E. A. (1939): A polysaccharide in tumors due to a virus of leukosis and sarcoma of fowls. J. Biol. Chem. *130:* 143–147.

KENDALL, F. E., M. HEIDELBERGER, M. H. DAWSON (1937): A serologically inactive polysaccharide elaborated by mucoid strains of group A hemolytic streptococcus. J. Biol. Chem. *118:* 61–69.

KENNEDY, J. F., H. C. TUN (1972): The degradation of hyaluronic acid by ferrous ions. Carbohydr. Res. *22:* 43–51.

KLEIN, U., K. VON FIGURA K. (1980): Characterization of dermatan sulfate in mucopolysaccharidosis VI. Evidence for the absence of hyaluronidase-like enzymes in human skin fibroblasts. Biochim. Biophys. Acta *630:* 10–14.

KNEPPER, P. A., A. I. FARMAN, A. G. TELSER (1984): Exogenous hyaluronidases and degradation of hyaluronic acid in the rabbit eye. Invest. Opthalmol. Vis. Sci. *25:* 286–93.

KNUDSON, W., C. BISWAS, B. P. TOOLE (1984): Interactions between human tumor cells and fibroblasts stimulate hyaluronate synthesis. Proc. Natl. Acad. Sci. USA *81:* 6767–71.

KNUDSON, W., C. BISWAS, X. Q. LI, R. E. NEMEC, B. P. TOOLE (1989): The role and regulation of tumour-associated hyaluronan. Ciba Found. Symp. *143:* 150–9.

KRAEMER, P. M., B. J. BARNHART (1978): Elevated cell-surface hyaluronate in substrate-attached cells. Exp. Cell Res. *114:* 153–157.

KUJAWA, M. J., D. J. PECHNAK, M. Y. FIZMAN, A. I. CAPLAN (1986): Hyaluronic acid bonded to cell culture surfaces inhibits the program of myogenesis. Dev. Biol. *113:* 10–16.

LACY, B. E., C. B. UNDERHILL (1987): The hyaluronate receptor is associated with actin filaments. J. Cell Biol. *105:* 1395–1404.

LARK, M. W., L. A. CULP (1982): Selective solubilization of hyaluronic acid from fibroblast substratum adhesion sites. J. Biol. Chem. *257:* 14073–80.

LATERRA, J., L. A. CULP (1982): Differences in hyaluronate binding to plasma and cell surface fibronectins. J. Biol. Chem. *257:* 719–726.

LAURENT, T. C., I. M. DAHL, L. B. DAHL, A. ENGSTROEM-LAURENT, S. ERIKSSON, J. R. FRASER, K. A. GRANATH, C. LAURENT, U. B. LAURENT, K. LILJA (1986 a): The catabolic fate of hyaluronic acid. Connect. Tissue Res. *15:* 33–41.

LAURENT, T. C. (1970): Structure of hyaluronic acid In: BALAZS E. A. (Ed): Chemistry and Molecular Biology of the intercellular matrix. Vol 2, pp. 703–732, Acad. Press, London.

LAURENT, T. C., J. R. FRASER, H. PERTOFT B. SMEDSROD (1986 b): Binding of hyaluronate and chondroitin sulphate to liver endothelial cells. Biochem. J. *234:* 653–8.

LEBOEUF, R. D., R. H. RAJA, G. M. FULLER, P. H. WEIGEL (1986): Human fibrinogen specifically binds hyaluronic acid. J. Biol. Chem. *261:* 12586–92.

LEMBACH, K. J. (1976): Enhanced synthesis and extracellular accumulation of hyaluronic acid during stimulation of quiescent human fibroblasts by mouse epidermal. J. Cell. Physiol. *89:* 277–288.

LESLEY, J., R. SCHULTE, R. HYMAN (1990): Binding of hyaluronic acid to lymphoid cell lines is inhibited by monoclonal antibodies against Pgb-1. Exp. Cell Res. *187:* 224–233.

LUBEN, R. A., J. F. GOGGINS, L. G. RAISZ (1974): Stimulation by parathyroid hormone of bone hyaluronate synthesis in organ culture. Endocrinology *94:* 737–45.

MAPLESON, J. L., M. BUCHWALD (1981): Effect of cycloheximide and dexamethasone phosphate on hyaluronic acid synthesis and secretion in cultured human skin fibroblasts. J. Cell. Physiol. 109: 215 – 22.

MARKOWITZ, A., A. DORFMAN (1962): Hyaluronic acid synthesizing system form group A Streptococcus. Methods Enzymology 5: 155 – 158.

MARKS, M. S., G. CHI-ROSSO, B. P. TOOLE (1990): Hyaluronate-binding proteins of murine brain. J. Neurochem. 54: 171 – 180.

MASON, R. M., C. d'ARVILLE, J. H. KIMURA, V. C. HASCALL (1982): Absence of covalently linked core protein from newly synthesized hyaluronate. Biochem. J. 207: 445 – 57.

MASON, R. M., J. D. LINEHAM, M. A. PHILLIPSON, C. M. BLACK (1984): Selective inhibition of proteoglycan and hyaluronate synthesis in chondrocyte cultures by cyclofenil diphenol, a non-steroidal weak oestrogen. Biochem. J. 223: 401 – 12.

MASON, R. M., M. V. CROSSMAN, C. SWEENEY (1989): Hyaluronan and hyaluronan-binding proteins in cartilaginous tissues. Ciba Found. Symp. 143: 107 – 16.

MAUSOLF, A., J. JUNGMANN, H. ROBENEK, P. PREHM (1990) : Shedding of hyaluronate synthase from Streptococci. Biochem. J. 267: 191 – 196.

McGARY, C. T., R. H. RAJA, P. H. WEIGEL (1989): Endocytosis of hyaluronic acid by rat liver endothelial cells. Evidence for receptor recycling. Biochem. J. 257: 875 – 84.

McCARTY, C. T., B. P. TOOLE (1989): Membrane-associated hyaluronate-binding activity of chondrosarcoma chondrocytes. J. Cell. Physiol. 141: 191 – 202.

McCORD, J. M. (1974): Free radicals and inflammation, Protection of synovial fluid by superoxide dismutase. Science 185: 529 – 531.

McGUIRE, P. G., J. R. CASTELLOT, R. W., ORKIN (1987): Size dependent hyaluronate degradation by cultured cells. J. Cell. Physiol. 133: 267 – 276.

McNEILL, U. D., O. W. WIEBKIN, W. H. BETTS, E. G. CLELAND (1985): Depolymerisation products of hyaluronic acid after exposure to oxygen-derived free radicals. Annals Rheumat. Dis. 44: 780 – 789.

MEIER, B., H. H. RADEKE, S. SELLE, N. YOUNES, H. SIES, K. RESCH, G. G. HABERMEHL (1989): Human fibroblasts release reactive oxygen species in response to interleukin-1 of tumour necrosis factor-α Biochem. J. 263: 530 – 545.

MEYER, K., J. W. PALMER (1934): The polysaccharide of the vitreous humor. J. Biol. Chem. 107: 629 – 634.

MEYER, K. (1947): The biological significance of hyaluronic acid and hyaluronidase. Physiol. Rev. 27: 335 – 359.

MEYER, F. A., I. YARON, V. MASHIAH, M. YARON (1989): Effect of diclofenac on prostaglandin E and hyaluronic acid production by human synovial fibroblasts stimulated with interleukin-1. Br. J. Clin. Pharmacol. 28: 193 – 196.

MIAN, N. (1986 a): Analysis of cell-growth-phase-related variations in hyaluronate synthase activity of isolated plasma-membrane fractions of cultured human skin fibroblasts. Biochem. J. 237: 333 – 342.

MIAN, N. (1986 b): Characterization of a high Mr plasma membrane bound protein and assessment of its role as a constituent of hyaluronate synthase complex. Biochem. J. 237: 343 – 357.

MIKUNI-TAKAGAKI, Y., B. P. TOOLE (1979): Shedding of hyaluronate from the cell surface of Rous sarcoma virus-transformed chondrocytes. J. Biol. Chem. 254: 8409 – 15.

MITCHELL, D., T. HARDINGHAM (1982): Monesin inhibits synthesis of proteoglycan, but not of hyaluronate in chondrocytes. Biochem. J. 202: 249 – 54.

MIYAKE, K., C. B. UNDERHILL, J. LESLEY, P. W. KINCADE (1990): Hyaluronate can function as cell adhesion molecule and CD44 participates in hyluronate recognition. J. Exp. Med. 172: 69 – 75.

MOTOHASHI, N., I. MORI (1985): The effect of synovial fluid proteins in the degradation of hyaluronic acid induced by acorbic acid J. Inorg. Biochem. 24: 69 – 74.

MYERS, S. L. (1985): Suppression of hyaluronic acid synthesis in synovial organ cultures by corticosteroid suspensions. Arthritis Rheum. 28: 1275 – 1282.

MYINT, P., D. J. DEEBLE, P. C. BEAUMONT, S. M. BLAKE, G. O. PHILLIPS (1978): The reactivity of various free radicals with hyaluronic acid, steady-state and pulse radiolysis studies. Biochim. Biophys. Acta 925: 194 – 202.

NG, K. F., N. B. SCHWARTZ (1989): Solubilization and partial purification of hyaluronate synthetase from oligogodendroglioma cells. J. Biol. Chem. *264:* 11776 – 83.

NISHIKAWA, H., I. MORI, J. UMEMOTO (1988): Glycosaminoglycan polysulfate-induced stimulation of hyaluronic acid synthesis in rabbit knee synovial membrane involvement of binding protein and calcium ion. Arch. Biochem. Biophys. *266:* 201 – 9.

OBERLEY, L. W., G. R. BUETTNER (1979): Role of superoxide dismutase in cancer. A review. Cancer Res. *39:* 1141 – 1149.

OESTERLIN, S. E. (1968): The synthesis of hyaluronic acid in vitreous. 3. In vivo metabolism in the owl monkey. Exp. Eye Res. *7:* 524 – 33.

OESTERLIN, S. E., B. JACOBSON (1968 a): The synthesis of hyaluronic acid in vitreous. I. Soluble and particulate transferases in hyalocytes. Exp. Eye Res. *7:* 497 – 510.

OESTERLIN, S. E., B. JACOBSON (1968 b): The synthesis of hyaluronic acid in vitreous II. The presence of soluble transferase and nucleotide sugar in the acellular vitreous gel. Exp. Eye Res. *7:* 511 – 23.

OESTERLIN, S. E. (1969): The synthesis of hyaluronic acid in the vitreous. IV. Regeneration in the owl monkey. Exp. Eye Res. *8:* 27 – 34.

OHASHI, Y., A. HONDA, T. IWAI, Y. MORI (1988): Stimulatory effect of vanadate on hyaluronic acid synthesis in mesothelial cells from rabbit pericardium. Biochem. Int. *16:* 293 – 302.

ORKIN, R. W., B. P. TOOLE (1978): Hyaluronidase activity and hyaluronate content of the developing chick embryo heart. Dev. Biol. *66:* 308 – 20.

ORKIN, R. W., B. P. TOOLE (1980): Isolation and characterization of hyaluronidse from cultures of chick embryo skin- and muscle-derived fibroblasts. J. Biol. Chem. *255:* 1036 – 1042.

ORKIN, R. W., C. B. UNDERHILL, B. P. TOOLE (1982): Hyaluronate degradation in 3T3 and simian virus-transformed 3T3 cells. J. Biol. Chem. *257:* 5821 – 6.

ORKIN, R. W., W. KNUDSON, B. P. TOOLE (1985): Loss of hyaluronate-dependent coat during myoblast fusion. Dev. Biol. *107:* 527 – 30.

PARTSCH, G., C. SCHWARZER, J. NEUMULLER, A. DUNKY, P. PETERA, H. BROLL, G. ITTNER, S. JANTSCH (1989): Modulation of the migration and chemotaxis of PMN cells by hyaluronic acid. Z. Rheumatol. *48:* 123 – 8.

PERIDES, G., W. S. LANE, D. ANDREWS, D. DAHL, A. BIGNAMI (1989): Isolation and partial characterization of a glial hyaluronate-binding protein. J. Biol. Chem. *264:* 5981 – 7.

PHILIPSON, L. H., N. B. SCHWARTZ (1984): Subcellular localization of hyaluronate synthetase in oligodendroglioma cells. J. Biol. Chem. *259:* 5017 – 5023.

PHILIPSON, L. H., J. WESTLEY, N. B. SCHWARTZ (1985): Effect of hyaluronidase treatment of intact cells on hyaluronate synthetase activity. Biochem. *24:* 7899 – 7906.

PRATT, R. M., M. A. LARSEN, M. C. JOHNSTON (1975): Migration of cranial neural crest cells in a cell-free hyaluronate-rich matrix. Dev. Biol. *44:* 298 – 305.

PREHM, P. (1980): Induction of hyaluronic acid synthesis in teratocarcinoma stem cells by retinoic acid. FEBS Lett. *111:* 295 – 8.

PREHM, P., W. DESSAU, R. TIMPL (1982): Rates of Synthesis of Basement Membrane Proteins and Their Modulation by Differentiating Teratocarcinoma Cells. Connective Tissue Res. *10:* 33 – 43.

PREHM, P. (1983 a): Synthesis of hyaluronate in differentiated teratocarcinoma cells. Characterization of the synthase. Biochem. J. *211:* 181 – 9.

PREHM, P. (1983 b): Synthesis of hyaluronate in differentiated teratocarcinoma cells. Mechanism of chain growth. Biochem. J. *211:* 191 – 198.

PREHM, P. (1984): Hyaluronate is synthesized at plasma membranes. Biochem. J. *220:* 597 – 600.

PREHM, P. (1985): Inhibition of hyaluronate synthesis. Biochem. J. *225:* 699 – 705.

PREHM, P., A. MAUSOLF (1986): Isolation of streptococcal hyaluronate synthase. Biochem. J. *235:* 887 – 889.

PREHM, P. (1989): Identification and regulation of the eukaryotic hyaluronate synthase. Ciba Found. Symp. *143:* 21 – 30.

PREHM, P. (1990): Release of hyaluronate from eukaryotic cells. Biochem, J. *267:* 185 – 189.

PULKKI, K. (1986): The effects of synovial fluid macrophages and interleukin-1 on hyaluronic acid synthesis by normal synovial fibroblasts Rheumatol. Int. *6:* 121 – 5.

RAJA, R. H., C. T. MCGARY, P. H. WEIGEL (1988): Affinity and distribution of surface and intracellular hyaluronic acid receptors in isolated rat liver endothelial cells. J. Biol. Chem. 263: 16661 – 16668.

RIPELLINO, J. A., M. BAILO, R. U. MARGOLIS, R. K. MARGOLIS (1988): Light and electron microscopic studies on the localization of hyaluronic acid in developing brain. J. Cell. Biol. 106: 845 – 855.

RODEN, L., P. CAMPBELL, J. R. FRASER T. C. LAURENT, H. PERTOFT, J. N. THOMPSON (1989): Enzymic pathways of hyaluronan catabolism. Ciba Found. Symp. 143: 60 – 76.

SAARNI, H., M. TAMMI, E. VUORI (1977): Effects of cortisol on glycosaminoglycans synthesized by normal and rheumatoid synovial fibroblasts in vitro. Scand. J. Rheumatol. 6: 222 – 4.

SAARNI, H., V. K. HOPSU-HAVU (1978): The decrease of hyaluronate synthesis by anti-inflammatory steroids in vitro. Br. J. Dermatol. 98: 445 – 9.

SALUSTRI, A., M. YANAGISHITA, V. C. HASCALL (1989): Synthesis and accumulation of hyaluronic acid and proteoglycans in the mouse cumulus cell-oocyte complex during follicle-stimulating hormone-induced mucification. J. Biol. Chem. 264: 13840 – 7.

SISSON, J. C. (1977): Effects of glucosamine, dibutyryl cyclic AMP and lymphocytes on retrobulbar fibroblast synthesis of hyaluronic acid. Proc. Soc. Exp. Biol. Med. 154: 467 – 70.

SMEDSROD, B., H. PERTOFT, S. ERIKSSON, J. R. FRASER, T. C. LAURENT (1984): Studies in vitro on the uptake and degradation of sodium hyaluronate in rat liver endothelial cells. Biochem. J. 223: 617 – 26.

SMITH, M. M., P. GHOSH (1987): The synthesis of hyaluronic acid by human synovial fibroblasts is influenced by the nature of the hyaluronate in the extracellular environment. Rheumatol. Int. 7: 113 – 122.

SMITH, T. J. (1987): n-Butyrate inhibition of hyaluronate synthesis in cultured human fibroblasts. J. Clin. Invest. 79: 1493 – 7.

SOLURSH, M., S. A. VAEREWYCK, R. S. REITER (1974): Depression by hyaluronic acid of glycosaminoglycan synthesis by cultured chick embryo chondrocytes. Dev. Biol. 41: 233 – 44.

STACK, M. T., K. D. BRANDT (1980): Dibutyryl cyclic AMP affects hyaluronate synthesis and macromolecular organization in normal adult articular cartilage in vitro. Biochim. Biophys. Acta 631: 264 – 4.

STOOLMILLER, A. C., A. DORFMAN (1969): The biosynthesis of hyaluronic acid by Steptococcus. J. Biol. Chem. 244: 236 – 246.

SUGAHARA, K., N. B. SCHWARTZ, A. DORFMAN (1979): Biosynthesis of hyaluronic acid by Streptococcus. J. Biol. Chem. 254: 6252 – 6261.

TAMMI, R. M. TAMMI (1986): Influence of retinoic acid on the ultrastructure and hyaluronic acid synthesis of adult human epidermis in whole skin organ culture. J. Cell. Physiol. 126: 389 – 98.

TOMIDA, M., H. KOYAMA, T. ONO (1975): Induction of hyaluronic acid synthetase activity in rat fibroblasts by medium change of confluent cultures. J. Cell. Physiol. 86: 121 – 30.

TOMIDA, M., H. KOYAMA, T. ONO (1977 a): A serum factor capable of stimulating hyaluronic acid synthesis in cultured rat fibroblasts. J. Cell. Physiol. 91: 323 – 8.

TOMIDA, M., H. KOYAMA, T. ONO (1977 b): Effects of adenosine 3' 5'-cyclic monophosphate and serum on synthesis of hyaluronic acid in confluent rat fibroblasts. Biochem. J. 162: 539 – 43.

TOOLE, B. P., J. GROSS (1971): The extracellular matrix of the regenerating newt limb synthesis and removal of hyaluronate prior to differentiation. Dev. Biol. 25: 57 – 77.

TOOLE, B. P., R. L. TRELSTAD (1971): Hyaluronate production and remocal during corneal development in the chick. Dev. Biol. 26: 28 – 35.

TOOLE, B. P. (1972): Hyaluronate turnover during chondrogenesis in the developing chick limb and axial skeleton. Dev. Biol. 29: 321 – 9.

TOOLE, B. P., G. JACKSON, J. GROSS (1972): Hyaluronate in morphogenesis. Inhibition of chondrogenesis in vitro. Proc. Natl. Acad. Sci. USA 69: 1384 – 1386.

TOOLE, B. P., C. BISWAS, J. GROSS (1979): Hyaluronate and invasiveness of the rabbit V2 carcinoma. Proc. Natl. Acad. Sci. USA 76: 6299 – 6303.

TOOLE, B. P., S. I. MUNAIM, S. WELLES, C. B. KNUDSON (1989): Hyaluronate-cell interaction and growth factor regulation of hyaluronate synthesis during limb development. Ciba Found. Symp. 143: 138 – 45.

TRISCOTT, M. X., I. VAN DE RIJN (1986): Solubilization of hyaluronic acid synthetic activity from strep-tococci and its activation with phospholipids. J. Biol. Chem. *261:* 6004 – 9.

TURLEY, E. A., P. BOWMAN, M. A. KYTRYK (1985): Effects of hyaluronate and hyaluronate binding proteins on cell motile and contact behaviour J. Cell. Sci *78:* 133 – 45.

TURLEY, E. A., J. TORRANCE (1985): Localization of hyaluronate and hyaluronate-binding protein on motile and non-motile fibroblasts. Exp. Cell. Res. *161:* 17 – 28.

TURLEY, E. A. D. MOORE, L. J. HAYDEN (1987): Characterization of hyaluronate binding proteins iso-lated from 3T3 and murine sarcoma virus transformed 3T3 cells. Biochemistry *26:* 2997 – 3005.

TURLEY, E., N. AUERSPERG (1989): A hyaluronate binding protein transiently codistributes with p21k-ras in cultured cell lines. Exp. Cell. Res. *182:* 340 – 8.

TURLEY, E. A. (1989a): The role o a cell-associated hyaluronan-binding protein in fibroblasts beha-viour Ciba Found. Symp. *143:* 121 – 33.

TURLEY, E. A. (1989b): Hyaluronic acid stimulates protein kinease activity in intact cells and in an iso-lated protein complex. J. Biol. Chem. *264:* 8951 – 5.

TZAICOS, C., J. R. E. FRASER, E. TSOTSIS, W. G. KIMPTON (1989): Inhibition of hyaluronan uptake in lymphatic tissue by chondroitin sulphate proteoglycan. Biochem. J. *264:* 823 – 828.

UCHIYAMA, H., Y. DOBASHI, K. OHKOUCHI, K. NAGASAWA (1990): Chemical cange involved in the oxidative reductive depolymerization of hyaluronic acid. J. Biol. Chem. *265:* 7753 – 7759.

ULLRICH, S. J., S. P. HAWKES (1983): The effect of the tumor promoter, phorbol myristate acetate (PMA), on hyaluronic acid (HA) synthesis by chicken embryo fibroblasts. Exp. Cell. Res. *148:* 377 – 386.

UNDERHILL, C. B. (1982): Interaction of hyaluronate with the surface of simian virus 40-transformed 3T3 cells. J. Cell. Sci. *131:* 177 – 89.

UNDERHILL, C. B., B. P. TOOLE (1982): Transformation-dependent loss of the hyaluronate-containing coats of cultured cells. J. Cell. Physiol. *110:* 123 – 8.

UNDERHILL, C. B., A. L. THURN, B. E. LACY (1985): Characterization and identification of the hyalu-ronate binding site from membranes of SV-3T3 cells. J. Biol. Chem. *260:* 8128 – 33.

UNDERHILL, C. B., G. TARONE, A. T. KAUSZ (1987): The hyaluronate-binding site from the plasma membrane is distinct from the binding protein present in brain. Connect. Tissue Res. *16:* 225 – 35.

VUORIO, E., I. TAKALA, K. PULKKI, S. EINOLA (1979): Effects of sodium aurothiomalate on hyalu-ronic acid synthesis in normal and rheumatoid synovial fibroblast cultures. Scand. J. Rheumatol. *8:* 173 – 6.

WEIGEL, P. H., G. M. FULLER, R. D. LEBOEUF (1986): A model for the role of hyaluronic acid and fibrin in the early events during the inflammatory response and wound healing. J. Theor. Biol. *119:* 219 – 34.

WEIGEL, P. H., S. J. FROST, R. D. LEBOEUF, C. T. MCGARY (1989): The specific interaction between fibrin(ogen) and hyaluronan, possible consequences in haemostasis, inflammation and wound healing. Ciba Found. Symp. *143:* 248 – 264.

WEST, D. C., I. N. HAMPSON, F. ARNOLD, S. KUMAR (1985): Angiogenesis induced by degradation products of hyaluronic acid. Science *228:* 1324 – 6.

WEST, D. C., S. KUMAR (1989a): The effect of hyaluronate and its oligosaccharides on endothelial cell proliferation and monolayer integrity. Exp. Cell. Res. *183:* 179 – 96.

WEST, D. C., S. KUMAR (1989b): Hyaluronan and angiogenesis. Ciba Found. Symp. *143:* 187 – 201.

WESTERGREN-THORNSSON, G., B. SAERNSTRAND, L. A. FRANSSON, A. MALMSTROEM (1990): TGF-beta enhances the production of hyaluronan in human lung but not in skin fibroblasts. Exp. Cell Res. *186:* 192 – 195.

WIEBKIN, O. W., H. MUIR (1977): Synthesis of proteoglycans by suspension and monolayer cultures of adult chondrocytes and de novo cartilage nodules – the effect of hyaluronic acid. J. Cell. Sci. *27:* 199 – 211.

WONG, G. L., G. N. KENT, K. Y. KU, D. V. COHN (1978): The interaction of parathormone and cal-cium on the hormone-regulated synthesis of hyaluronic acid and citrate decarboxylation in isolated bone cells. Endocrinology *103:* 2274 – 82.

WONG, S. F., B. HALLIWELL, R. RICHMOND, W. R. SKOWRONECK (1981): The role of superoxide and hydroxyl radicals in the degradation of hyaluronic acid induced by metal ions and by ascorbic acid. J. Inhorg. Biochem. *14:* 127–34.

WU, R., M. M. WU (1986): Effects of retinoids on human bronchial epithelial cells differential regulation of hyaluronate synthesis and keratin protein synthesis and keratin protein synthesis. J. Cell. Physiol. *127:* 73–82.

YARON, M. C.W. CASTOR (1969): Leukocyte-connective tissue cell interaction I Stimulation of hyaluronate synthesis by live and dead leukocytes. Arthritis Rheum. *12:* 265–73.

YARON, M., I. YARON, C. WILETZKI, U. ZOR (1978): Interrelationship between stimulation of prostaglandin E and hyaluronate production by poly (I). poly (C) and interferon in synovial fibroblast culture. Arthritis Rheum. *21:* 694–698.

YARON, M., I. YARON (1986): The effect of diflunisal on hyaluronic acid production by 'activated' human synovial fibroblasts. Br. J. Clin. Pharmac. *12:* 423–426.

YONEDA, M., S. SUZUKI, K. KIMATA (1990): Hyaluonic acid associated with the surfaces of cultured fibroblasts is linked to a serum-derived 85-kDa protein. J. Biol. Chem. *265:* 5247–5257.

YOSHIMURA, M. (1985): Change of hyaluronic acid synthesis during differentiation of myogenic cells and its relation to transformation of myoblasts by Rous sarcoma virus. Cell. Differ. *16:* 175–185.

*Anatomisches Institut der Universität Erlangen-Nürnberg*

# Histochemical and immunohistochemical localization of hyaluronan and hyaluronan synthase in the anterior eye segment

### E. Lütjen-Drecoll

In recent studies we were able to localize hyaluronan (HA) and the HA synthesizing enzyme HA-synthase (HAS) in different tissues of the anterior segment of the eye (Lütjen-Drecoll et al., 1990; Rittig et al., 1992 a,b). The visualization of HA has been made possible by the work of Tengblad (1979). Using an affinity purification method, he isolated a protein from cartilage, which specifically binds to HA. This probe, the HA binding region, binds to HA with high specificity and affinity (Hardingham and Muir, 1972; Hascall and Heinegård, 1974; Hascall and Hascall, 1981; Lütjen-Drecoll et al., 1990). For the histochemical demonstration the probe was linked to biotin, the complex purified and visualized in the tissue by staining the probe using the avidine-biotin-complex (ABC) technique. In order to reduce loss of HA during preparation and staining, HA was precipitated in the tissue with cetylpyridinium chloride (CPC).

As has been described by Prehm in this volume, HA is not formed in the Golgi apparatus like other proteoglycans, but is synthesized from precursors by a membrane bound enzyme, HAS, releasing the growing HA-chain directly into the extracellular space. Prehm et al. have identified this enzyme in streptococcus protoplast membrane as a 52 000 Mr protein. Biochemical and immunohistochemical studies by Prehm and Mausolf (1986) as well as immunohistochemical studies by our group (Rittig et al., 1992 a), indicate that there is a cross reactivity between the streptococcal and primate enzyme.

For the immunohistochemical demonstration of HAS in the anterior segment of primate eyes, we used the streptococcal anti HAS-antibody, which was kindly provided by P. Prehm.

### 1. Cornea

Both the cell membranes of the corneal epithelium and endothelium stained intensely for the synthesizing enzyme HAS, whereas the keratozytes in the corneal stroma were only weakly stained. In the corneal epithelium HAS-staining was found in the cell membranes of all cell layers. Only the basolateral membranes of

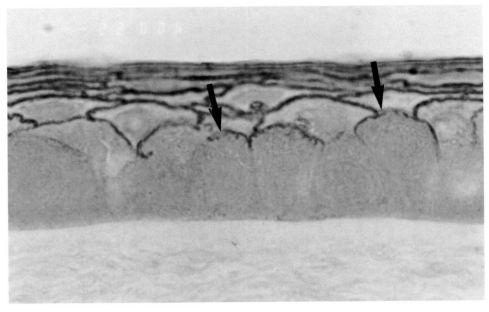

Fig. 1. Cornea epithelium stained with antibodies against HAS visualized with the peroxidase technique (x 800). Note that the cell membranes of the corneal epithelium are intensely stained. The small
unstained dots represent the locations of the desmosomes (arrows), where no staining is present. In
the basal layer of the epithelium the staining of the apical surface of the cells is less intense and is lacking at the basal and lateral cell surfaces.

the basal cells appeared unlabelled (Fig. 1). Histochemical staining for the HA-
molecule was found only at the inner surface of the cornea. Here the corneal endothelium was covered by a prominent layer of HA (Fig. 2).

Even if the specimens are fixed in the presence of CPC, hyaluronan molecules
are lost during the embedding procedure, if they are not bound to any structure in
the tissue. A stained HA-layer on the surface of the endothelium therefore
indicates that the HA-molecule is bound to the cell membrane. In fact, MADSEN·et
al. (1989) demonstrated binding sites for HA in the corneal endothelium, so that at
this location the freshly synthesized HA-molecule might bind to the cell surface.

The functional significance of the HA covering the corneal endothelium is still
not known. In experimental studies GRAUE, POLACK and BALAZS (1980) were able
to demonstrate, that Na-hyaluronate injected into the anterior segment of the eye
had a protective effect for endothelial cells when exposed to mechanical stress. It is
not known, whether physiologically hyaluronan in this location serves the same
function. On the other hand, hyaluronan due to its surrounding "water coat" is a
quite inert molecule, which hinders adhesion of particles transported in the aque-

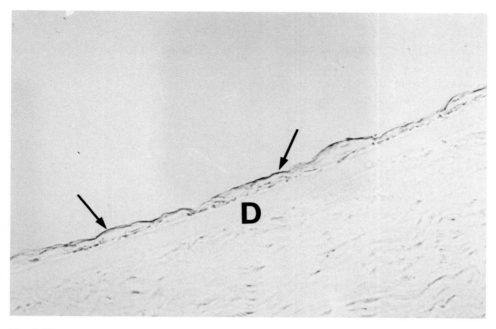

Fig. 2. Histochemical staining for hyaluronan in the cornea (x 250). Note that the surface of the corneal endothelium is covered by a HA positively stained layer (arrows). (D = Descemet's membrane).

ous humor. Therefore, a hyaluronan film covering the endothelium could play a protective role also for the translucence of the cornea.

Interestingly no staining for HA was seen between the epithelial cells or on the outer surface of the corneal epithelium, even if the cell membranes were intensely stained for HAS. This differences in staining between presence of the molecule and the synthesizing enzyme indicates that HA in this location is not bound to the cell membranes and is lost from the tissue. This suggestion is supported by the finding of UNDERHILL (1989) who did not find binding sites for HA in the corneal epithelium.

On the outer surface of the eye, the epithelium is not only protected by a HA-film, but by the complicated layers of the tear film. Our findings indicate that HA might be released into the tear film, but possibly the surface of the epithelium is not covered by a HA-layer to allow the inner layer of the tear film to adhere to the corneal epithelium.

## 2. Lens

The outer and lateral cell membranes of the lens epithelium stained intensely for HAS. In this location the outer surface of the epithelium was covered by a stained HA-layer similar to what was seen in the corneal endothelium. Possibly HA in the lens serves similar functions as described for the corneal endothelium.

## 3. Trabecular meshwork

In the transition zone to the trabecular meshwork the cells covering the operculum found in monkey eyes also stained intensely for HAS and HA. In contrast, the trabecular meshwork proper showed differences between HA- and HAS-staining. Only the inner uveal and corneoscleral trabecular cells stained for HAS (Fig. 3), whereas staining for HA was mainly seen in the cribriform layer underneath the

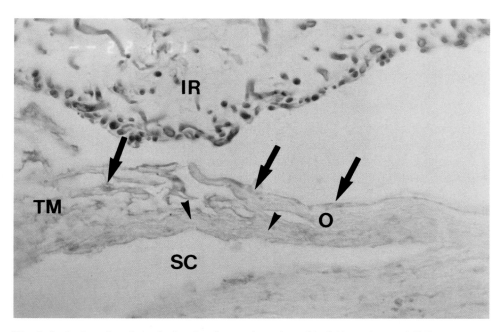

Fig. 3. Sagittal section through the chamber angle region with Schlemm's canal (SC), trabecular meshwork (TM) and iris root (IR) (staining for HAS, x 304). Note that the cells covering the operculum (O) – the posterior extension of the corneal endothelium – are intensely stained as are the trabecular cells covering the uveal and inner corneoscleral lamellae (arrows). The cells of the cribriform region underlying the inner wall of Schlemm's canal remain nearly unstained (arrowheads). At the anterior surface of the iris there are also cells with stained membranes. Due to the pigmentations of the cells this staining is difficv' to demonstrate in the picture.

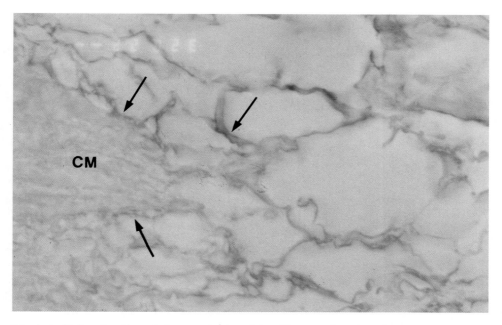

Fig. 4. Sagittal section through the anterior tips of the ciliary muscle stained for HAS (x 304). Note that the cells covering the anterior tips in the socalled trabeculum ciliare are stained (arrows), whereas the muscle (CM) itself remains unstained.

endothelial lining of Schlemm's canal. In this region no cells stained for HAS (Fig. 3). We therefore assume that the HA deposited in the cribriform layer is not produced locally, but reaches the cribriform region by aqueous flow. It has been shown that during anterior chamber perfusion experiments in monkeys (KAUFMAN et al., 1988) there is a decrease in outflow resistance due to wash-out of extra-cellular material. If there is loss of HA from the inner wall region also in human eyes, this HA could be regenerated from the cells of the inner portion of the trabe-cular meshwork.

## 4. Ciliary body

Intense staining for HAS was also seen in the cells of the trabeculum ciliare covering the anterior tips of the ciliary muscle (Fig. 4). The ciliary muscle fibers themselves and the fibroblasts within the stroma of the muscle showed nearly no staining for HAS. There was also no HA-staining in this region. These findings are in contrast to those seen in the rabbit, where the ciliary body, especially in front of the muscle, was intensely stained (Fig. 5), (LÜTJEN-DRECOLL et al., 1990). These

Fig. 5. Schematic drawing of the distribution of HA-staining in monkey (top) and rabbit eyes (bottom). Note that there is intense staining in the uveoscleral pathways of the rabbit, whereas this region in monkey eyes remains unstained.

staining differences between the two species could explain differences in uveoscleral outflow. In rabbits only little aqueous humor leaves the eye via ciliary body-sclera, whereas in primates in the relaxed state of the ciliary muscle there is little

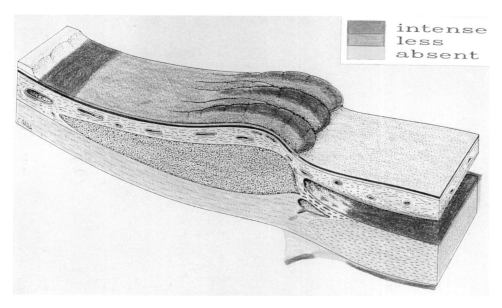

intense
less
absent

Fig. 6. Schematic drawing demonstrating the regional differences of HAS staining in the primate eye.

resistance to the aqueous flow through the wide intermuscular spaces, and uveo-scleral flow can increase to more than 30% of the total outflow. Possibly some HA in this area can be regenerated from the cells of the trabeculum ciliare.

## 5. Iris

In the iris staining for both HA and HAS was observed. The most intense staining for HA was seen at the anterior iris surface (Fig. 3). Here also most cells stained for HAS, indicating that HA in the iris is produced locally.

## 6. Ciliary epithelium

In the ciliary epithelium three different regions could be distinguished with regard to HA- and HAS-staining: 1. the anteriormost pars plicata extending into the aqueous humor of the posterior chamber; 2. the posterior pars plicata and the anterior pars plana which faces the vitreous; and 3. the posterior pars plana, where the zonule is directly attached to the nonpigmented epithelium (NPE).

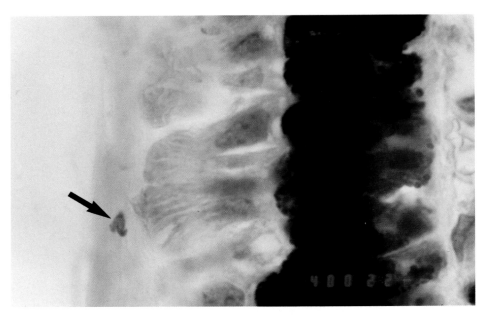

Fig. 7. Ciliary epithelium of the posterior pars plana (staining for HAS x 1600). Note the intense stain-ing of the cell membranes of the NPE-cells and the hyalocyte adjacent to the vitreous surface of the NPE-cell (arrow).

    The most intense staining for HAS was seen in the NPE of the posterior pars plana (region 3) (Figs. 6, 7). The hyalocytes found in the cortical layer of the vitre-ous in this region also showed intense staining for HAS, supporting previous studies by Balazs et al. (BALAZS et al., 1964; FREEMAN et al., 1979), which indicated that hyalocytes may produce HA for the vitreous. On the other hand, the HAS-positive NPE cells of the posterior pars plana might also be responsible for HA-production for the vitreous, as it has been postulated by ZIMMERMANN et al. and FINE (1964).

    In the ciliary epithelium of the posterior pars plicata and anterior pars plana (region 2) no staining for HAS was seen (Fig. 6).

    Staining for HAS was also found in the NPE at the tips of the anterior pars pli-cata (Fig. 8). Since these cells are immediately adjacent to the posterior chamber, we assume that HA produced by these cells is released into the aqueous humor. The presence of HA in the aqueous humor has been demonstrated by LAURENT et al. (1981). These authors noted that the total amount of HA turned over in the an-terior chamber is larger than that in the vitreous, indicating significant synthesis of HA in the anterior ocular segment (LAURENT and FRASER, 1983, LAURENT and GRANATH, 1983). Based on our staining results we assume that the sources of HA

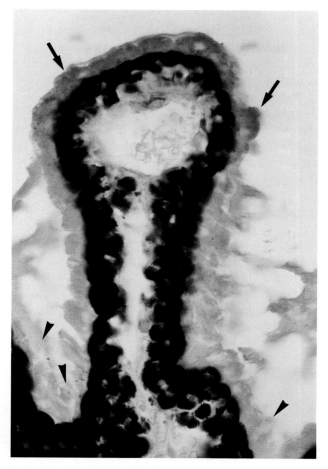

Fig. 8. Section through the anterior pars plicata of the ciliary processes (staining for HAS x 320). The NPE-cells at the top of the process (arrows) show a more intense staining of their basolateral cell membranes than those of the valleys (arrowheads).

in the aqueous humor are the NPE-cells of the anterior pars plicata, but the anterior layer of the iris and the corneal endothelium might also contribute.

## 7. Conjunctiva

The most intense staining for the HA-molecule was seen in the *stroma* of the conjunctiva where HA forms most of the ground substance (Fig. 5). The source for the molecule could either be the stromal fibroblasts which showed a faint staining for HAS or the conjunctival epithelium which stained intensely for HAS (Fig. 9a). The molecule is, however, not only released to the stromal site, but also to the intercellular spaces of the epithelium itself and to the epithelial surface. In these locations there was staining for the HA-molecule indicating that the conjunctival epithelium also should have binding sites for HA.

Possibly HA in the conjunctival epithelium due to its water binding capacities might help to prevent the cornea from drying out. In the transition zone to the cornea, in the socalled *limbal conjunctiva*, staining for HAS stopped, but occured again in the corneal epithelium (Fig. 9b,c). The functional significance of this special staining pattern in the limbal conjunctiva is still not clear. In previous studies we have demonstrated, that the epithelial cells of this small region stained for the membrane bound enzymes NA-K-ATPase and Carbonic anhydrase, indicating active pumping capacities of these cells. We do not know, whether secretion of HA interfers with this pump-function.

On the other hand, there is still staining for the HA molecule in the intercellular spaces and on the surface of the epithelium in the limbal region. If water is pumped from the most peripheral cornea into the epithelium, this water can be bound by the HA within the epithelium so that also the limbal portion of the conjunctiva is prevented from drying out.

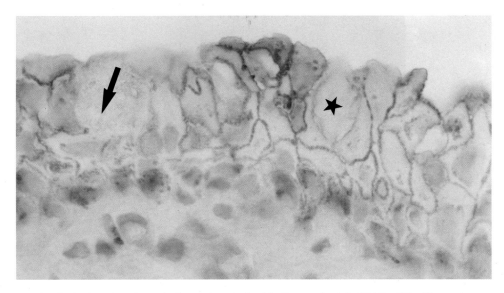

Fig. 9a. Sagittal section through the conjunctival epithelium stained for HAS x 800. All membranes except the basolateral ones of the basal cells are intensely stained. There are two different types of globlet cells with respect to HAS-staining: One type with (asterisks) and one without membrane staining (arrow).

# Conclusion

Summarizing our results on the distribution of hyaluronan (HA) and hyaluronan-synthase (HAS) we can state that at least in the anterior segment of the primate eye HA is found at the same location where the HA-synthesizing enzyme

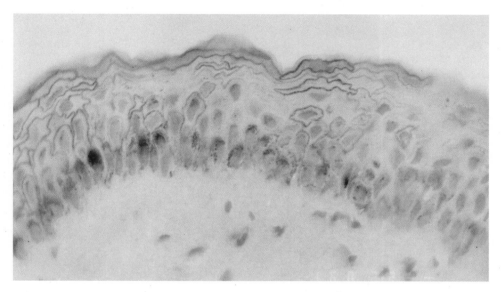

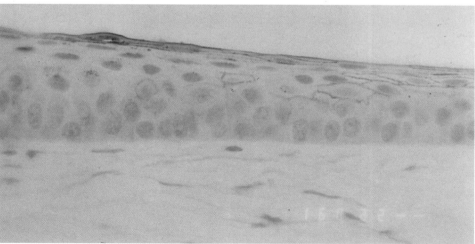

Fig. 9b + c. In the transition zone from the fornix to the limbal conjunctiva the membrane staining for HAS stops (right side of the picture) (x 800) (Fig. 9c). At the transition zone of the limbal conjunctiva to the cornea (right side of the picture), membrane staining occurs again (x 800).

(HAS) is also located at the cell membranes. This indicates that the HA is produced locally. There are only two exceptions, i. e. the epithelium of the cornea and the trabecular meshwork (Fig. 10).

At the surface of the cornea epithelium a layer of HA was lacking although the membranes of the superficial cell layers stained positively for HAS. We assume that in this region the locally produced HA is incorporated into the tear film and

## Distribution of HA and HA-Synthase in the anterior segment of the eye

|  | HA | HA-Synthase |
|---|---|---|
| Corneaepithel | − | + |
| Conjunctiva epithelium | | |
| limbal | + | − |
| fornix | + | + |
| Corneal endothelium | + | + |
| Operculum | + | + |
| Trabecular meshwork | | |
| non filtering portion | + | + |
| filtering portion | | |
| uveal, inner corneoscleral | − | + |
| outer corneoscleral, cribriform | + | − |
| inner, outer wall-endoth. | + | + |

Fig. 10. Distribution of HA and HA-synthase in the anterior segment of the eye.

washed away during lid movements. It might also be that the HA-layer in this zone is so small that it is lost in the process of fixation and tissue embedding. Further studies are needed in this respect.

In the trabecular meshwork the cells of the uveal and inner corneoscleral part revealed HAS, whereas the cribriform cells did not stain positively for HAS. In contrast, the cribriform layer and the inner as well as the outer wall of Schlemm's canal contained HA but did not stain for HAS. In this case, the HA might be produced by the inner portion of the trabecular meshwork and the corneal endothelium but washed away by aqueous flow through the trabecular meshwork and aqueous outflow pathways. If so, this could become an important factor for outflow resistance regulation, but final decisions cannot be made at this stage of investigation.

# References

BALAZS, E. A., L. Z. J. TOTH, A. P. MITCHELL (1964): Studies on the structure of the vitreous body. XII. Cytological and histochemical studies on the cortical tissue layer. Exp. Eye Res. *3*: 57 – 71.

FREEMAN, M. I., B. JACOBSON, E. A. BALAZS (1979): The chemical composition of vitreous hyalocyte granules. Exp. Eye Res. *29*: 479 – 484.

GRAUE, E. L., F. M. POLACK, E. A. BALAZS (1980): The protective effect of Na-hyaluronate to corneal endothelium. Exp. Eye Res. *31*: 119 – 127.

HARDINGHAM, T. E., H. MUIR (1972): The specific interaction of hyaluronic acid with cartilage proteogylcans. Biochem. Biophys. Acta *279*: 401 – 5.

HACALL, V. C., (1974): D. HEINEGÅRD, Aggregation of cartilage proteoglycans. J. Biol. Chem. *49*: 4232 – 56.

HASCALL, V. C., G. K. HASCALL (1981): Proteoglycans. Cell Biology of the Extracellular Matrix. Hay, E. D. (Ed.), Plenum Press. New York, Pp. 39 – 63.

KAUFMANN, P. L., B. A. TRUE-GABELT, K. A. ERICKSON-LAMY (1988): Time-dependence of perfusion outflow facility in the cynomologus monkey. Curr. Eye Res. *7*: 721 – 726.

LAURENT, U. B. G., (1981): Hyaluronate in aqueus humour. Exp. Eye Res. *33*: 147 – 155

LAURENT, U. B. G., J. R. E. FRASER (1983): Turnover of hyaluronate in the aqueous humor and vitreous body of the rabbit. Exp. Eye Res. *36*: 493 – 504.

LAURENT, U. B. G., K. A. GRANATH, (1983): The molecular weight of hyaluronate in the aqueous humour and vitreous body of rabbit and cattle eyes. Exp. Eye Res. *36*: 481 – 492.

LÜTJEN-DRECOLL, E., M. SCHENHOLM, E. TAMM, A. TENGBLAD (1990): Visualization of hyaluronic acid in the anterior segment of rabbit and monkey eyes. Exp. Eye Res. *51*: 55 – 63.

MADSEN, K., M. SCHENHOLM, G. JAHNKE, A. TENGBLAD (1989): Hyaluronate binding to intact corneas and cultured endothelial cells. Invest. Ophthalmol. Vis. Sci. *30*: 2132 – 2137.

PREHM, P.: Cellular functions of hyaluronate. In: E. Lütjen-Drecoll (Ed.) (1992): Basic Aspects of Glaucoma Research III. Schattauer, Stuttgart.

PREHM, P., A. MAUSOLF (1986): Isolation of streptococcal hyaluronate synthase. Biochem J. *235*: 887 – 889.

RITTIG, M., E. LÜTJEN-DRECOLL, P. PREHM (1992a): Immunohistochemical localization of hyaluronan synthase in cornea and conjunctiva of cynomolgus monkey: Exp. Eye Res. *54*: 455 – 460.

RITTIG, M., C. FLÜGEL, P. PREHM, E. LÜTJEN-DRECOLL (1992b): Hyaluronan synthase immunoreactivity in the anterior segment of the primate eye. Graefes Arch. Klin. exp. Opthalm. (in press).

TENGBLAD, A. (1979): Affinity chromatography on immobilized hyaluronate and its application to the isolation of hyaluronate binding proteins from cartilage. Biochem. Biophys. Acta *578*: 281 – 9.

UNDERHILL, C. B. (1989): The interaction of hyaluronate with the cell surface: the hyaluronate receptor and the core protein. In: The biology of hyaluronan (Ciba Foundation Symposium 143). Wiley, Chichester, pp. 87 – 106.

ZIMMERMANN, L. E., B. FINE (1964): Production of hyaluronic acid by cysts and tumors of the ciliary body. Arch. Ophthal. *72*: 365 – 379.

*Departments of Ophthalmology and Pathology, State Universty*
*of New York Health Science Center at Syracuse*

# Elastic fibers and microfibrils in the eye

### B. W. STREETEN

Knowledge of the elastic tissue system has increased greatly in the past decade, but still lags behinds that of the collagens and many of the nonfibrillar matrix molecules. It is highly likely that an intact elastic system is essential for the normal development and function of the eye, although elastic fibers comprise less than 2–7% of ocular structural protein where specific regions have been analysed (MOSES et al. 1978; HORSTMANN, ROHEN, SAMES 1983). The first disease of elastic tissue affecting the eye to be identified with a specific genetic defect is the Marfan syndrome (DIETZ et al. 1991; LEE et al. 1991), although many others are postulated.

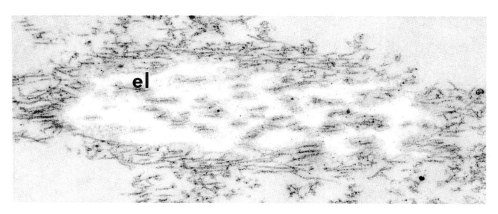

Fig. 1. Young elastic fiber showing electron lucent homogeneous elastin (el) being deposited in linear cords on 10nm elastic microfibrils (x 67,500)

## Composition and structure of fibers in the elastic system

The basic unit of the elastic fiber is the microfibril (Fig. 1), a 10nm periodic fibril which serves as a template for deposition of the amorphous elastin (GREENLEE, ROSS and HARTMANN 1966). Investigation of elastin is much more advanced than that of the microfibril. Elastin is a 68kDa very insoluble protein, rich in the hydrophobic amino acids, proline, glycine, alanine, and valine (see review by ROSEN-

BLOOM, 1984). It is highly crosslinked by the Cu-requiring enzyme, lysyl oxidase, producing two unique lysine crosslinks, desmosine and isodesmosine. The elastin molecule is thought to have a random coil structure with random lysine crosslinks between adjacent molecules. The hydrophobic regions between crosslinks confer elasticity, and result in a very mobile elastomer. Since elastin contains hydroxyproline and about a third of its amino acids are glycine (Table I), it may be phylogeneti-

Table 1: Amino acid composition of elastin, zonules and other elastic microfibrils (in residues/1000 amino acid residues)

|  | Elastin[1] (Human aorta) | Zonule[2] (Human) | Zonule[2] (Bovine) | Elastic Microfibrils[3] (Calf Ligament) |
|---|---|---|---|---|
| Aspartic Acid | 6 | 104 | 108 | 114 |
| Threonine | 12 | 48 | 54 | 55 |
| Serine | 8 | 66 | 64 | 59 |
| Glutamic acid | 18 | 129 | 137 | 111 |
| Proline | 131 | 69 | 66 | 70 |
| Glycine | 295 | 118 | 108 | 120 |
| Alanine | 233 | 66 | 49 | 59 |
| Cystine/2 | (2)* | 74 | 83 | 80 |
| Valine | 143 | 48 | 48 | 54 |
| Methionine | 0 | 10 | 16 | 16 |
| Isoleucine | 23 | 34 | 41 | 45 |
| Leucine | 58 | 67 | 60 | 57 |
| Tyrosine | 23 | 23 | 30 | 30 |
| Phenylalanine | 22 | 33 | 41 | 32 |
| Lysine | 4 | 37 | 38 | 37 |
| Histidine | 0.5 | 16 | 17 | 14 |
| Arginine | 9 | 44 | 40 | 45 |
| Hydroxyproline | 10 | 0 | 0 | 0 |
| Hydroxylysine | 0 | 0 | 0 | 0 |
| Isodesmosine | 2.2 | ND | ND | ND |
| Desmosine | 2.8 | ND | ND | ND |

[1] STARCHER and GALIONE 1976
[2] STREETEN et al. 1983
[3] ROSS and BORNSTEIN 1969
* Two cysteine residues discovered on sequencing (INDIK et al. 1989)
ND = Not determined

cally a distant relative of collagen. The elastin molecule is now sequenced (INDIK et al. 1989) and its gene identified on chromosome 2 (EMANUEL et al. 1985). Tropoelastin, a 70kDa molecule, is the primary gene product, requiring cleavage of a small signal peptide to produce the functional elastin. Regulation of elastin gene expression is being intensively studied, to give some insight into how elastin synthesis is controlled (FAZIO et al. 1990).

The elastic microfibril is quite different from elastin, being composed of cysteine-rich acidic glycoprotein which has proven very difficult to isolate since its first crude extraction (ROSS and BORNSTEIN 1969). Quantities available for analysis are small, and show a significant amount of associated carbohydrate, as well as frequent admixture with other matrix molecules. Experimentally the bovine elastic neck ligament (ligamentum nuchae) has been the standard source of microfibrillar protein for analysis.

A new and especially concentrated source of relatively pure elastic microfibrils was uncovered by RAVIOLA in 1971, when she suggested that zonular fibrils resembled ultrastructurally the then recently discovered microfibrils of elastic tissue. This hypothesis was confirmed immunologically by demonstrating crossreactivity between zonular fibrils and elastic microfibrils of both ocular and nonocular types in several species (STREETEN et al. 1981, STREETEN and LICARI 1983). Amino acid and partial carbohydrate analysis of bovine zonular fibers was first reported by BUDDECKE and WOLLENSAK in 1966. Similar profiles were shown for bovine and human zonules (Table I), and a similarity noted as well between amino acid profiles and soluble peptides of zonular fibrils and elastic microfibrils from other sources (STREETEN et al. 1983; STREETEN and GIBSON 1988). These findings established that zonular fibers are a type of elastic microfibril, and justify their frequent use as a model for these structures (MECHAM et al. 1988).

Several microfibrillar proteins have been reported to cross-react immunologically with elastic microfibrils in tissues, usually proteins of 31–36kDa MW (KAWAGUCHI 1982; GIBSON et al. 1986; STREETEN and GIBSON 1988), and 250–350kDa MW (SEAR, GRANT, JACKSON 1981; SAKAI, KEENE, ENGVALL 1986; STREETEN and GIBSON 1988; GIBSON, KUMARATILAKE and CLEARY 1989). Isolation and characterization is most advanced on the 350kDa protein given the name fibrillin (SAKAI, KEENE, ENGVALL 1986). Fibrillin has an amino acid profile similar to that of elastic microfibrillar extracts and of whole zonule, and is even higher in cysteine. The cysteine content of the zonule is of great interest because a number of lens-dislocating diseases have defects in cystine metabolism, for example homocystinuria, implying that the disulfide bonds of cystine are important for linking zonular fibrils together. Fibrillin is now partially sequenced (MASLEN et al. 1991) and has been localized to chromosome 15 q21 although there appear to be 2 other fibrillin genes on chromosomes 5 and 17 (LEE et al. 1991). Monoclonal antibody to fibrillin binds strongly to all types of elastic microfibrils, including zonular fibrils (SAKAI, KEENE, ENGVALL 1986; STREETEN, GIBSON, DARK 1986). It is very likely that fibrillin is the main microfibril protein. Two other elastic microfibril-associated proteins have also been sequenced, – the 21kDa MAGP from bovine nuchal ligament (GIBSON et al. 1991) and the 58kDa AMP from bovine zonule (HORRIGAN et al. 1992).

An unexpected advance in understanding of the microfibril came from rotary shadowing of the chick vitreous by WRIGHT and MAYNE in 1988. Among the type II collagen fibrils of vitreous, they found a beaded fibril composed of 29nm beads strung together by 6–8 fine filaments, composing a stable-appearing microfibril

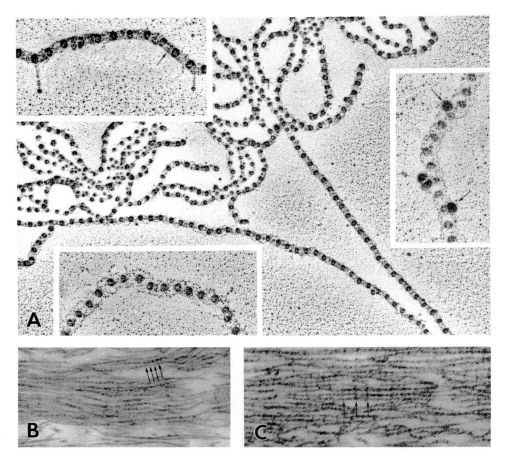

Fig. 2. Rotary shadowing of human zonular fibrils. A. Clump of typical zonular beaded fibrils with 29nm beads, in tightly aggregated conformation (x 67,800). Upper inset: Double banding is sometimes visible across the interbead filaments (arrow). Two drumstick forms extend down from beads or inter-bead areas. (x 107,700). Lower inset: Fine filaments seen more clearly between the beads when in looser conformation (x 107,700). Right inset: Zonular fibril immunostained with monoclonal fibrillin antibody. The round gold-labeled antibody complex binds to the junction of beads and outer filaments (arrows) (x 107,700). B. 12nm microperiodicity (arrows) of zonular fibrils in epon sections (x 86,400). C. 45 – 55nm macroperiodicity (arrows) sometimes seen across bundles of zonular fibrils in epon sections. (x 86,400). (In part from WALLACE, STREETEN and HANNA 1991).

they suggested might be zonular in type. While the fibril did not conform to the classical description of zonular and other elastic microfibrils as 10nm tubular structures with a 12 – 14nm microperiodicity, the frequency of beading at 49 – 52nm was very similar to the 45 – 55nm macroperiodicity often noted across bundles of bovine and human zonular fibrils (Fig. 2B, C) (RAVIOLA 1971, STREETEN et al. 1981).

By rotary shadowing freshly dissected human and bovine zonular fibers, beaded fibrils (Fig. 2A) identical to those in the vitreous were found, and also in bovine neck ligament (WALLACE, STREETEN, HANNA 1991). Fibrillin antibody bound to one side of the beaded components, confirming their identification as elastic microfibrils. Three protein fragments immunologically related to native fibrillin resemble portions of this beaded fibril (MADDOX et al. 1989), strengthening the claim for fibrillin as the major elastic microfibrillar protein. The NH2-terminal sequences for two of these fragments were determined, and the fibrillin molecule is presently being sequenced (MASLEN et al. 1991). Clearly tools are rapidly becoming available for understanding not only the normal structure of the elastic system but genetic and other abnormalities as well.

Characterization of the elastic system into 3 components has been helpful for 3-dimensional conceptualization of this complex system (COTTA-PEREIA et al. 1976). The simplest units are bundles of nonelasticized microfibrils known as oxytalan (FULLMER and LILLIE 1958), typified by fibers in the zonule of Zinn (GABLER and SCHEUNER 1965). Oxytalan bundles characteristically attach to basement membranes of epithelial cells such as ciliary pigmented or non-pigment-

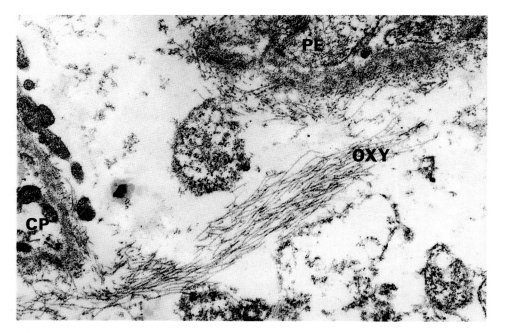

Fig. 3. Oxytalan fibers (OXY) connecting basement membrane of ciliary pigment epithelium (PE) with basement membrane of an underlying capillary wall (CP) Bovine. x 36,750. (From Streeten and Licari 1983).

ed epithelial cells, and to basement membranes of vascular and lymphatic endothelium and muscle cells (Fig. 3). In complex tissues they also blend into partially elasticized small elastic fibers called elaunin (GAWLIK 1965), which in turn join mature elastic fibers at a deeper level.

The nature of the binding between the elastic microfibril and the elastin molecule to form elastic fibers is unknown. Lysine crosslinks, in the form of lysinonorleucine (RICHMOND 1981), and cystine crosslinks (KUCICH et al. 1988) have both been suggested. A fascinating question is what prevents oxytalan fibers from becoming elasticized, since in most instances the same cells can produce both microfibrils and elastin. A 67kDa cell surface receptor for elastin (MECHAM et al. 1989 a) appears to be the same as the laminin receptor (MECHAM et al. 1989 b). Reciprocal binding of the receptor to galactoside sugars suggested a way for directing interaction between elastin and the glycosylated microfibrils. The progression from immature elaunin to mature elastic fibers, the normal course in maturation, also involves unknown controlling factors. Elaunin fibers in many sites remain as immmature microfibril-rich structures with nonfused cables of elastin passing through them for life. Although elaunin fibers bind elastin antibody, they do not stain with Verhoeff's iron hematoxylin stain, the previous gold standard for elastin, implying other differences besides size. It is not clear what advantage an incompletely elasticized fiber would have other than for some modification of its elasticity.

Oxytalan fibers are thought to play a role in resisting tractional stresses, inferred from their typical position between two surfaces or tissues subject to considerable traction. Zonular bundles placed on stretch in enucleated eyes have elastic characteristics and show elastic recoil on release, although there is no evidence they contain elastin in mammals. Small foci of tropoelastin on zonular bundles have been described only in the chick (GORDINI et al. 1990). The variable periodicity of zonular fibrils in tissues, and the variable length of their interbead filaments on rotary shadowing, suggest that their elasticity may reside in the extensibility of their interbead filaments (WALLACE, STREETEN, HANNA 1991).

## Elastogenesis within the eye

Some component of the elastic system is present in every tissue of the eye although its distribution and variety may be severely limited. The iris for example has only oxytalan fibers, most of them closely associated with the dilator and sphincter smooth muscles (ALEXANDER and GARNER, 1983). The retina is reported to have no elastic fibers in the walls of its blood vessels or in the extravascular tissue (ANDERSON 1969 a; HOGAN, ALVARADO, WEDDELL 1971 a). Histochemical demonstration of apparent elastic components in retinal vessels of some older eyes (Fig. 4) may represent induction of expression under pathologic conditions, such as

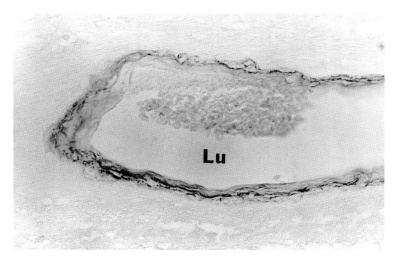

Fig. 4. Retinal vessel wall showing apparent linear elastic components after staining with orcein. Lu = lumen, containing red cells. x 330.

systemic hypertension. The lens has only oxytalan fibers, inserting on its capsule. The cells found close to the elastic components are usually their cells of origin, illustrating how many different kinds of cells are able to express elastin and/or microfibril genes. Mesenchymal cells deriving from both mesoderm and neural crest appear to be competent, as do neuroectodermal smooth muscle cells in the iris, and smooth muscle cells in the ciliary body. Mesodermal skeletal muscle cells produce copious elastic fibers.

All the epithelial and other basement-membrane secreting cells in the eye appear capable of producing oxytalan in the normal state or as a pathologic expression. From the second decade, the lens epithelial cells produce microfibrils with oxytalan staining characteristics as inclusions in the lens capsule (DARK et al. 1969; STREETEN et al. 1984). The corneal endothelial cells secrete oxytalan as detected by histochemical staining in many dystrophic conditions (ALEXANDER, GRIERSON, GARNER 1981). Indirect evidence suggests that the ciliary nonpigment epithelium synthesizes zonular fibrils (GLOOR 1974; RHODES et al. 1982; BENNETT and HADDAD 1986), although lens epithelial cells in culture can also synthesize microfibrillar components (BRIGLIN, LI, STREETEN 1991). It is possible that the retinal pigment epithelium contributes to the elastin of Bruch's membrane, and the ciliary pigment epithelium to its underlying elastic layer, but this has not been shown in vitro (NEWSOME et al. 1988). Whether there are any differences in elastic components from these different cells is at present unknown.

The course of ocular elastogenesis during development has been little studied although the eye is an excellent organ for such study. It is relatively small, with development proceeding at different rates regionally, and presumably requires different degrees of elasticity during those periods. In a histochemical study, ALEXANDER and GARNER (1983) found that oxytalan fibers were the most common elastic components in the neonate. The change to more mature elastic fibers occurred progressively from the anterior to the posterior regions of the eye with a few important exceptions, as will be noted under specific regions of the eye.

## Renewal of elastic tissue components, and additional proteins associated with elastic fibers during aging

Information is limited concerning the turnover of elastin after maturation, but in the skin the rate appears to be constant for many decades (FAZIO et al. 1988). There is little basis for an opinion about renewal of elastic microfibrils since their composition is incompletely known, although rapid turnover of a fucose-containing glycoprotein has been described in zonules of the rabbit (RHODES et al. 1982) and the adult rat (BENNETT and HADDAD 1986).

An interesting association has been reported of several serum proteins and elastic fibers post-natally. Amyloid P component shows non-covalent binding to elastic fibers from the age of 4 (BREATHNACH, PEPYS, HINTNER 1989), and vitronectin becomes bound sometime in the following decade (DAHLBACK et al. 1989, 1990). The normal function of amyloid P is unknown but vitronectin is a multifunctional adhesion protein. Amyloid P can inhibit elastolysis in vitro (LI and MCADAM 1984). Whether this occurs in vivo is not known. There is controversy about whether amyloid P and vitronectin bind to elastin or to the microfibrils. We have found that amyloid P binds to the surface of elastic fibers (LI et al. 1989), and vitronectin somewhat irregularly to zonular and other microfibrils (STREETEN et al., unpublished). C3 complex of complement also binds to elastic microfibrils in skin during the third decade or later, possibly as a reaction to actinic injury (DAHLBACK et al. 1989).

Fibronectin, another adhesion protein, is associated with normal elastic microfibrils (SCHWARTZ et al. 1985), including zonular fibrils (GOLDFISCHER et al. 1985), and as a contaminant in their peptide profile (STREETEN and GIBSON 1988). INOUE et al. (1986) suggested that ocular zonular fibrils have cores of amyloid P held together by bands of fibronectin. We have found no amyloid P in direct association with normal zonular fibrils in the human (LI, STREETEN, YOHAI 1989), and fibronectin appeared to be more related to bundles of zonular microfibrils than to individual fibrils (STREETEN and GIBSON, 1988).

## Cornea

As described by ALEXANDER and GARNER (1983), the very young human cornea has extensive staining histochemically for oxytalan fibers in its inner two-thirds, especially in the preDecemet's region, but most of these disappear in early childhood. An appearance of tubular microfibrils in the fetal rabbit cornea at 15 days gestation, and in highly regular bundles presumed to be of the same type in newborn rabbits, has been seen ultrastructurally (CINTRON, COVINGTON, KUBLIN 1983). A similar distribution was reported in kittens with the disappearance of all but peripheral bundles in adult cat corneas (CARRINGTON, ALEXANDER, GRIERSON 1984). This late disappearance has recently been questioned because bundles similar to elastic microfibrils have been noted ultrastructurally in adult rabbit and mice corneas, between the collagen lamellae (KANAI and KAUFMAN 1973; PRATT and MADRI 1985; CARLSON and WARING 1988). These microfibrils are straighter than the usual oxytalan, only occasionally show tubular profiles, and are almost hidden by fibrogranular material. They fragment on incubation with pepsin, are digested by prolonged trypsin and elastase treatment but are not affected by hyaluronidase or chondroitinase ABC. PRATT and MADRI found these microfibrillar bundles reative with polyclonal antibodies to types III and IV collagen and laminin, but concluded the fibrils were composed of neither these proteins nor oxytalan. These interesting fibrillar structures are undoubtedly the same as those reported by BRUNS, PRESS and GROSS (1987), forming startlingly regular orthogonal arrays throughout the cornea of most animals, although not adult humans. BRUNS et al. thought this network belonged to the elastic microfibrillar system, and suggested it had a structural or light-diffracting function. Its exact nature and apparent absence in humans deserves further study.

Although the expression of elastic components appears to be significantly inhibited in the normal human cornea beyond childhood, oxytalan is made in quantities in a great variety of stromal scars and dystrophies (ALEXANDER and GARNER, 1977; GARNER and ALEXANDER 1981), in congenital anomalies of the cornea (STREETEN, KARPIK, SPITZER 1983; NORTON and STREETEN 1988), and in Descemet's membrane region in Fuchs and other endothelial dystrophies (reviewed in ALEXANDER, GRIERSON and GARNER 1983; GARNER and ALEXANDER 1981). Elastic fibers have been reported in sclerocornea (KANAI et al. 1971). Desmosine and isodesmosine, the characteristic elastin crosslinkage sites, were noted biochemically in bovine Descemet's membrane in one report (HEATHCOTE, EYRE, GROSS 1982).

## Sclera

In the neonate, scleral elastic tissue is limited to a diffuse distribution of oxytalan fibers as in other ocular tissues, except that the peripapillary sclera has fully mature elastic fibers (ALEXANDER and GARNER 1983). A large proportion of the scleral elastic fibers continue to show some elaunin characteristics with nonfused elastin cores and persistent peripheral microfibrils throughout life (STREETEN et al. 1989). They also show an accumulation of 55nm fibrogranular banded material on their outer surfaces, and lesser quantities of 100nm banding ("long-spacing collagen") more peripherally, like the better known "zebra-banding" in the trabecular region. This banding pattern begins in the anterior sclera in the second decade, progressing thereafter into the posterior sclera, the reverse direction from that inferred for scleral elastic fiber maturation based on early maturity of fibers around the optic disc (ALEXANDER & GARNER 1983). No study of elastic fibers in the sclera of large myopic eyes has been reported but there are changes in nanophthalmic sclera, varying from focal deficiency of elastic fibers in eyes under 17 mm anteroposterior diameter, to small elastic fibers with reduced peripheral banded material in somewhat larger eyes (STEWART et al. 1991). The outer sclera and episclera have a phlethora of small elastic fibers which merge with the conjunctival stromal elastica anteriorly, and a large number of elastic fibers are present in the tendons of the inserting rectus muscles.

## Trabeculum

The presence of elastic tissue in the trabecular beams was recognized early because of a positive Verhoeff's elastic stain. However, its resistance to digestion by elastase was disconcerting, and its unusual appearance by electron microscopy puzzling, since the presumed elastic fibers had a variety of appearances unlike normal fibers (summarized in IWAMOTO 1964). During development however these fibers show a typical pattern of amorphous elastin deposited on bundles of elastic microfibrils (TRIPATHI and TRIPATHI 1982) and bind elastin antibody at all ages (MURPHY et al. 1987; GONG, TRINKAUS-RANDALL, FREDDO 1989; STREETEN, LI, STEWART 1989), also showing some sensitivity to elastase (LÜTJEN-DRECOLL, FUTA, ROHEN 1981).

The trabecular elastic fibers stain moderately well with Verhoef's stain, but remain ultrastructurally immature with unfused cords of elastin and many associated elastic microfibrils, more like elaunin fibers (STREETEN, LI, SEWART 1989). Their unusual ultrastructural appearance is due to the gradual accumulation of granular and banded material on their peripheries, beginning in the first decade, with obscuration of peripheral microfibrils by age 20. When the fiber is cut longitudi-

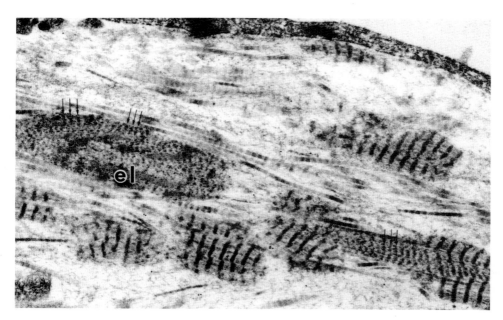

Fig. 5. Trabecular beam showing many aggregates of long-spacing collagen ("zebra-banding"). An elaunin-type elastic fiber (el) has two dense cords of elastin, immunostained with 10nm gold-labeled elastin antibody. Surrounding granular material aggregates into a 55nm narrow-banding pattern when cut longitudinally (arrows). Another elastic fiber on the right is cut through its periphery, showing only narrow-banding material (arrows), with wide spacing fibers at the edges (x 35,400).

nally, the granular material shows a 55nm banding pattern (Fig. 5), often dwarfing the elastin content. With further aging, 100nm banded material may be seen peripherally, partially blending into the inner 55nm banded zone, although it is more common closer to the endothelial cell basement membrane. A similar process obscures the elastin in small elaunin type fibers inserting via oxytalan fibers on the basement membranes of the inner and outer walls of Schlemm's canal and the collecting channels.

Understanding of the trabecular elastic system, particularly in the juxtacanalicular (cribriform) region has been contributed by many investigators, especially by ROHEN, LÜTJEN-DRECOLL and colleagues in a series of papers over more than three decades, and can only be touched upon here. The unusual banded materials around the elastic fibers in the juxtacanalicular region were early on referred to as types II and III plaque, and as sheath material surrounding elastic-like fibers (ROHEN and LÜTJEN-DRECOLL 1971). This material was noted to increase with age (McMENAMIN and LEE 1980; TRIPATHI and TRIPATHI 1982; LÜTJEN-DRECOLL et al. 1986; McMENAMIN, LEE, AITKEN 1986), with greater increase in chronic simple glaucoma (ROHEN and WITMER 1972; LEE and GRIERSON 1974; RODRIGUES et al.

1976; ROHEN, FUTA, LÜTJEN-DRECOLL 1981; LÜTJEN-DRECOLL, FUTA, ROHEN
1981), calculated morphometrically to be 23 % higher in POAG after the age of 40
years (ALVARADO, YUN and MURPHY 1986). No increase was seen in exfoliation-
associated glaucoma (LUTJEN-DRECOLL et al. 1986). Serial sections showed a network of heavily banded elastic fibers in the inner cribriform region, which was
named the cribriform plexus (ROHEN, FUTA and LÜTJEN-DRECOLL 1981). These
fibers merged with fibers passing to the wall of Schlemm's canal (connecting
fibers) and with the trabecular elastic system.

Elastic fibers around the tips of the anterior ciliary muscles were found to join
the cribriform plexus and also the trabecular elastic system (Fig. 6), with densifica-

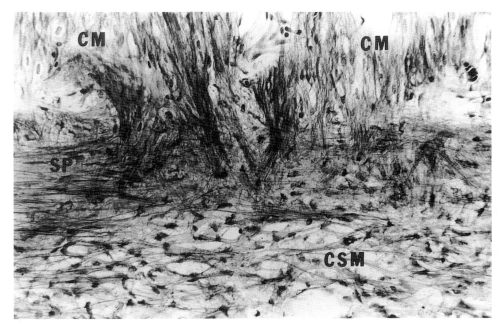

Fig. 6. Tangential section showing fine black elastic fibers extending from the ends of the longitudinal
ciliary muscle (CM), and joining the circumferential elastica of the scleral spur (SP) and the corneoscleral meshwork (CSM). Verhoeff elastic stain. x 500.

tions of the adjacent muscle cell plasma membranes suggesting that the fibers were
functioning like elastic tendons (ROHEN, LÜTJEN, BARANY 1967; ROHEN, FUTA,
LÜTJEN-DRECOLL 1981), as described for the arrector pili muscles of the skin
(RODRIGO, COTTA-PEREIRA, DAVID-FERREIRA 1975). It was hypothesized that
these tendons would pull the cribriform plexus inward and spread the subendothe-

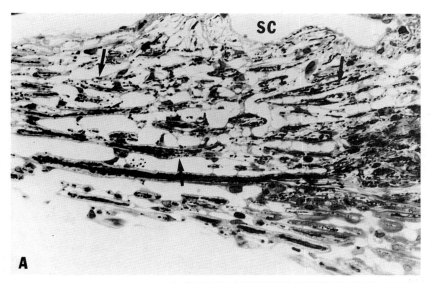

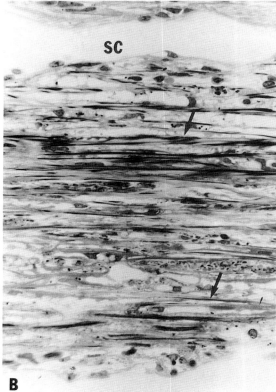

Fig. 7. Comparison of elastic fibers seen in A as dark dots (arrows) in an anteroposterior section of Schlemm's canal (SC) and trabeculum, and in B as circumferential fibers (arrows) in coronal section thru the posterior trabeculum. Anterior chamber below. Toluidine blue stain on 1 μm epoxy sections. Both x500.

lial layers, as well as prevent collapse of Schlemm's canal during ciliary muscle contraction.

There was a marked circumferential arrangement of elastic fibers in the cribriform plexus, also evident in the trabecular beams and scleral spur when cut in coronal or tangential planes (ROHEN, FUTA, LÜTJEN-DRECOLL 1981; TRIPATHI and TRIPATHI 1982). This distribution explains the dotted appearance of the trabecular elastic fibers in routine anteroposterior sections (Fig. 7). The predominant circular pattern is partially converted to an anteroposterior one by interconnecting fibers, and by oxytalan and elaunin fibers passing from the trabeculum to the outer surface of Descemet's membrane, Schlemm's canal, the scleral spur, ciliary muscle and iris root (CHIJIIWA and STREETEN, in preparation). The impression given is that the elastic system in this region is designed to modulate both anteroposterior and outwardly expansile stresses.

The accumulation of abnormal granular, banded and fibrillar material associated with the elastic fibers, especially in the juxtacanalicular region, is of great interest because of its frequency and possible pathogenetic significance in glaucoma. The 100nm banded material is a common finding in aging and pathologic connective tissues such as Descemet's membrane, or as Luse bodies in neurilemommas, and has also been referred to as zebra fibers, wide-spacing collagen, and banded basement membrane (FINE and YANOFF 1979). It has recently been hypothesized to result from abnormal aggregation of type VI collagen, which normally has a 100nm periodicity (BRUNS et al. 1986). Similar banding can be produced by incubation of collagen VI-containing tissues, such as trabeculum or cornea, at an acidic pH with or without ATP (HIRANO et al. 1989). Chondroitin sulfate, present at the banding sites, may be necessary for this type of aggregation (SCHLUMBERGER et al. 1989). Immunostaining of 100nm banding in the trabecular region by collagen VI antibody has been reported by LÜTJEN- DRECOLL et al. (1989). It is not clear whether the more frequent 55nm banding around elastic fibers is a separate or related phenomenom. Outside the ocular region we have found banded elastic fibers to date only in small elaunin-type elastic fibers of tendons.

Many groups have shown accumulation of anionic material histochemically in the ageing trabecular and juxtacanalicular aggregates, interpreting it as mucopolysaccharide or proteoglycan (reviewed in TAWARA, VARNER and HOLLYFIELD 1989). Dermatan sulfate, chondroitin sulfate and heparan sulfate have been specifically identified by immunostaining or enzyme digestions in some of these aggregates (LÜTJEN-DRECOLL, FUTA, ROHEN 1981; LÜTJEN-DRECOLL et al. 1989; TAWARA et al. 1989). No proteoglycans were found associated with elastic fibers by TAWARA et al. (1989), but chondroitin and hyaluronic acid were found in the greatly expanded elastic fiber "sheaths" (LÜTJEN-DRECOLL, FUTA, ROHEN 1981). We have noted that many aggregates in the juxtacanalicular region are non-oriented clumps of elastic microfibrils staining with microfibrillar antibody (LI et al., unpublished). Amyploid P component, a frequent elastin-associated aging protein, is also present. This further evidence of elastic-related or elastotic components in the clumps of "type I plaques" (ROHEN and LÜTJEN-DRECOLL 1971) under the endothelium of Schlemm's canal is of interest. These materials would possibly be resistant to normal enzymatic removal or other hypothesized "wash-out" mechanisms for aiding aqueous outflow (GRIERSON and LEE 1975). The fact that cultured trabecular cells synthesize elastin when stimulated with dexamethasone (YUN et al. 1989) is a fascinating new finding. It raises the question of whether persons who are high "steroid-responders" have an inherent abnormality involving elastic component metabolism in this region, or are simply demonstrating reduced outflow capacity of other etiology.

## The zonular apparatus

As a representative of exytalan, the simplest form of elastic material, the zonular fibril can serve as a model for the elastic microfibril, informing us abut its composition, regulation of synthesis, mechanism of basement membrane attachment, range of function, and particularly the nature of its elasticity. Whether there are any singificant differences between the highly aggregated zonular fibrils and other elastic microfibrils is still to be determined. Molecular biology will eventually tell us how the zonular fibril molecule or associated molecules are abnormal in the hereditary lens-dislocating diseases, the location of the gene or genes for this structural fibril, as well as the cell or cells of origin. Evidence that there is more than one fibrillin gene which can be defective in Marfan syndrome and its variants, and that there are at least two other closely associated proteins (see pg. 3), points the way to future great advances in understanding the lens-dislocating diseases.

Many groups contributed to elucidating the course of the zonular fibers by scanning and transmission electron microscopy over the past two decades, as reviewed in FARNSWORTH and BURKE (1977), ROHEN (1979), and STREETEN (1982 a). There has been general consensus about the pattern of zonular attachments to the anterior, equatorial and posterior lens capsule and the origin of most zonular fibers on the posterior pars plana within the vitreous. The fact that the zonular fibers must pursue a somewhat curved rather than straight course from origin to insertion and that the fibers to the posterior capsule deviate sharply from the main zonular course at the zonular "fork", presents a problem of stable fixation, resolved somewhat differently by several investigators. FARNSWORTH and BURKE (1977) found that zonular fibers to the equatorial and posterior capsule originated from or were strongly fixed to the ciliary body. ROHEN (1979) noted attachment of the main zonular bundles to the ciliary process epithelium by finer "tension fibers", leaving the main stream and anchoring the larger bundles. We found anchoring fibrils joining the main zonular stream to the epithelium over the whole pars plana, but more profuse on the ciliary processes and minor plicae, and especially strongly attaching the anterior zonules in the ciliary valleys (STREETEN 1982 a). The redundant "folding" of zonular fibers seen sometimes in extreme accommodation clinically and experimentally (NEIDER et al. 1990) may be further evidence of strong attachment at the ciliary processes, limiting their elastic recoil rather than allowing it to spread along the whole zonular course.

Since most zonular fibrils blend into the lens and ciliary basement membranes quite superficially, usually less than 1.6 μ on the lens capsule, additional adhesion molecules are likely to be involved in their attachments, and indeed in attachments of all oxytalan fibers.

## Ciliary body elastic tissue and accommodation

Just as the bulk of the ciliary body is muscle dedicated to the accommodative process, the prime function of its elastic system also appears directed towards modulating accommodative movements, aiding return to the resting state. In a series of imaginative experiments on primates, the dramatic anterior and inward movement of the ciliary processes during stimulated accommodation has been photographed, as well as their withdrawal during disaccommodation (NEIDER et al. 1990), with documentation of zonular reactions as alluded to above. This technique promises to be an exciting tool for investigating accommodation in vivo, testing assumptions based on morphological and other indirect methods.

Maintaining a close relation between the zonular fiber-ciliary epithelial layer and the stroma during accommodative movements, oxytalan and small elaunin fibers attach the basement membrane of the ciliary pigment epithelium to stromal blood vessels and to larger deep elastic fibers (Fig. 3) (STREETEN 1982 c; STREETEN and LICARI 1983). This inner elastic system is very robust in the cow, blending in with elastic tissue around the ciliary muscle fibers as they insert into the pectinate ligament. The general plan in the human is similar, as oxytalan and elastic fibers increase around the anterior ends of the longitudinal ciliary muscle, connecting them to the elastica of the scleral spur, the juxtacanalicular tissues and trabecular beams (Fig. 7), and functioning like elastic tendons (ROHEN, FUTA, LÜTJEN-DRECOLL 1981), as discussed under Trabeculum. These connections give the elastic system a second role, in the control of aqueous outflow during accommodation.

In young eyes the circular and radial fibers are close to the pigment epithelial basement membrane and connect to it by oxytalan and elastic fibers running in an anteroposterior direction. The strongest component of the ciliary elastic system is in the posterior pars plana, where there are several elastic layers. The ones directly under the pigment epithelium are continuous with Bruch's membrane in the anterior choroid (STREETEN 1982 b, c; KORTE and D'AVERSA 1989).

Exactly what constitutes the posterior insertion of the meridional ciliary muscle has long been in question. Recently ultrastructural evidence has been adduced that the elastic fiber layers in the posterior pars plana function as elastic tendons of the posterior ciliary muscle like those of the anterior region, with plasmalemmal densities of the muscle cells adjacent to the elastic fibers, continuous with the elastic network of Bruch's membrane (TAMM, LÜTJEN-DRECOLL, ROHEN, JUNGKUNZ 1990). These investigators found an increase in collagen around the elastic tendons with aging, suggesting that resultant stiffening of the elastic system could interfere with accommodation. Further description of this elastic tendon system is awaited, to finally resolve the elusive posterior insertion of the ciliary muscle. Few of the ciliary muscle fibers appear to extend posterior to the ora serrata but the elastic fibers do, so that the peripheral choroid and retina could be placed under some tension by these fibers during accommodation.


## Choroid and Bruch's membrane


The elastic tissue of the choroid has been studied primarily in the posterior pole, with greatest interest in Bruch's membrane because of its strategic position in the path of diffusion between the choriocapillaris and the retinal pigment epithelium. Extensive degenerative changes in the aging Bruch's membrane are postulated to interfere with diffusion by an increase in anionic sites acting as a barrier to molecular filtration (DAS et al. 1990). The elastic layer itself has been suggested as a barrier to removal of retinal pigment epithelial debris by choriocapillaris cells (FEENEY-BURNS and ELLERSIECK 1985).

There is some ambiguity about which cell or cells synthesize the elastic components of Bruch's membrane. In the primate the first elastic microfibrils and early elastic fibers originate closer to the endothelium of the choriocapillaris than to the retinal pigment epithelium, coinciding with the appearance of fibroblasts in this region. (TAKEI and OZANICZ 1975). These fibroblasts are described mostly as thin processes, and their number is unclear but they decrease by day 100 and are gone by day 110. Since gestation is 160 days, and growth of the elastic tissue must continue until maturity, it is likely that either the choriocapillaris endothelium or the retinal pigment epithelium is the primary synthesizer of Bruch's elastica. No fibroblasts have been described in the development of Bruch's membrane in the chick (OLSON 1975).

The 0.8 μm elastic layer of Bruch's membrane extends over the entire choroid up to the edge of the optic disc where it is continuous with concentric bundles running

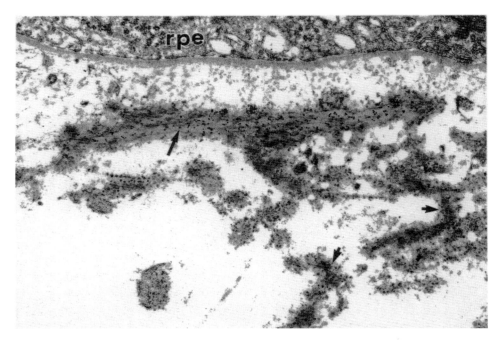

Fig. 8. Elastic fiber in aging Bruch's membrane, surrounded by granular dense material. Its amorphous elastin center stains well with 10nm gold labeled elastin antibody (large arrow). Some of the adjacent dense elastotic material also binds elastin (small arrows). (x 27,500).

around the nerve canal (HOGAN, ALVARADO and WEDDELL 1971 b). At the ora serrata it continues directly into the subepithelial elastic layers in the pars plana (STREETEN 1982 b). Oblique and flat sectioning through Bruch's membrane shows that the elastic fibers form a network of thin straight fibers, interlacing with surrounding collagen fibrils which extend between its bundles (FEHER and VALU 1967), often two-layered in the macula.

Histochemically Bruch's membrane elastica matures through an elaunin stage to mature elastic fibers (ALEXANDER and GARNER 1983). Extensive smaller new elastic fibers may surround the original fibers of Bruch's membrane with aging (Fig. 8), besides the addition of an extensive granular coating (HOGAN, ALVARADO and WEDDELL 1971 c). With aging there is increased autofluorescence of the elastic layer (NEWSOME et al. 1987), and increased quantitative staining for elastin histochemically (NEWSOME, HUH, GREEN 1987). These changes in the elastic tissue of Bruch's membrane have some similarities to those in the trabeculum. 55nm banding on the fibers has not been described although a suggestive association can be seen in some published figures (Fig. 8 – 12 in HOGAN, ALVARADO and WEDDELL 1971). Calcification is more frequent on Bruch's membrane elastic fibers. DAS et al. (1990) noted collagen VI immunoreacitivty amongst the elastic fibers of Bruch's membrane, suggesting it was associated with collagen fibers connecting the two collagenous layers of Bruch's membrane.

Oxytalan and elaunin fibers are reported to join Bruch's elastica to the retinal pigment epithelium in the rat (ESSNER and GORDON 1984). Recently KORTE and D'ADVERSA (1989) observed attachments of Bruch's membrane to surrounding structures in both the choroid and ciliary body using high voltage electron microscopy, which allows a 3-dimensional view of these rather sparse connecting fibers. The connections were by oxytalan fibers in the rabbit and oxytalan and elaunin fibers in the human, joining the elastica of Bruch's membrane with bundles of elastic fibers in the deeper choroid, through the intercapillary spaces.

Oxytalan bundles inserting into vascular basement membranes in the uvea and optic nerve of the rabbit were shown by a combination of confocal scanning laser microscopy and electron microscopy (KORTE and MANCHE 1990). These connecting elements linked the ocular elastic system to the whole vascular system, by inserting into the basement membranes of arteriolar smooth muscle cells, and of endothelium and pericytes in the venules and capillaries. This association was suggested as contributing to vasoresponsiveness related to variations in blood pressure and intraocular pressure. A more direct effect of these ubiquitous basement membrane connections of oxytalan may be modulation of vasoresponsive vessel movements on the surrounding tissues.

The outer choroid contains an extensive network of elastic fibers which have delicate interconnections with elastic fibers in the inner sclera.

### Optic nerve and meninges

A definitive view of the elastic tissue in and around the optic nerve, like that in other complex tissues, had to await the development of electron microscopy as exemplified in early reports by ANDERSON (1969 a, b), ANDERSON and HOYT (1969), and HOGAN, ALVARADO and WEDDELL (1971 d). These studies showed that the whole scleral canal was lined by glia, except where bridged by the sheets of connective tissue composing the lamina cribosa, which extended into the sclera and apparently derived from the sclera. The laminal sheets were lined by glia, as were their perforations thru which the optic nerve fibers run, showing fidelity to the principle that neuroectodermal tissue is everywhere protected from mesodermal connective tissue by glia. HOGAN, ALVARADO and WEDDELL (1971 d) noted an "impressive amount" of elastic fibers in the lamina cribosa although ANDERSON found them more variable, and even absent in some specimens (1969 a). These and other discrepancies have been clarified in the past decade, particularly by the addition of immunostaining in both humans and primates.

By scanning electron microscopy, the lamina was visualized as containing up to 10 layers of stacked plates with their perforations in register (QUIGLEY and ADDICKS 1981). In young eyes the laminal plates contain fine elastic fibers with more type III than type I collagen, type I being the primary collagen of the sclera (HERNANDEZ, IGOE and NEUFELD 1986, 1987). Elastin and type I collagen increase with aging as the laminal connective tissue thickens (HERNANDEZ et al. 1989, MORRISON et al. 1989 b), and its composition becomes more similar to that of the peripapillary and posterior sclera (MORRISON et al. 1989 b). This increase in density and widening of the elastic fibers can be seen also in histochemical staining (Fig. 9). Concentrically arranged elastic fibers surround the whole optic nerve-scleral junction (HERNAN-DEZ et al. 1987), visible even in the newborn, with increasing numbers also in the peripapillary sclera (Fig. 9). These concentric fibers around the scleral canal in the laminal and prelaminal regions appear to be those which show early maturity histochemically (ALEXANDER and GARNER 1983), indicating their structural importance. Elastic fibers from the laminal plates join this concentric ring, but few extend as far into the sclera as do the astroglial processes of the laminal plates, with their basement membranes (HERNANDEZ et al. 1987; GOLDBAUM et al. 1989). The presence of elastic fibers but little collagen I in the young lamina cribosa may help to explain the prompt reversal of cupping after treatment of glaucoma in the young, and its failure to reverse in older eyes may be explained by the stiffening resulting from increased laminal fibrous collagen with age (QUIGLEY 1977; ANDERSON 1982; MORRISON 1989 a).

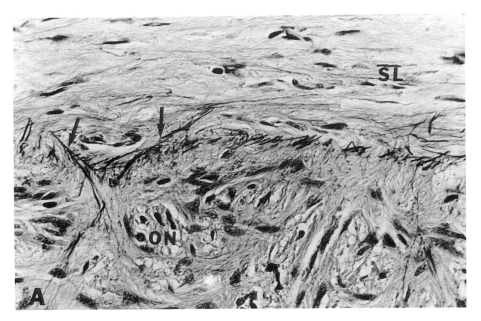

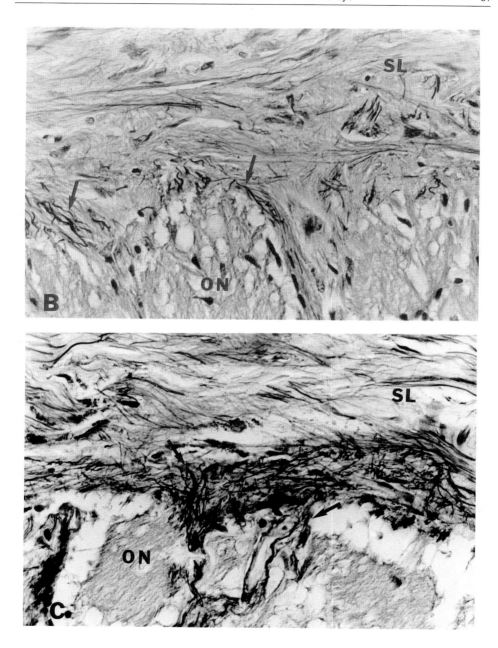

Fig. 9. Elastic fibers running circumferentially in the sclera (SL) around the optic nerve (ON), joining the elastica of the lamina cribrosa (arrows). Fibers increase in number and thickness with age. A. 22 day old infant, B. 25 year old, C. 75 year old. Cross-sections. Verhoeff elastic stain. All x 500.

A study of the laminal plate cells in culture suggested that they were neither typical scleral fibroblasts nor astrocytes as they grew in a flat polygonal pattern, synthesizing predominantly types III and IV collagen with associated fibronectin and elastin (HERNANDEZ et al. 1988). Further studies of this possible new cell type will be of great interest.

Laminal collagen and elastic fibers continue into the central vascular core of the nerve, with an internal elastic lamina and medial elastic fibers around the central retinal artery. No elastic fibers were found in the prelaminal or retinal arteries (ANDERSON 1969 a; HOGAN, ALVARADO and WEDDELL 1971 a). Whether this deficiency of vascular elastic components may change in pathologic conditions (Fig. 3) has not been specifically studied. "Microfibrils" and small "striated fibrils" recently reported in the outer basement membranes of aging retinal arterioles reacted with antibodies to types I and III collagen and were presumably small collagen fibrils (DAS et al. 1990; MARSHALL, KONSTAS, LEE 1990).

Elastic fibers are also present in the postlaminal optic nerve septae but have a more random and sparser distribution compared to their horizontal disposition in the lamina cribosa. They interconnect with elastic fibers in the pia mater. A plethora of quite large elastic fibers is present in the dura with both longitudinal and circumferential distribution (ANDERSON 1969 b; HERNANDEZ et al. 1989). Bundles of oxytalan fibers and individual 10nm elastic microfibrils are plentiful throughout the meninges (ANDERSON 1969 b). This significant content of elastic components in the meninges completes the picture of another ocular tissue which has considerable ability to respond to the stresses of its environment, including changes in subarachnoid fluid volume and bending during versional ocular movements.

## Acknowledgements

Supported in part by Research Grant EY01602 from the National Eye Institute, National Institutes of Health.

## References

ALEXANDER, R. A., A. GARNER (1977): Oxytalan fibre formation in the cornea. A light and microscopical study. Histopathol. *1:* 189–199.

ALEXANDER, R. A., A. GARNER (1983): Elastic and precursor fibres in the normal human eye. Exp. Eye Res. *36:* 305.

ALEXANDER, R. A., I. GRIERSON, A. GARNER (1981): Oxytalan fibers in Fuchs endothelial dystrophy. Arch. Ophthalmol. *99:* 1622–1627.

ALVARADO, J. A., A. J. YUN, C. G. MURPHY (1986): Juxtacanalicular tissue in primary open angle glaucoma and in nonglaucomatous normals. Arch. Ophthalmol. *104:* 1517–1528.

ANDERSON, D. R. (1969a): Ultrastructure of human and monkey lamina cribrosa and optic nervehead. Arch. Ophthalmol. *82:* 800–814.

ANDERSON, D. R. (1969b): Ultrastructure of meningeal sheaths in human and monkey optic nerves. Arch. Ophthalmol. *82:* 659–674.

ANDERSON, D. R. (1982): The posterior aspect of glaucomatous eyes. In: Basic Aspects of Glaucoma Research, E. LÜTJEN–DRECOLL (Ed.), F. K. Schattauer Verlag, Stuttgart-New York, pg.178.

ANDERSON, D. R., W. F. HOYT (1969): Ultrastructure of intraorbital portion of human and monkey optic nerve. Arch. Ophthalmol. *82:* 506–530.

BENNETT, J., A. HADDAD (1986): Synthesis and migration of $^3$H-fucose labeled glycoproteins in the ciliary repithelium of the eye: Effects of microtubule-disrupting drugs. Am. J. Anat. *177:* 441–455.

BREATHNACH, S. M., M. B. PEPYS, H. HINTNER (1989): Tissue amyloid P component in normal human dermis is non-covalently associated with elastic fiber microfibrils. J. Invest. Dermatol. *92:* 53–58.

BRIGLIN, C. A., Z.-Y. LI, B. W. STREETEN (1991): Cultured lens epithelial cells synthesize matrix immunopositive for elastic microfibrillar proteins, including fibrillin and a zonular peptide. Invest. Ophthalmol. Vis. Sc. *32* (Suppl.): 777, 1991.

BRUNS, R. R., W. PRESS, E. ENGVALL, R. TIMPEL, J. GROSS (1986): Type VI collagen extracellular 100nm-periodic filaments and fibrils: identification by immunoelectron microscopy. J. Cell Biol. *103:* 393– 404.

BRUNS, R. R., W. PRESS, J. GROSS (1987): A large-scale, orthogonal network of microfibril bundles in the corneal stroma. Invest. Ophthalmol. Vis. Sc. *28:* 1939–1946.

BUDDECKE, E., J. WOLLENSAK (1966): Zur Biochemie der Zonularfaser des Rinderauges. Z. Naturforsch. *216:* 337–341.

CARLSON, E. C., G. O. WARING (1988): Ultrastructural analyses of enzyme-treated microfibrils in rabbit corneal stroma. Invest. Ophthalmol. Vis. Sc. *29:* 578–585.

CARRINGTON, S. D., R. A. ALEXANDER, I. GRIERSON (1984): Elastic and related fibres in the normal cornea and limbus of the domestic cat. J. Anat. *139:* 319–332.

CINTRON, C., H. COVINGTON, C. L. KUBLIN (1983): Morphogenesis of rabbit corneal stroma. Invest. Ophthalmol. Vis. Sc. *24:* 543–556.

COTTA-PEREIRA, G., F. G. RODRIGO, S. BITTENCOURT-SAMPAIO (1976): Oxytalan, elaunin and elastic fibers in the human skin. J. Invest. Derm. *66:* 143.

DAHLBACK, K., A. LJUNGQUIST, H. LOFBERG et al.: (1990): Fibrillin immunoreactive fibers constitute a unique network in the human dermis: Immunohistochemical comparison if the distibutions of fibrillin, vitronectin, amyloid P compenent and orcein stainable structures in normal skin and elastosis. J. Invest. Dermatol. *94:* 284–291.

DAHLBACK, K., H. LOFBERG, J. ALUMETS, B. DAHLBACK (1989): Immunohistochemical demonstration of age-related deposition of vitronectin (S-protein of complement) and terminal complement complex on dermal elastic fibers. J. Invest. Dermatol. *93:* 727– 733.

DARK, A. J., B. W. STREETEN, D. B. JONES (1969): Accumulation of fibrillar protein in the ageing human lens capsule. With special reference to the pathogenesis of pseudoexfoliative disease of the lens. Arch. Ophthalmol. *82:* 815–821.

DAS, A., R. N. FRANK, N. L. ZHANG, T. J. TURCZYN (1990): Ultrastructural localization of extracellular matrix components in human retinal vessels and Bruch's membrane Arch. Ophthalmol. *108:* 421– 429.

DIETZ, H., G. R. CUTTING, R. E. PYERITZ et al. (1991): Marfan syndrome caused by a recurrent de novo missense mutation in the fibrillin gene. Nature *352:* 337.

EMANUEL, B. S., L. CANNIZZARO, N. ORNSTEIN-GOLDSTEIN et al. (1985): Chromosomal localization of the human elastin gene. Am. J. Hum. Genet. *37:* 873–882.

ESSNER, E., S. R. GORDON (1984): Demonstration of microfibrils in Bruch's membrane of the eye. Tissue Cell. *16:* 779–788.

FARNSWORTH, P. M., P. BURKE (1977): Three-dimensional architecture of the suspensory apparatus of the lens of the rhesus monkey. Exp. Eye Res. *25:* 563–576.

FAZIO, M. J., V. M. KAHANI, M. M. BASHIR, B. SAITTA, J. ROSENBLOOM, J. UITTO (1990): Regulation of elastin gene expression: evidence for functional promoter activity in the 5'- flanking region of the human gene. J. Invest. Dermatol. *94:* 191 – 196.

FAZIO, M. J., D. R. OLSEN, H. KUIVANIEMI, M. L. CHU, J. M. DAVIDSON, J. ROSENBLOOM, J. UITTO (1988): Isolation and characterization of human elastin cDNAs, and age-associated variation in elastin gene expression in cultured skin fibroblasts. Lab. Invest. *58:* 270 – 277.

FEENEY-BURNS, L., M. R. ELLERSIECK (1985): Age related changes in the ultrastructure of Bruch's membrane. Am. J. Ophthalmol. *100:* 686 – 697.

FEHER, J., L. VALU (1967): Zur Struktur des Bruchschen Membran. v. Graefes Arch. Klin. Exp. Ophthal. *173:* 162 – 167.

FINE, B. S., M. YANOFF (1972): Ocular Histology. a Text and Atlas. 2nd Edition. Harper and Row. New York, pg.47.

FULLMER, H. M., R. D. LILLIE (1958): Oxytalan fibers: A previously undescribed connective tissue fiber. J. Histochem. Cytochem. *6:* 425.

GABLER, V. W., G. SCHEUNER (1965): Untersuchungen zur Histochemie der Zonulafasern. Acta Histochem. *21:* 393 – 403.

GARNER, A., R. A. ALEXANDER (1981): Pre-elastin (oxytalan) fibres in corneal pathalogy, in Proceedings of 6th Congress of the European Society of Ophthalmology. Brighton, London, Academic Press/Royal Society of Medicine, p. 213 – 216.

GAWLIK, Z. (1965): Morphological and morphochemical properties of the elastic system in the motor organ of man. Folia Histochem. et. Cytochem. *3:* 233.

GIBSON, M. A., J. L. HUGHES, J. C. FANNING, E. G. CLEARY (1986): The major antigen of elastin-associated microfibrils is a 31-kDa glycoprotein. J. Biol. Chem. *24:* 11429 – 11436.

GIBSON, M. A., J. S. KUMARATILAKE, E. G. CLEARY (1989): The protein components of the 12-nanometer microfibrils of elastic and non-elastic tissues. J. Biol. Chem. *264:* 4590 – 4598.

GIBSON, M. A., L. B. SANDBERG, L. E. GROSSO, E. G. CLEARY (1991): Complementary DNA cloning establishes microfibril-associated glycoprotein (MAGP) to be a discrete component of the elastin-associated microfibrils. J. Biol. Chem. *266:* 7596 – 7601.

GLOOR, B. P. (1974): Zur Entwicklung des Glaskörpers und der Zonula. VI Autoradiographische Untersuchungen zur Entwicklung der Zonula der Maus mit $^3$H-markierten Aminosäuren und $^3$H Glucose. A. v. Graefes Arch. Ophth. *189:* 105 – 124.

GOLDBAUM, M. H., S. JENG, R. LOGEMANN, R. N. WEINROB (1989): The extracellular matrix of the human optic nerve. Arch. Ophthalmol. *107:* 1225 – 1231.

GOLDFISCHER, S., B. COLTOFF-SCHILLER, M. GOLDFISCHER (1985): Microfibrils, elastic anchoring components of the extracellular matrix, are associated with fibronectin in the zonule of Zinn and aorta. Tissue and Cell *17:* 441 – 450.

GONG, H., V. TRINKHAUS-RANDALL, T. F. FREDDO (1989): Ultrastructural immunocytochemical localization of elastin in normal human trabecular meshwork. Curr. Eye Res. *8:* 1071 – 1082.

GORDINI, D. D., I. CASTELLANI, D. VOLPIN, G. M. BRESSAN (1990): Ultrastructural immuno-localization of tropoelastin in the chick eye. Cell Tissue Res. *260:* 137 – 146.

GREENLEE, T. K. Jr., R. ROSS, J. L. HARTMAN (1966): The fine structure of elastic fibers. J. Cell Biol. *30:* 59 – 71.

GRIERSON, I., W. R. LEE (1975): The fine structure of the trabecular meshwork at graded levels of intraocular pressure. 1. Pressure effects within the near-physiological range (8-30 mm Hg). Exp. Eye Res. *20:* 505 – 521.

HEATHCOTE, J. G., D. R. EYRE, J. GROSS (1982): Mature bovine descemet's membrane contains desmosine and isodesmosine. Biochem. Biophys. Res. Commun. *108:* 1588 – 1594.

HERNANDEZ, M. R., F. IGOE, A. H. NEUFELD (1986): Extracellular matrix of the human optic nerve. Am. J. Ophthalmol. *102:* 139 – 148.

HERNANDEZ, M. R., F. IGOE, A. H. NEUFELD (1987): Extracellular matrix of the human lamina cribrosa. Am. J. Ophthalmol. *104:* 567 – 576.

HERNANDEZ, M. R., X. X. LUO, F. IGEO, A. H. NEUFELD (1988): Cell culture of the lamina cribrosa. Invest. Ophthalmol. Vis. Sc. *29:* 78 – 89.

HERNANDEZ, M. R., X. X. LUO, W. ANDRZEJEWSKA, A. H. NEUFELD (1989): Age-related changes in the extracellular matrix of the human optic nervehead. Am. J. Ophthalmol. *107:* 476 – 484.

HIRANO, K., M. KOBAYASHI, K. KOBAYASHI, T. HOSHINO, S. AWAYA (1989): Experimental formation of 100nm periodic fibrils in the mouse corneal stroma and trabecular meshwork. Invest. Ophthalmol. *30:* 869 – 874.

HOGAN, M. J., J. A. ALVARADO, J. E. WEDDELL (1971): Histology of the Human Eye, A Text and Atlas. W. B. Saunders Co., Philadelphia, (1971 a. pg. 508, b. pg. 342, c. pg. 336 – 361, d. pg. 561 – 570).

HOLLISTER, D. W., M. GODFREY, L. Y. SAKAI, R. E. PYERITZ (1990): Marfan syndrome: immunohistochemical abnormalities of the microfibrillar fiber system. N. E. J. Med. *323:* 152 – 159.

HORRIGAN, S. K., C. B. RICH, B. W. STREETEN, Z-Y LI, J. A. FOSTER (1992): Characterization of an associated microfibril protein through recombinant DNA techniques. J. Biol. Chem. *267:* 10087 – 10095.

HORSTMANN, H. J., J. W. ROHEN, K. SAMES (1983): Age-related changes in the composition of proteins in the trabecular meshwork of the human eye. Mech. Ageing Dev. *21:* 121.

INDIK, Z., H. YEH, M. ORNSTEIN-GOLDSTEIN, V. KUCICH, W. ABRAMS, J. C. ROSENBLOOM, J. ROSENBLOOM (1989): Structure of the elastin gene and alternative splicing of elastin mRNA: implications for human disease. Am. J. Med. Genet *34:* 81 – 90.

INOUE, S., C. P. LEBLOND, D. S. GRANT, P. RICO (1986): The microfibrils of connective tissue: II. Immunohistochemical detection of the amyloid P component. Amer. J. Anat. *176:* 139 – 152.

IWAMOTO, T. (1964): Light and electron microscopy of the presumed elastic components of the trabeculae and scleral spur of the human eye. Invest. Ophthalmol. Vis. Sc. *3:* 144 – 156.

KAINULAINEN, K., L. PULKKINEN, A. SAVOLAINEN, I. KAITILA, L. PELTONEN (1990): Location on chromosome 15 of the gene defect causing Marfan syndrome. N. E. J. Med. *323:* 935 – 939.

KANAI, A., H. E. KAUFMAN (1973): Electron microscopic study of rabbit corneal stroma: elastic-like fibers. Ann. Ophthalmol. *5:* 667 – 674.

KANAI, A., T. C. WOOD, F. M. POLOCK, H. E. KAUFMAN (1971): The fine structure of sclerocornea. Invest. Ophthalmol. *10:* 687 – 694.

KAWAGUCHI, T. (1982): Isolation of glycoproteins from bovine nuchal ligament. Connect. Tiss. Res. *9:* 241 – 245.

KORTE, G. E., G. D'AVERSA (1989): The elastic tissue of Bruch's membrane. Connections to choroidal elastic tissue and the ciliary epithelium of the rabbit and human eyes. Arch. Ophthalmol. *107:* 1654 – 1658.

KORTE, G. E., E. E. MANCHE: Microfibril-microvessel connections in the rabbit eye. Correlative confocal scanning microscopy and electron microscopy . J. Electr. Micro. Tech. *18:* 74 – 81, 1991.

KUCICH, V., W. ABRAMS, G. WEINBAUM, J. ROSENBLOOM (1988): Evidence that elastin is covalently crosslinked to other extracellular macromolecules. J. Cell Biol. (Suppl.) *107:* 3415.

LEE, B., M. GODFREY, E. VITALE et al. (1991): Linkage of Marfan syndrome and a phenotypically related disorder to two different fibrillin genes. Nature *352:* 330.

LEE, W. R., I. GRIERSON (1974): Relationships between intraocular pressure and the morphology of the outflow apparatus. Trans. Ophthalmol. Soc. UK. *94:* 43 – 449.

LI, J. J., W. J. McADAM (1984): Human amyloid P component: an elastase inhibitor, Scand. J. Immunol. *20:* 219 – 226.

LI, Z-Y, B. W. STREETEN, N. YOHAI (1989): Amyloid P protein in pseudoexfoliative fibrillophaty. Curr. Eye Res. *8:* 214 – 227.

LÜTJEN-DRECOLL, E., R. FUTA, J. W. ROHEN (1981): Ultrahistochemical studies on tangential sections of the trabecular meshwork in normal and glaucomatous eyes. Invest. Ophthalmol. Vis. Sc. *21:* 563 – 573.

LÜTJEN-DRECOLL, E., T. SHIMIZU, M. ROHRBACH, J. W. ROHEN (1986): Quantitative analysis of "plaque material" in the inner and outer wall of Schlemm's canal in normal and glaucomatous eyes. Exp. Eye Res. *42:* 443 – 455.

LÜTJEN-DRECOLL, E., M. RITTIG, J. RAUTERBERG, R. JANDER, J. MOLLENHAUER (1989): Immunoelectron microscopical study of type VI collagen in the trabecular meshwork of normal and glaucomatous eyes. Exp. Eye Res. *48:* 139 – 147.

MADDOX, B. K., L. Y. SAKAI, D. R. KEANE, R. W. GLANVILLE (1989): Connective tissue microfibrils. Isolation and characterization of three large pepsin-resistant domains of fibrillin. J. Biol. Chem. *264:* 21, 381–385.

MARSHALL, G. E., A. G. KONSTAS, W. R. LEE (1990): Ultrastructural distribution of collagen types I-IV in aging human retinal vessels. Br. J. Ophthalmol. *74:* 228–232.

MASLEN, C. L., G. M. CORSON, B. K. MADDOX, R. W. GLANVILLE, L. Y. SAKAI (1991): Parial sequence of a candidate gene for the Marfan syndrome. Nature *353:* 334–337.

MCMENAMIN, P. G., W. R. LEE (1980): Age-related changes in extracellular materials in the inner wall of Schlemm's canal. v. Graefes Arch. Klin Exp. Ophthalmol. *212:* 159–172.

MCMENAMIN, P. G., W. R. LEE, D. A. AITKEN (1986): Age-related changes in the human outflow apparatus. Ophthalmol. *93:* 194–209.

MECHAM, R. P., A. HINEK, E. G. CLEARY, V. KUCICH, S. J. LEE, J. ROSENBLOOM (1988): Development of immunoreagents to ciliary zonules that react with protein components of elastic fiber microfibrils and with elastin-producing cells. Biochem. Biophys. Res. Commun. *151:* 822–826.

MECHAN, R. P., A. HINEK, R. ENTWISTLE, D. S. WRENN, G. L. GRIFFIN, R. M. SENIOR (1989a): Elastin binds to a multifunctional 67-kilodalton peripheral membrane protein. Biochem. *28:* 3716–3722.

MECHAM, R. P., A. HINEK, G. L. GRIFFIN, R. M. SENIOR, L. A. LIOTTA (1989b): The elastin receptor shows structural and functional similarities to the 67-KDA tumor cell laminin receptor. J. Biol. Chem. *264:* 16,652–16,657.

MORRISON, J. C., J. A. JERDAN, M. E. DORMAN, H. A. QUIGLEY (1989a): Structural proteins of the neonatal and adult lamina cribrosa. Arch. Ophthalmol. *107:* 1220–1224.

MORRISON, J. C., N. L. L'HERNAULT, H. A. QUIGLEY (1989b): Ultrastructural location of extracellular matrix components in the optic nerve head. Arch. Ophthalmol *107:* 123–129.

MOSES, R. A., W. J. GRODSKI JR., B. C. STARCHER, M. J. GALIONE (1978): Elastin content of the scleral spur, trabecular mesh, and sclera. Invest. Ophthalmol. Vis. Sc. *17:* 817–818.

MURPHY, C. G., A. J. YUN, D. A. NEWSOME, J. A. ALVARADO (1987): Localization of extracellular proteins of the human trabecular meshwork by indirect immunofluorence. Am. J. Ophthalmol. *104:* 33–43.

MOSES, R. A., W. J. GRODSKI JR., B. C. STARCHER, M. J. GALIONE (1978): Elastin content of the scleral spur, trabecular mesh, and sclera. Invest. Ophthalmol. Vis. Sc. *17:* 817–818.

MURPHY, C. G., A. J. YUN, D. A. NEWSOME, J. A. ALVARADO (1987): Localization of extracellular proteins of the human trabecular meshwork by indirect immunoflourence. Am. J. Ophthalmol. *104:* 33–43.

NEIDER, M. W., K. CRAWFORD, P. L. KAUFMAN, L. Z. BITO (1990): In vivo videography of the rhesus monkey accommodative apparatus age-related loss of ciliary muscle response to control stimulation. Arch. Ophthalmol. *108:* 69–74.

NEWSOME, D. A., A. T. HEWITT, W. HUH, P. G. ROBEY, J. R. HASSELL (1987): Detection of specific extracellular matrix molecules in drusen, Bruch's membrane and ciliary body. Am. J. Ophthalmol. *104:* 373–381.

NEWSOME, D. A., W. HUH, W. R. GREEN (1987): Bruch's membrane age-related changes vary by region. Curr. Eye Res. *6:* 1211–1221.

NEWSOME, D. A., B. A. PFEFFER, A. T. HEWITT, P. G. ROBEY, J. R. HASSELL (1988): Detection of extracellular matrix molecules synthesized in vitro by monkey and human retinal pigment epithelium and influence of donor age and multiple passages. Exp. Eye Res. *46:* 305–321.

NORTON, S. W., B. W. STREETEN (1988): Corneal rupture in the neonate: Management and pathology. In Cornea: Transactions of the World Congress, III. Ed. D. Cavanagh, Raven Press, NY, *88:* pg. 351–358.

OLSEN, M. D. (1979): Development of Bruch's membrane in the chick: An electron microscopic study. Invest. Ophthalmol. Vis. Sc. *18:* 329–338.

PRATT, B. M., J. A. MADRI (1985): Immunolocalization of type IV colagen and laminin in nonbasement membrane structures of murine corneal stroma. A light electron microscopic study. Lab. Invest. *52:* 650–656.

QUIGLEY, H. A. (1977): The pathogenesis of reversible cupping in congenital glaucoma. Am. J. Ophthalmol. *84:* 358–370.

QUIGLEY, H. A., E. M. ADDICKS (1981): Regional diferrences in the structure of the lamina cribrosa and their relation to glaucomatous optic nerve damage. Arch. Ophthalmol. *99:* 137–143.

RAVIOLA, G. (1971): The fine structure of the ciliary zonule und ciliary epithelium. With special regard to the organization and insertion of the zonular fibrils. Invest. Ophthalmol. Vis. Sc. *10:* 851.

RHODES, R. H., S. H. MANDELBAUM, D. S. MINCKLER, P. E. CLEARY (1982): Tritiated fucose incorporation in the vitreous body, lens and zonules of the pigmented rabbit. Exp. Eye Res. *34:* 921–931.

RICHMOND, V. L. (1981): The microfibrillar components of porcine lung elastic tissue. Biochem. Biophys. Acta *669:* 193–205.

RODRIGO, F. G., G. COTTA-PEREIRA, J. F. DAVID-FERREIRA (1975): The fine structure of the elastic tendons in the human arrector pili muscle. Br. J. Dermotol. *93:* 631–637.

RODRIGUES, M. M., G. L. SPAETH, E. LIVALINGAM, S. WEINREB (1976): Histopathology of 150 trabeculectomy specimens in glaucoma. Trans. Ophthalmol. Soc. U. K. *96:* 245–255.

ROHEN, J. W. (1979): Scanning electron microscopic studies of the zonular apparatus in human and monkey eyes. Invest. Ophthalmol. Vis. Sc. *18:* 133–144.

ROHEN, J. W., R. FUTA, E. LÜTJEN-DRECOLL (1981): The fine structure of the cribriform meshwork in normal and glaucomatous eyes as seen in tangential sections. Invest. Ophthalmol. Vis. Sc. *21:* 574–585.

ROHEN, J. W., E. LÜTJEN-DRECOLL (1971): Age changes of the trabecular meshwork in human and monkey eyes. In: Ageing and Development. H. Bredt and J. W. Rohen Eds. Vol. I., Schattauer, Stuttgart, pg. 1–36.

ROHEN, J. W., E. LÜTJEN, E. H. BARANY (1967): The relation between the ciliary muscle and the trabecular meshwork and its importance for the effects of miotics on aqueous outflow resistance. v. Graefes Arch. Klin Exp. Ophthalmol. *172:* 23–47.

ROHEN, J. W., R. WITMER (1972): Electron microscopic studies on the trabecular meshwork in glaucoma simplex. v. Graefes Arch. Klin Exp. Ophthalmol. *183:* 251–266.

ROSENBLOOM, J. (1984): Elastin: Relation of protein and gene structure to disease. Lab. Invest. *51:* 605–623.

ROSS, R., P. BORNSTEIN (1969): The elastic fiber. I. The separation and partial characterization of its macromolecular components. J. Cell Biol. *40:* 366.

SAKAI, L. Y, D. R. KEENE, E. ENGVALL (1986): Fibrillin, a new 350-kD glycoprotein, is a component of extracellular microfibrils. J. Cell Biol. *103:* 2499–2509.

SCHLUMBERGER, W., M. THIE, J. RAUTENBERG, H. KRESSE, H. ROBENEK (1989): Deposition and ultrastructural organization of collagen and proteoglycans in the extracellular matrix of gel-cultured fibroblasts. Eur. J. Cell Biol. *50:* 100–110.

SCHWARTZ, E., S. GOLDFISCHER, B. COLTOFF-SCHILLER, O. O. BLUMENFELD (1985): Extracellular matrix microfibrils are composed of core proteins coated with fibronectin. J. Histochem. Cytochem. *33:* 268–274.

SEAR, C. H. J., M. E. GRANT, D. S. JACKSON (1981): The nature of the microfibrillar glycoproteins of elastic fibers. A biosynthetic study. Biochem. J. *194:* 587.

STARCHER, B. C., M. J. GALIONE (1976): Purification and comparison of elastins from different animal species. Anal. Biochem. *74:* 441–447.

STEWART, D. H. III, B. W. STREETEN, R. J. BROCKHURST, D. R. ANDERSON, T. HIROSE, D. M. GASS (1991): Abnormal scleral collagen in nanophthalmos, an ultrastructural study. Arch. Ophthalmol. *109:* 1017–1025.

STREETEN, B. W. (1982a): Zonular Apparatus. In: Biomedical Foundations of Ophthalmology, Vol. I. T. D. DUANE and E. A. JAEGER, Eds. Harper & Row, Pa., Chapter 12, pg. 4–21.

STREETEN, B. W. (1982b): Ciliary Body. In: Biomedical Foundations of Ophthalmology. Vol. I. T. D. DUANE and E. A. JAEGER, Eds. Harper & Row, Pa., Chapter 13, pg. 15–31.

STREETEN, B. W. (1982c): The nature of the ocular zonule. Trans. Am. Ophthalmol. Soc. *80:* 823–854.

STREETEN, B. W., A. J DARK, C. W. BARNES (1984): Pseudoexfoliative material and oxytalan fibers. Exp. Eye Research *38:* 523–531.

STREETEN, B. W., S. A. GIBSON (1988): Identification of extractable proteins from the bovine ocular zonule: Major zonular antigens of 32kD and 250kD. Curr. Eye Res. *7:* 139–146.

STREETEN, B.W., S. A. GIBSON, A. J. DARK (1986): Pseudoexfoliative material contains an elastic microfibrillar-associated glycoprotein. Trans. Am. Ophthalmol. Soc. *84:* 304–320.

STREETEN, B.W., A. G. KARPIK, K. H. SPITZER (1983): Posterior Keratoconus Associated With Systemic Abnormalities. Arch. Ophthalmol. *101:* 616–622.

STREETEN, B.W., Z.-Y. LI, D. H. STEWART, T. CHIJIIWA, R.W. WALLACE (1989): Elastin and amyloid P immunolocalization on elastic fibers in the human trabeculum and sclera. Invest. Ophthalmol. Vis. Sc. *30* (Suppl): 204.

STREETEN, B.W., P. A. LICARI (1983): The zonules and the elastic microfibrillar system in the ciliary body. Invest. Ophthalmol. Vis. Sc. *24:* 667–681.

STREETEN, B.W., P. A. LICARI, A. A. MARUCCI, R. M. DOUGHERTY (1981): Immunohistochemical comparison of the zonular fibrils and elastic tissue microfibrils. Invest. Ophthalmol. Vis. Sc. *21:* 130.

STREETEN, B.W., D. A. SWANN, P. A. LICARI, M. R. ROBINSON, S. A. GIBSON, N. J. MARSH, J.P. VERGNES, I. L. FREEMAN (1983): The protein composition of the ocular zonules. Invest. Ophthalmol. Vis. Sc. *24:* 119–123.

TAKEI, Y., V. OZANICS (1975): Origin and development of Bruch's membrane in monkey fetuses: An electron microscopic study. Invest. Ophthalmol. *14:* 903–916.

TAMM, E., E. LÜTJEN-DRECOLL, J.W. ROHEN, W. JUNGKUNZ (1991): Posterior attachment of the ciliary muscle in young, accommodating and old presbyoptic rhesus monkeys. Invest. Ophthalmol. Vis. Sc. *32:* 1678–1692, 1991.

TAWARA, A., H. H. VARNER, J. G. HOLLYFIELD (1989): Distribution and characterization of sulfated proteoglycans in the human trabecular tissue. Invest. Ophthalmol. Vis. Sc. *30:* 2215–2231.

TRIPATHI, R. C., B. J. TRIPATHI (1982): Functional Anatomy of the Anterior Chamber Angle. In: Biomedical Foundations of Ophthalmology, Vol. 1. Harper & Row, Pa., Chapter 10, pg. 13–44

WALLACE, R. N., B.W. STREETEN, R. B. HANNA (1991): Rotary shadowing of elastic system microfibrils in the ocular zonule, vitreous, and ligamentum nuchea Curr. Eye Res. *10:* 99–109.

WRIGHT, D.W., E. R. MAYNE (1988) Vitreous humor of chicken contains two fibrillar systems. J. Ultrastruct. & Molec. Res. *100:* 224–234.

YUN, A. J., C. G. MURPHY, J. R. POLANSKY, D. A. NEWSOME, J. A. ALVARADO (1989): Proteins secreted by human trabecular cells. Glucocorticoid and other effects. Invest. Ophthalmol Vis. Sc. *30:* 2012–2022.

*Max-Planck-Society, Clinical Research Units for Rheumatology*
*at the Medical Clinic III of the University of Erlangen-Nürnberg*

# Structure and function of collagens in the eye

### K. von der Mark

## 1. Introduction

There is probably no other organ in the vertebrate organism that has found so much interest in collagen research and has contributed so much to our understanding of the functions of the collagens as the eye. No other organ contains that many different collagen types and collagenous tissues or compartments so closely associated, yet clearly separabel and easily accessible for biochemical, histological or cell culture analysis. There is the cornea and its three layers containing at least 8 collagens (I, II, IV, V, VI, VII, VIII and IX), the lens capsule with type IV collagen, the vitreous humour with II, IX and XI collagen, the neural retina (type II) or the trabecular meshwork (VI) besides others. There is probably no part of the eye whose particular function is not intimately associated with a distinct collagen type or pattern of collagen types. Thus, the dense hexagonal lattice of Descemet's membrane whose chemical nature has remained obscure for a long time has now been identified as a type VIII collagen meshwork (SAWADA et al., 1990); the secret of the regular diameter (and therefore probably also for the transparency) of the collagen fibrils in the corneal stroma was elucidated by clarifying the role of type V collagen in controlling the diameter of type I/V collagen heterofibrils (FITCH et al., 1984; BIRK et al., 1988; ADACHI and HAYASHI, 1985; for review see BURGESON, 1988).

This articles adresses to scientists working both in eye and in collagen research, and tries to summarize in brief the collagenous composition of the various parts of the eye to illustrate the variety of structures the different collagens are able to give rise to.

## 2. The collagens – a family of structural proteins
## for diverse tissues and functions

The unique feature of all collagens is the triple helix, a rigid, inflexible structure made of three α-chains that wind around each other in a left handed helix and hold together firmly through hydrogen-bonds (KÜHN 1987; RAMACHANDRAN and REDDI

Table 1: Vertebral Collagens

**Fibril forming collagens**

| Type | Subunits | mol wt | Molecular composition | Occurence | Extracellular Architecture |
|---|---|---|---|---|---|
| I | α1 α2 | 95 K 95 K | $[\alpha1(I)]_2$, α2(I) | skin, bone *cornea, sclera* | crossbanded fibrils |
| II | α1(II) | 95 K | $[\alpha1(II)]_3$ | cartilage, *vitreous* humour *avian prim. corneal stroma*, notochord | crossbanded fibrils |
| III | α1(III) | 95 K | $[\alpha1(III)]_3$ | reticular fibres skin, placenta *mammalian corneal stroma, sclera* | crossbanded and unbanded fibrils |
| V | α1(V) α2(V) α3(V) | 105 K 105 K 105 K | α1, α2, α3 (V) | skin, smooth muscle placenta, *corneal stroma* | heterofibrils with with type I collagen |
| XI | α1(XI) α2(XI) α3(XI)[a] | 105 K 105 K | α1, α2, α3 (XI) | hyaline cartilage *vitreous* | heterofibrils with with type II |

**FACIT (Fibril Associated Collagens with Interrupted Tripelhelix) Collagens:**

| Type | Subunits | mol wt | Molecular composition | Occurence | Extracellular Architecture |
|---|---|---|---|---|---|
| IX | α1[b] α2[c] α3 | 80 K 120 K 60 K | α1, α2, α3 (IX) | cartilage vitreous humour | linked to type II collagen fibrils |
| XII | α1 | 220 K | $[\alpha1(XII)]_3$ | perichondrium tendon, ligaments | linked to type I collagen fibrils? |
| XIX | ? | ? | ? | skin, tendon | |

[a] homologous or identical to α1(II);
[b] shorter form in cornea, lacking NC 1 domain;
[c] contains a chondroitin sulfate side chain

1976). Prerequisite for the formation of a triple helix is a glycine residue in every third position of the polypeptide chain, and a high proportion – around 10 % each – of proline and hydroxyproline. In type I collagen, the longest known and best studied collagen found in skin, bone, tendon, corneal stroma and in other fibril forming collagens (see Table 1) the triple helix has a length of about 300 nm and repre-

**Short chain collagens**

| Type | Subunits | MW | Molecular composition | Occurence | Extracellular Architecture |
|---|---|---|---|---|---|
| VI | $\alpha 1(VI)$<br>$\alpha 2(VI)$<br>$\alpha 3(VI)$ | 140 000<br>140 000<br>240 000 | $(\alpha 1,\ \alpha 2,\ \alpha 3)\ VI$ | skin, ligaments<br>cartilage<br>*Corneal stroma*<br>*Zonula trabecules* | microfibrils,<br>beaded<br>filaments |
| VIII | $\alpha 1(VIII)$<br>$\alpha 2(VIII)$ | 64 000 | ? | Endothlial cells<br>*Descemet's<br>membrane* | hexagonal<br>meshwork |
| X | $\alpha 1(X)$ | 66 000 | $[\alpha 1(X)]_3$ | hypertrophic<br>cartilage | hexagonal<br>meshwork |
| XIII | $\alpha 1(XIII)$ | ? | ? | fibroblasts | ? |

**Basement membrane collagens**

| Type | Subunits | MW | Molecular composition | Occurence | Extracellular Architecture |
|---|---|---|---|---|---|
| IV | $\alpha 1(IV)$ | 160 000 | $[\alpha 1(IV)]_2\ \alpha 2(IV)$ | Basement<br>Membranes | "chicken wire"<br>meshwork |
| | $\alpha 2(IV)$ | 150 000 | | *Lens capsule*<br>*Bowman's membrane* | |
| | $(\alpha 3 - \alpha 6)$ | $\approx 150\,000$ | ? | | |

**Other collagens**

| Type | Subunits | MW | Molecular composition | Occurence | Extracellular Architecture |
|---|---|---|---|---|---|
| VII | $\alpha 1(VII)$ | 150 000 | $[\alpha 1(VII)]_3$ | Epidermis<br>*Cornea epithelium* | anchoring fibrils<br>(connects BM with<br>mesenchyme) |

sents almost the entire molecule, with the exception of short telopeptides (15-30 residues) at both ends of the molecule (KÜHN et al. 1987; BURGESON 1988; VAN DER REST and GARRONE 1991).

Most important for our understanding of the function and structure of collagens in tissues are the molecular interactions they undergo either with a homologous collagen molecule or another collagen type, with proteoglycans, glycoproteins and other components of the extracellular matrix. These interactions produce a large variety of structures such as thick or thin fibrils of strictly controlled diameter (e.g. in the cornea), transparent gels (in the vitreous), dense textures that prohibit influx of water (e.g. Descemet's membrane), tough fibres of extreme endurance (trabecular meshwork) or elastic microfibrillar meshworks. All collagens are synthesized as precursor molecules with large non-triplehelical domains at both amino- and carboxyl ends; from all fibril forming collagens the C-terminal extensions, from type I also the amino terminal extensions are removed by specific proteases before their assembly in the extracellular space. In most other collagens such as type IV or VI collagen the extensions remain on the molecule; they are essential for homologous or heterologous interactions with other collagen molecules or other matrix components and form two- or three-dimensional structures such as hexagonal meshworks, beaded filaments and other networks (BORNSTEIN and SAGE 1980; VON DER MARK 1981; MAYNE and BURGESON 1987; BURGESON 1988; VAN DER REST and GARRONE 1991).

In the past the molecular structure of most of the presently known collagen types (15) has been elucidated by protein sequencing analysis, physico-chemical studies and molecular cloning. Much of the present activities in collagen research are directed towards analysis of the molecular interactions of collagens with other tissue components and cells in order to understand their role in tissue development, structure and remodelling.

Attempts are being made to classify the various collagen which may have very little in common in terms of structure, function and evolutionary traits except the triple helical domains (see e.g. BURGESON 1988; VAN DER REST and GARRONE 1991).

## 2.1. The fibril forming collagens I, II, III, V and XI

Most banded collagen fibrils in tendon, skin, bone, or cornea with a repetitive cross-banding pattern of a 67 nm period are heterofibrils consisting of mixtures of I, III and V collagens, or in cartilage of II and XI collagens (KÜHN 1987; BIRK et al. 1988; MENDLER et al. 1989), associated with other collagens (FACIT-collagens, see below). The fibril forming collagen molecules with a 300 nm triplehelix are characterized by a periodic pattern of hydrophobic lateral interaction sites that allow their assembly into a staggered array with a 67 nm period (D-period), about one fifth of the length of a molecule (BRODSKY and EIKENBERRY 1985). The highly tensile strength of collagen fibrils results from covalent bonds forming between amino group and aldehyde groups derived from lysine and hydroxylysine residues, and histidine residues (for review see Bailey et al. 1974). Although such fibrils form spontaneously in vitro from solutions of processed type I, II or III collagen molecules, the fibril formation in situ is much more complex and not yet fully understood. There is good evidence that the type I collagen fibril diameter is controlled in part by the incorporation of type V collagen molecules retaining their amino terminal propeptides (ADACHI and HAYASHI 1985; BIRK et al. 1988). Similarly, type III collagen fibrils are smaller in diameter than type I collagen fibrils due to the presence of the unprocessed amino terminal extension (FLEISCHMAYER et al. 1981) (Fig. 1). However, the growth and size of collagen fibrils is also regulated by small chondroitin and dermatan-sulfate proteoglycans that are intimately associated with most collagen fibrils (SCOTT et al. 1985).

## 2.2. FACIT collagen

In many, if not all tissues so-called FACIT-collagens (Fibril-Associated-Collagens with Interrupted Triplehelix (GORDON et al. 1990)) are covalently linked and incorporated into collagen fibrils. For example, electron microscopic analysis of cartilage heterofibrils consisting of type II and XI collagen revealed short collagenous stubs with globular domains decorating the surface of the fibrils (VAUGHAN et al. 1988). These stubs are part of type IX collagen, a FACIT collagen consisting of three stretches of triplehelix interrupted with non-triplehelical domains, and a large globular domain (NC 4) at the amino and of the $\alpha1(IX)$ chain (YASUI et al. 1984; VAN DER REST et al. 1985) (see Table 2). The interruptions in the triplehelix provide the molecule with a high flexibility. Type IX collagen molecules are covalently linked to type II collagen through a hydroxypyridinium crosslink (EYRE et al. 1987; VAN DER REST et al. 1988). Outside hyaline cartilage, type IX collagen exists also in another form: In the cornea, the first 6 exons of the $\alpha1(IX)$ gene including exon 1 coding for the NC 4 domain are not transcribed; instead, a cornea-specific

Table 2: Collagen distribution in the vertebrate eye (overview)

*Cornea*

| | | |
|---|---|---|
| Primary stroma: | fibrils: | I, II, IX[*] |
| Secondary stroma: | fibrils: avian | I, V |
| | mammalian | I, III, V |
| interfibrillar meshwork | | VI |
| nerves | | IV |
| Bowman's membrane: | fibrils | I, V |
| | basal lamina | IV |
| | anchoring fibrils | VII |
| Descemet's membrane | | VIII |
| Endothelial basal lamina | | IV |

| | |
|---|---|
| Lens capsule | IV |

| | |
|---|---|
| Neural retina | II, IV |
| Vitreous humour | II, IX[*], XI |
| Trabecular meshwork | VI |
| Sclera (mammalian) | I, III, V |
| Scleral cartilage (avian) | II, IX, XI |
| Pigmented epithelium (avian, embryonic) | II |

promotor and exon are located in the intron between exon 6 and 7, giving rise to a shorter α1(IX) transcript (NISHIMURA et al. 1989; MURAGAKI et al. 1990).

The structure of type XII collagen is similar to that of type IX collagen (GORDON et al. 1987). The N-terminal NC 1 domain is larger (190 kD) and appears cross-shaped in the electron microscope (DUBLET 1989). It is located in perichondrium, periosteum, tendon, and ligaments (SUGRUE et al. 1989) and may be associated with type I collagen fibrils in a similar manner as type IX collagen being linked to type II collagen fibrils. Also type XIV collagen is a homotrimeric collagen homologous to type IX collagen and is found in bone and tendon (DUBLET 1991).

## 2.3. Short chain collagens

Although this classification may be only historical, types VI, VIII and X collagen may be considered as short chain collagen as their triplehelical core is only about 100 nm in length. While types VIII and X collagen are homologous in their sequence and form hexagonal meshworks (see below), type VI collagen is structurally unrelated to these collagens, carries considerably larger globular domains on both ends and forms a microfibrillar network of beaded filaments (TIMPL and ENGEL 1987; RAUTERBERG et al. 1986).

*Type VI collagen* is a carbohydrate- and cystine-rich, highly cross-linked collagen which owing to its insolubility has long been known only in form of its pepsin-resistant collagenous domains (JANDER et al. 1981; VON DER MARK et al. 1984). The molecules consist of 3 different α-subunits. The α3(VI) chain is considerable larger than the α1 and α2(VI) chains due to a large aminoterminal globular domain (Mr180K). Four type VI collagen molecules assemble into tetrades with their globular domains overlapping (FURTHMAYR 1983). The meshwork of beaded filaments with a 100 nm periodicity identified as type VI collagen fibrils in fibroblast cultures (BRUNS et al. 1986) in skin (KEENE et al. 1988) or in the trabecular meshwork of the eye (LÜTJEN-DRECOLL et al. 1989) can best be explained by oligomerization of such tetrades (TIMPL and ENGEL 1987). Type VI collagen has been identified in a large variety of tissues including skin (KEENE 1988), cartilage (AYAD et al. 1984), nucleus pulposus (VON DER MARK et al. 1984), cornea (LINSENMAYER et al. 1986; ZIMMERMANN et al. 1986) and others.

*Type VIII collagen* was first identified in the culture medium of endothelial cells and was therefore called endothelial cell (EC) collagen (SAGE et al. 1980; QUARONI and TRELSTAD 1980). Due to the formation of covalent bonds between the α-subunits the structure of the native molecules was obscured for some time. Biochmical analysis (BENYA and PADILLA 1986) and cDNA cloning (YAMAGUCHI et al. 1989) revealed that the size of an α-chain is 64 kD, with a triplehelical domain of 45 kD and two globular domains at both ends. In an elegant reconstitution study with

type VIII collagen molecules isolated from bovine corneal endothelial cells in vitro
SAWADA et al. (1990) could demonstrate that type VIII collagen assembles into
hexagonal sheets identical to those seen after electronmicroscopical examination
of Descemet's membrane (SAWADA et al. 1982, 1984).

*Type X collagen*, a collagen made exclusively by hypertrophic chondrocytes
(SCHMID and LINSENMAYER 1987) is homologous to type VIII collagen in its sequence (YAMAGUCHI et al. 1989; THOMAS et al. 1991; REICHENBERGER et al. 1991) and
forms a similar hexagonal network after reconstitution in vitro (KWAN et al. 1991).
As a constituent of the calcifying hypertrophic cartilage in the fetal growth plate it
binds calcium (KIRSCH and VON DER MARK 1991) and may thus be involved in cartilage calcification.

*Type XIII collagen* is about the same size as VIII and X collagen and was first
cloned from a HT-1080 tumor cell cDNA library (PIHLAJANIEMI et al. 1987).
However, in contrast to type X collagen it consists of three collagenous and four
noncollagenous transcripts and undergoes complex alternative splicing (PIHLAJA-
NIEMI and TAMMINEN 1990).

### 2.4. Basement membrane collagens

Basement membranes contain a chicken-wire like network of *type IV collagen*
molecules which undergo homologous interactions at their C-terminal extensions
(NC 1 domains), the aminoterminal 7S domains as well along their triplehelix
(KÜHN et al. 1981, for review see MARTIN et al. 1988; TIMPL 1989; YURCHENCO and
SCHITTNY 1990). Type IV collagen molecules have a triplehelical core somewhat
longer than type I collagen with several short interruptions that make the molecules
flexible and allow them to bend into interlaced meshwork structures. In addition to
the most common $[\alpha1(IV)]_2$ $\alpha2(IV)$ molecule, tissue-specific a-chain variants ($\alpha3$,
$\alpha4$, $\alpha5$ and $\alpha6(IV)$) have been described. A defect in $\alpha5(IV)$ was elucidated as the
genetic cause of Alport's syndrom (HOSTIKKA et al. 1990).

### 2.5. Other collagens

Among other vertebrate collagens, *type VII collagen*, the collagenous constituent
of anchoring fibrils, deserves a closer look in view of its importance in the intercon-
nection between epithelium and underlying stroma. Type VII collagen is the largest known collagen with a triplehelix of 424 nm length and a total molecular mass
of 1.050 kDa (MORRIS et al. 1986; SAKAI et al. 1986). The molecule carries a globular domain (NC 2) of Mr 30 kDA at the carboxyl end, and a large cross-shaped Mr
150 KDa domain (NCI) at the amino end (LUNSTRUM et al. 1986; PARENTE et al.

1991). Two molecules align antiparallel at their N-terminal domains; in the anchoring fibril these dimers assemble laterally to form bundes of filaments which are anchored through the C-terminal domains on the one side within the basal lamina, and with the C-terminal domain on the other side within a collagenous plaque (anchoring plaque) in the stroma. Ultrastructurally and immunohistochemically type VII collagen anchoring fibrils have been located in the epidermis, cornea-epithlium, oral and vaginal mucosa, sclera and amnion, but not in other basement membranes (SAKAI et al. 1986; LUNSTRUM et al. 1986).

### 3. The collagens of the vertebrate cornea

Transparency of the *corneal stroma* requires extreme regular arrangements and strictly controlled size of the collagen fibrils. In the avian cornea, collagen fibrils are 25 nm thick and are packed with a uniform distance into orthogonal layers (HAY and REVEL 1969; TRELSTAD and COULOMBRE 1971; for review see HAY et al. 1979; HAY 1980). The layers of collagen fibrils are stacked in an angle somewhat above 90° on top of each other, resulting in a spiraling configuration of over 200° along the optical axis (COULOMBRE 1965).

The morphogenetic principles controlling this unusual arrangement of collagen fibrils is a fascinating problem. From studies on the isolated embryonic chick cornea epithelium it has been elucidated that the entire primary corneal stroma is synthesized and secreted by the epithelium after induction by the underlying lens capsule (DODSON and HAY 1974; MEIER and HAY 1974). The orthogonal pattern of collagen fibrils in the acellular, primary stroma is laid out by the corneal epithelial cells (TRELSTAD et al. 1971; 1974) which protrude collagen fibrils from cellular invaginations in two directions at an angle of about 90°.

*The primary corneal stroma* of the embryonic chick eye is synthesized by the cornea epithelial cells; it consists of type I and type II collagen which seem to assemble to hybrid fibrils (LINSENMAYER et al. 1973; VON DER MARK et al. 1977; HENDRIX et al. 1978). The synthesis of type II collagen, a collagen found elsewhere only in cartilage, by embryonic epithelia was somewhat unexpected as only mesenchymal cells had been assumed to synthesize fibril forming collagens. Curiously, also other avian epithelia secrete type II collagen at sites of presumptive chondrogenesis: the notochord (LINSENMAYER et al. 1974; VON DER MARK et al. 1976), pigmented epithelium (NEWSOME et al. 1973), otic vesicle or mandibular mesenchyme (THOROGOOD et al. 1986), suggesting that type II collagen may be involved in chondrogenesis, for example of the avian cartilaginous sclera (NEWSOME 1976).

Similar to type II collagen, there is a transient brief expression of type IX collagen by embryonic corneal epithelium at the time when endothelial cells begin to immigrate from the limbus and spread on the posterior surface of the primary

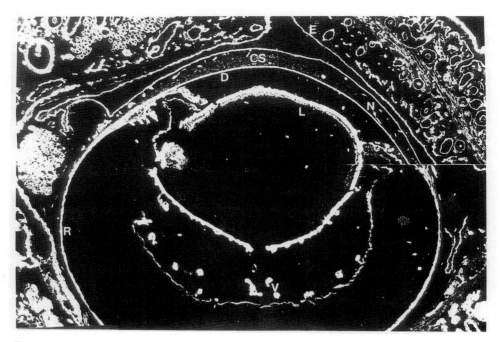

Fig. 1. Immunofluorescence localization of type IV collagen in the 19d fetal mouse eye. The antibody was raised against some type IV collagen prepared from the EHS-tumour (TIMPL et al. Eur. J. Biochem. *84* (1978) 43 – 52) and was kindly provided by Dr. R. Timpl, Martinsried Germany CS = Corneal stroma. D = Descemet's Membrane, E = Eyelid, L = Lens capsule, N = Nerves, R = Neural Retina, V = Vitreous humous (Photograph: K. von der Mark). Magnification: 60x.

stroma (FITCH et al. 1988). It disappears when the cornea begins to swell, while type II collagen remains for a longer period. The $\alpha$1-chain of this type IX collagen lacks the aminoterminal NC4 domain (NISHIMURA et al. 1989; MURAGAKI et al. 1990) due to a cornea specific transcription start (see also 2.4). The function of this transiently appearing type IX collagen is still unclear.

*The secondary corneal stroma* is laid down by invading keratocytes, using the primary stroma as a scaffold. Thus, the collagen fibrils of the avian corneal stroma are arranged in the same orthogonal pattern. Chemical analysis of the collagens revealed the presence of about 20 % type V, but not of type II collagen in the avian (PÖSCHL and VON DER MARK 1980) and in the bovine cornea (DAVISON et al. 1979). Immunofluorescence analysis with polyclonal (PÖSCHL and VON DER MARK 1980) and monoclonal antibodies (VON DER MARK and ÖCALAN 1982; LINSENMAYER et al. 1983) showed a codistribution of type V and I collagen in the corneal stroma. Electronmicroscopical investigations after double labeling with gold-labeled antibodies indicated codistribution of types I and V collagen in the same fibril (FITCH et al. 1985). This was also suggested from the observation that immunolabeling of type V collagen required partial dissolution of the collagen fibrils by acid treatment or enzymes (VON DER MARK and ÖCALAN 1982; LINSENMAYER et al. 1983, 1984; FITCH 1984). In vitro reconstitution experiments of collagen fibrils with various ratios of type I and type V collagen further suggest that a content of 20 % type V collagen regulates the diameter of the heterofibrils to about 25 nm, the size observed in the corneal stroma (ADACHI and HAYASHI 1985).

Interestingly, the avian corneal stroma is completely devoid of type III collagen (VON DER MARK et al. 1977; CONRAD et al. 1980), while this collagen is present in the mouse and bovine cornea (SCHMUT et al. 1977; DAVISON et al. 1979). Chick corneal fibroblasts, however, are able to synthesize type III collagen when taken into culture (CONRAD et al. 1980). The reason why type III collagen synthesis is completely suppressed in the corneal stroma, while it codistributes with type I collagen in the adjacent limbus and most other tissues of the chicken, is yet unclear. It may have to do with the expression of keratan sulfate proteoglycan in precisely the same region.

By immunofluorescence analysis using a monoclonal antibody, type VI collagen was also localized in the stroma of the chick (LINSENMAYER et al. 1986) and human cornea (ZIMMERMANN et al. 1986). The presence of type VI in the human was confirmed by pepsin extraction, SDS-gelelectrophoresis and immunoblotting (ZIMMERMANN et al. 1986). It represents about 7-10 % of the dry weight of the cornea and forms an independent microfibrillar meshwork independent of the type I/V collagen fibrils (LINSENMAYER et al. 1986; see also KEENE et al. 1988).

*The cornea epithelium* is interconnected to the underlying stroma by anchoring fibrils and anchoring plaques (KEENE et al. 1987). The anchoring fibrils consist of bundles of antiparallel dimers of type VII collagen (MORRIS et al. 1986; SAKAI et al. 1986). The anchoring plaques within the stroma may correspond to the type IV collagen plaques observed by PRATT and MADRI (1985). At the basement membrane side, the anchoring fibrils terminate adjacent to hemidesmosomes in the corneal epithelial cells. STEPP and coauthors (1990) have located a particular integrin ($\alpha6\beta4$) in the basal cell membrane adjacent to hemidesmosomes. The extracellular matrix ligand of this integrin is not yet clearly identified, but there is a good chance that it is the carboxyterminal globule of type VII collagen. Thus, the complete sequence of molecular links interconnecting the intracellular cytokeratin filaments of the corneal epithelial cells to the collagen fibrils of the stroma would involve hemidesmosomes, $\alpha6\beta4$ integrins, type VII collagen anchoring fibrils, type IV collagen plaques and type I/V collagen fibrils (see Fig. 2).

Type IV collagen is located, as expected, both in the epithelial and the endothelial basement membrane (Fig. 1) (HAY et al. 1979). Interestingly, it is also present in fine short bands or plaques within the corneal stroma (BEE et al. 1988), probably correlating with basal lamina-like plaques observed in the electron microscope (PRATT and MADRI 1985). Furthermore, it appears in the avian cornea coincident with the development of nerves and may indicate the presence of intra-stromal

# Collagens in the cornea

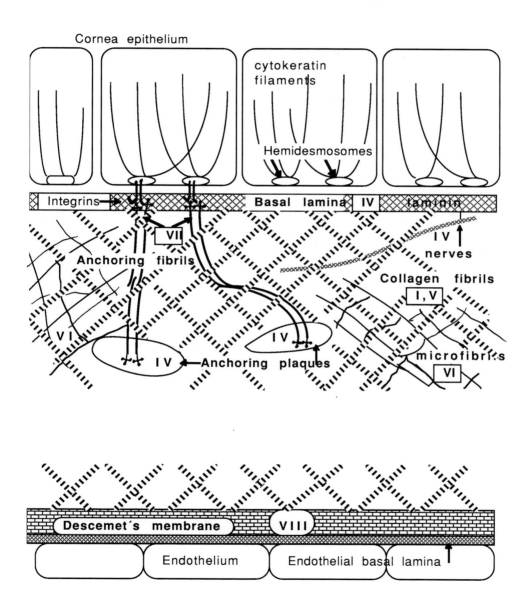

Fig. 2. Schematic illustration of the distribution of collagens in the vertebrate cornea. The collagen types are indicated in roman numbers.

Schwann cells accompanying the immigrating nerves (BEE et al. 1988). In addition, antibody staining revealed intra-stromal fibres of type IV collagen orthogonal to the epithelial basement membrane (BEE et al. 1988). Bowman's Membrane, the acellular collagenous layer underneath the epithelium consists primarily of type I and V collagen (VON DER MARK et al. 1977).

The collagenous constituent of *Descemet's membrane*, which consists of stacks of hexagonal lattices visible in the electron microscope (SAWADA et al. 1982, 1984) is collagen type VIII; this collagen is able to reconstitute to such hexagonal lattices by head-to-head assembly also in vitro (SAWADA et al. 1990). Previous suggestions that Descemet's membrane may consist of type VI or IV collagen were not confirmed (SAWADA 1990).

## 4. Lens capsule

The lens capsule is essentially a pure basement membrane, and has been therefore one of the first and most intensely studied object for the isolation and characterization of basement membrane collagen (DENDUCHIS and KEFALIDES 1969). Owing to the insolubility and high degree of crosslinking only collagen fragments of various length could be characterized which were different from other known collagens. Soluble type IV collagen molecules of complete size were obtained in cultures of chick lenses (GRANT et al. 1972; DEHM and KEFALIDES 1978). Further chemical characterization of the lens capsule collagen was possible after extraction with citrate (OLSEN et al. 1973) or after limited pepsin digestion (GAY and MILLER 1979) and suggested the existence of two $\alpha$-chains. Based on immunological cross-reaction with antibodies to type IV collagen (FITCH et al. 1983) and on the size of the pepsin fragments it is now clear that the major collagen of lens is type IV collagen. Immunofluorescence staining with monoclonal antibodies to type IV collagen showed a bright staining of the anterior chick lens capsule but hardly any staining of the posterior lens capsule (FITCH et al. 1983), which, however, seemed to be associated with type II collagen perhaps derived from the vitreous humour (VON DER MARK et al. 1977, NEWSOME et al. 1976). Final information on the $\alpha$-subunit composition of lens capsule type IX collagen is still missing.

## 5. Neural retina and vitreous humour

Embryonic chick neural retina cells synthesize type II collagen (SMITH et al. 1976; NEWSOME et al. 1976) and another higher Mr collagen (LINSENMAYER et al. 1978) which may be either type V or type XI collagen. In the embryonic chick eye, the retina is thus the source for the type II collagen found in the vitreous humour

(NEWSOME et al. 1976). In later stages of development, some of the vitreous type II collagen seems to be made also by hyalocytes (NEWSOME et al. 1976). The presence of type II collagen was also shown in the bovine vitreous (SWANN and SCOTSMAN 1980). CNBr-peptide analysis also indicated the existence of another collagen in the vitreous (SWANN and SCOTSMAN 1980), which may be type IX collagen (FITCH et al. 1988).

## 6. Trabecular meshwork

The trabecular meshwork underneath the Schlemm's canal contains cross-striated fiber bundles, also called "lattice collagen" or "long spacing-collagen" with a periodicity of 50 and 100 nm. This banding resembled that of type VI collagen fibres (FURTHMAYR et al. 1983; BRUNS et al. 1988). By antibody staining this collagen was shown to be type VI collagen (LÜTJEN-DRECOLL et al. 1989).

## 7. Conclusions and perspectives

Improved biochemical and molecular biological methods have in the past revealed a growing number of collagenous proteins with diverse structural and functional domains. Apart from the triple helix which defines the collagens as such and allows the fibril forming collagens I, II, III, V and XI to assemble to the well known crossbanded fibrils, other collagens contain globular domains at their ends which undergo specific interactions with other matrix components or homologous interactions; others have interrupted triple helices that render the molcules more flexible and allows them to bend into meshworks. Besides their structural importance, collagens have been shown to have a regulatory impact on migration, proliferation and differentiation of most body cells, which is mediated by specific cell surface receptors such as integrins or membrane intercalated heparan sulfate proteoglycans.

Thus, a repertoire of diverse structural molecules seems to be ready to fulfill almost any physiological or structural function required for a particular ocular tissue. The preparation of specific antibodies and cDNA-probes has allowed precise localization of the new collagens and the corresponding gene transcripts, and thus has contributed essential information for our understanding of structural-functional relationships of collagens in the eye. In the future, these tools will allow us the describe more precisely collagen-related molecular defects in ocular tissues.

# References

ADACHI, E., T. HAYASHI (1985): In vitro formation of fine fibrils with a D-periodic banding pattern from type V collagen. Collagen Rel. Res. *5:* 225–232.

AYAD, S., H. EVANS, J. B. WEISS, L. HOLT (1984): Type VI collagen but not type V collagen is present in cartilage. Collagen Rel. Res. *4:* 165–168.

BAILEY, A. J., S. P. ROBINS, G. BALIAN (1974): Biological significance of the intermolecular crosslinks of collagen. Nature *251:* 105–109.

BEE, J. A., U. KÜHL, U. EDGAR, D. EDGAR, K. VON DER MARK (1988): Avian corneal nerves: Co-Distribution with collagen type IV and acquisition of substance P immunoreactivity. Investigative Ophthalmology & Visual Science *29:* 101–107.

BENYA, P. D., S. R. PADILLA (1986): Isolation and characterization of type VIII collagen synthesized by cultured rabbit corneal endothelial cells. A conventional structure replaces the interrupted-helix model. J. Biol. Chem. *261:* 4160–4169.

BIRK, D. E., J. M. FITCH, J. P. BABIARZ, T. F. LINSENMAYER (1988): Collagen type I and type V are present in the same fibril in the avian corneal stroma. J. Biol. Chem. *106:* 999–1008.

BORNSTEIN, P., H. SAGE (1980): Structurally distinct collagen types. Ann. Rev. Biochem. *49:* 957–1003.

BRODSKY, B., E. F. EIKENBERRY (1985): Surpamolecular collagen assemblies. Ann. N.Y. Acad. Sci. *460:* 73–84.

BRUNS, R. R., W. ENGVALL, R. TIMPL, J. GROSS (1986): Type VI collagen in extracellular, 100-nm periodic filaments and fibrils: identification by immunoelectron microscopy. J. Cell Biol. *103:* 393–404.

BURGESON, R. E. (1988): New collagens, new concepts. Ann. Rev. Cell Biol. *4:* 551–577.

CONRAD, G. W., W. DESSAU, K. VON DER MARK (1980): Synthesis of type III collagen by fibroblasts from the embryonic chick cornea. J. Cell Biol. *84:* 501–512.

COULOMBRE, A. J. (1965): Problems in corneal morphogenesis. Adv. Morphog. *4:* 81.

DAVISON, P. F., B.-S. HONG, D. J. CANNON (1979): Quantitative analysis of the collagens in the bovine cornea. Exp. Eye Res. *29:* 97–107.

DEHM, P., N. A. KEFALIDES (1978): The collagenous component of lens basement membrane. The isolation and characterization of an α-chain size collagenous peptide and its relationship to newly synthesized lens components. J. Biol. Chem. *253:* 6680–6686.

DENDUCHIS, B., N. A. KEFALIDES (1970): Immunochemistry of sheep anterior lens capsule. Biochim. Biophys. Acta *221:* 357–366.

DODSON, J. W., E. D. HAY (1974): Secretion of collagen by corneal epithelium. II. Effect of the underlying substratum on secretion and polymerization of epithelial products. J. Exp. Zool. *189:* 51–72.

DUBLET, B., M. VAN DER REST (1991): Type XIV collagen, a new homotrimeric molecule extracted from bovine skin and tendon, with a triple helical disulfide-bonded domain homologous to type IX and type XII collagens. J. Biol. Chem. *266:* 6853–6858.

DUBLET, B., S. OH, S. P. SUGRUE, M.K. GORDON, D. R. GERECKE, D. R. OLSEN, M. VAN DER REST (1989): The structure of avian type XII collagen. α1(XII) chains contain 190-kDa non-triple helical amino-terminal domains and forms homotrimeric molecules. J. Biol. Chem. *264:* 13150–13156.

EYRE, D. R., S. APON, J.-J. WU, L. H. ERICSSON, K. A. WALSH (1987): Collagen type IX: Evidence for covalent linkages to type II collagen in cartilage. FEBS Lett. *220:* 337–341.

FITCH, J. M., R. MAYNE, T. F. LINSENMAYER (1983): Developmental acquisition of basement membrane heterogeneity: Type IV collagen in the avian lens capsule. J. Cell Biol. *97:* 940–943.

FITCH, J. M., J. GROSS, R. MAYNE, B. JOHNSON-WINT, T. F. LINSENMAYER (1984): Organization of collagen types I and V in the embryonic chicken cornea: Monoclonal antibody studies. Proc. Natl. Acad. Sci. USA *81:* 2791–2795.

FITCH, J. M., A. MENTZER, R. MAYNE, T. F. LINSENMAYER (1988): Acquisition of type IX collagen by the developing avian primary corneal stroma and vitreous. Develop. Biol. *128:* 396–405.

FLEISCHMAYER, R., R. TIMPL, L. TUDERMAN, L. RAISHER, M. WIESTNER, J. S. PERLISH, P. N. GRAVES (1981d): Ultrastructural identification of extension aminopropeptides of type I and type III collagens in human skin. P. Nas. Biol. *78:* 7360 – 7364.

FURTHMAYR, H., H. WIEDEMANN, R. TIMPL, E. ODERMATT, J. ENGEL (1983): Electron-microscopical approach to a structural model of intima collagen. Biochem. J. *211:* 303 – 311.

GAY, S., E. J. MILLER (1979): Characterization of lens capsule collagen: Evidence for the presence of two unique chains in molecules derived from major basement membrane structures. Arch. Biochem. Biophys. *198:* 370 – 378.

GORDON, M. K., D. R. GERECKE, B. R. OLSEN (1987): Type XII collagen: Distinct extracellular matrix component discovered by cDNA cloning. Pros. Natl. Acad. Sci. USA *84:* 6040 – 6044.

GRANT, M. E., N. A. KEFALIDES, D. J. PROCKOP (1972): The biosynthesis of basement membrane collagen in embryonic chick lens. J. Biol. Chem. *247:* 3539 – 3544.

HAY, E. D. (1980): Development of the vertebrate cornea. International Review of Cytology *63:* 263 – 321.

HAY, E. D., J. P. REVEL (1969): Fine structure of the developing avian cornea. In: Monographs in Developmental Biology. A. WOLSKY and P. S. CHEN, (Eds.) S. Karger AG, Basel, Switzerland, Vol. 1, pp.1-.

HAY, E. D., J. W. DODSON (1973): Secretion of collagen by corneal epithelium. I. Morphology of the collagenous products produced by isolated epithelia grown on frozen-killed lens. J. Cell Biol. *57:* 190 – 213.

HAY, E. D., T. F. LINSENMAYER, R. L. TRELSTAD, K. VON DER MARK (1979): Origin and distribution of collagens in the developing cornea. Curr. Top. Eye Res. *1:* 1 – 35.

HENDRIX, M. J. C., E. D. HAY, K. VON DER MARK, K. VON DER MARK (1978): Electron-microscopic localization of collagen types in embryonic chick cornea and tibia utilizing ferritin-conjugated antibodies. J. Cell Biol. *79:* 150 – 150.

HOSTIKKA, S. L., R. L. EDDY, M. G. BYERS, M. HÖYHTYÄ, T. B. SHOWS, K. TRYGGVASON (1990): Identification of a distinct type IV collagen α-chain with restricted kidney distribution and assignment of its gene to the locus of X chromosome-linked Alport syndrome. Proc. Natl. Acad. Sci. USA *87:* 1606 – 1610.

JANDER, R., J. RAUTERBERG, B. VOSS, D. R. VON BASSEWITZ (1981): A cysteine-rich collagenous protein from bovine placenta. Isolation of its constituent polypeptide chains and some properties of the non-denatured protein. Eur. J. Biochem. *114:* 17 – 25.

KEENE, D. R., L. Y. SAKAI, G. P. LUNSTRUM, N. P. MORRIS, R. E. BURGESON (1987): Type VII collagen forms an extended network of anchoring fibrils. J. Cell Biol. *104:* 611 – 621.

KEENE, D. R., E. ENGVALL, R. W. GLANVILLE (1988): Ultrastructure of type VI collagen in human skin and cartilage suggests an anchoring function for this filamentous network. J. Cell Biol. *107:* 1995 – 2006.

KIRSCH, T., K. VON DER MARK (1991): $Ca^{2+}$ binding properties of type X collagen. FEBS Lett. *294:* 149 – 152.

KÜHN, K. (1987): The classical collagens: Types I, II and III. Structure and Function of Collagen Types 1 – 41, Academic Press.

KÜHN, K., H. WIEDEMANN, R. TIMPL, J. RISTELI, H. DIERINGER, T. VOSS, G. GLANVILLE (1981): Macromolecular structure of basement membrane collagen. FEBS Lett. *125:* 123 – 128.

KWAN, A. P. L., C. E. CUMMINGS, J. A. CHAPMAN, M. E. GRANT (1991): Macromolecular organization of chicken type X collagen in vitro. J. Biol. Chem. *114:* 597 – 605.

LINSENMAYER, T. F., C. D. LITTLE (1978): Embryonic neural retina collagen – in vitro synthesis of high molecular weight forms of type II plus a new genetic type. Proc. Natl. Acad. USA *74:* 3235 – 3239.

LINSENMAYER, T. F., R. L. TRELSTAD, J. GROSS (1973): The collagen of chick embryonic notochord. Biochem. Biophys. Res. Commun. *53:* 39 – 45.

LINSENMAYER, T. F., G. N. SMITH, E. D. HAY (1977): Synthesis of 2 collagen types by embryonic chick corneal epithelium in vitro. Proc. Natl. Acad. Sci. USA *74:* 39 – 43.

LINSENMAYER, T. F., J. M. FITCH, T. M. SCHMID, N. B. ZAK, E. GIBNEY, R. D. SANDERSON, R. MAYNE (1983): Monoclonal antibodies against chicken type V collagen: Production, specificity, and use for immunocytochemical localization in embryonic cornea and other organs. J. Cell Biol. *96:* 124–131.

LINSENMAYER, T. F., J. M. FITCH, R. MAYNE (1984): Extracellular matrices in the developing avian eye: Type V collagen in corneal and noncorneal tissues. Investigative Ophthalmology & Visual Science *1:* 41–47.

LINSENMAYER, T. F., K. A. MENTZER, M. H. IRWIN, N. K. WALDREP, R. MAYNE (1986): Avian type VI collagen. Monoclonal antibody production and immunohistochemical identification as a major connective tissue component of cornea and skeletal muscle. Experimental Cell Research *165:* 518–529.

LUNSTRUM, G. P., L. Y. SAKAI, D. R. KEENE, N. P. MORRIS, R. E. BURGESON (1986): Large complex globular domains of type VII procollagen contribute to the structure of anchoring fibrils. J. Biol. Chem. *261:* 9042–9048.

LÜTJEN-DRECOLL, E., M. RITTIG, J. RAUTERBERG, R. JANDER, J. MOLLENHAUER (1989): Immunomicroscopical study of type VI collagen in the trabecular meshwork of normal and glaucomatous eyes. Exp. Eye Res. *48:* 139–147.

MARTIN, G. R., R. TIMPL, K. KÜHN (1988): Basement membrane proteins: Molecular structure and function. Advances in Protein Chemistry *39:* 1–50, Academic Press, Inc.

MAYNE, R., R. E. BURGESON (1987): Structure and Function of collagen types. Academic Press.

MEIER, S., E. D. HAY (1974): Control of corneal differentiation by extracellular materials. Collagen as a promoter and stabilizer of epithelial stroma production. Develop. Biol. *38:* 249–270.

MENDLER, M., S. G. EICH-BENDER, L. VAUGHAN, K. H. WINTERHALTER (1989): Cartilage contains mixed fibrils of collagen types II, IX and XI. J. Cell Biol. *108:* 191–197.

MORRIS, N. P., D. R. KEENE, R. W. GLANVILLE, H. BENTZ, R. E. BURGESON (1986): The tissue form of type VII collagen is an antiparallel dimer. J. Biol. Chem. *261:* 5638–5644.

MURAGAKI, Y., I. NISHIMURA, A. HENNEY, Y. NINOMIYA, B. R. OLSEN (1990): The $\alpha 1(IX)$ collagen gene gives rise to two different transcripts in both mouse embryonic and human fetal RNA. Proc. Natl. Acad. Sci. USA *87:* 2400–2404.

NEWSOME, D. A., K. R. KENYON (1973): Collagen production in vitro by the retinal pigmented epithelium of the chick embryo. Develop. Biol. *32:* 387–400.

NEWSOME, D. A. (1976): In vitro stimulation of cartilage in embryonic chick neural creast cells by products of retinal pigmented epithelium. Develop. Biol. *49:* 496–507.

NEWSOME, D. A., LINSENMAYER, T. F., R. L. TRELSTAD (1976): Vitreous body collagen – evidence for a dual origin from neural retina and hyalocytes. J. Cell Biol. Chem. *71:* 59–67.

NISHIMURA, I., Y. MURAGAKI, B. R. OLSEN (1989): Tissue-specific forms of type IX collagen-proteoglycan arise from the use of two widely separated promoters. J. Biol. Chem. *264:* 20033–20041.

OLSEN, B. R., R. ALPER, N. A. KEFALIDES (1973): Structural characterization of a soluble fraction from lens-capsule basement membrane. Eur. J. Biochem. *38:* 220–228.

PARENTE, M. G., L. C. CHUNG, J. RYYNÄMEN, D. WOODLEY, K. C. WINN, E. BAUER, M.-L. CHU, J. UITTO (1991): Human type VII collagen: cDNA cloning and chromosomal mapping of the gene. Proc. Natl. Acad. Sci. USA *88:* 6931–6935.

PIHLAJANIEMI, T., M. TAMMINEN (1990): The $\alpha 1$ chain of type XIII collagen consists of three collagenous and four noncollagenous domains, and its primary transcript undergoes complex alternative splicing. J. Biol. Chem. *265:* 16922–16928.

PIHLAJANIEMI, T., R. MYLLYLÄ, J. SEYER, M. KURKINEN, D. J. PROCKOP (1987): Partial characterization of a low molecular weight human collagen that undergoes alternative splicing. Proc. Natl. Acad. Sci. USA *84:* 940–944.

PÖSCHL, A., K. VON DER MARK (1980): Synthesis of type V collagen by chick corneal fibroblasts in vivo and in vitro. FEBS-Lett. *115:* 100–104.

PRATT, B. M., J. A. MADRI (1985): Immunolocalization of type IV collagen and laminin in non-basement membrane structures of murine corneal stroma: A light and electron microscope study. Lab. Invet. *52:* 650.

QUARONI, A., R. L. TRELSTAD (1980): Biochemical characterization of collagens synthesized by intestinal epithelial cell cultures. J. Biol. Chem. *255:* 8351 – 8361.

RAMACHANDRAN, G. N., A. H. REDDI (Eds.) (1976): Biochemistry of collagen. Plenum, New York.

RAUTERBERG, J., R. JANDER, D. TROYER (1986): Type VI collagen. A structural glycoprotein with a collagenous domain. In: Frontiers of Matrix Biology Vol. 11, pp. 90 – 109 (ed. L. ROBERT, Creteil) (Karger, Basel).

REICHENBERGER, E., T. AIGNER, K. VON DER MARK, H. STÖSS, W. BERTLING (1991): In situ hybridization studies on the expression of type X collagen in fetal human cartilage. Develop. Biol. *148:* 562 – 572.

SAGE, H., P. PRITZL, P. BORNSTEIN (1980): A unique, pepsin-sensitive collagen synthesized by aortic endothelial cells in culture. Biochem. *19:* 5747 – 5755.

SAKAI, L. Y., D. R. KEENE, N. P. MORRIS, R. E. BURGESON (1986): Type VII collagen is a major structural component of anchoring fibrils. J. Cell Biol. *103:* 1577 – 1586.

SAWADA, H. (1982): The fine structure of the bovine Descemet's membrane with special reference to biochemical nature. Cell Tissue Res. *226:* 241 – 255.

SAWADA, H. (1984): The basement membrane of bovine corneal endothelial cells in culture with β-aminopropionitrile: biosynthesis of hexagonal lattices composed of a 160 nm dumbbell-shaped structure. Eur. J. Cell Biol. *35:* 226 – 234.

SAWADA, H., H. KONOMI, K. HIROSAWA (1990): Characterization of the collagen in the hexagonal lattice of Descemet's membrane: Its relation to type VIII collagen. J. Cell Biol. *110:* 219 – 227.

SCHMID, T. M., T. F. LINSENMAYER (1987): Type X collagen. In: "Structure and Function of Collagen Types" R. MAYNE and R. E. BURGESON (Eds). Academic Press, pp 223 – 259.

SCHMUT, O. (1977): The identification of type III collagen in calf and bovine cornea and sclera. Exp. Eye Res. *25:* 505 – 509.

SCOTT, J. E., M. HAIGH (1985): 'Small'-proteoglycan: collagen interactions: Keratan sulphate proteoglycan associates with rabbit corneal collagen fibrils at the 'a' and 'c' bands. Biosci. Rep. *5:* 765 – 774.

SMITH J.R., G. N., T. F. LINSENMAYER, D. A. NEWSOME (1976): Synthesis of type II collagen in vitro by embryonic chick neural retina tissue. Biochemistry *12:* 4420 – 4423.

STEPP, M. A., S. SPURR-MICHAUD, A. TISDALE, J. ELWELL, I. K. GIPSON (1990): α6β4 integrin heterodimer is a component of hemidesmosomes. Proc. Natl. Acad. Sci. USA *87:* 8970 – 8974.

SUGRUE, S. P., M. K. GORDON, J. SEYER, B. DUBLET, M. VAN DER REST, B. R. OLSEN (1989): Immunoidentification of type XII collagen in embryonic tissues. J. Cell Biol. *109:* 939 – 945.

SWANN, D. A., S. S. SOTMAN (1980): The chemical composition of bovine vitreous-humour collagen fibres. Biochem. J. *185:* 545 – 554.

THOMAS, J. T., A. P. L. KWAN, M. E. GRANT, R. P. BOOT-HANDFORD (1991): Isolation of cDNAs encoding the complete sequence of bovine type X collagen. Biochem. J. *273:* 141 – 148.

THOROGOOD, P., J. BEE, K. VON DER MARK (1986): Transient expression of collagen type II at epithelio-mesenchymal interfaces during morphogenesis of the cartilaginous neurocranium. Develop. Biol. *116:* 497 – 509.

TIMPL, R. (1989): Structure and biological activity of basement membrane proteins. Eur. J. Biochem. *180:* 487 – 502.

TIMPL, R., J. ENGEL (1987): Type VI collagen. In: Structure and Function of Collagen Types, pp. 105 – 143. Academic Press Inc.

TRELSTAD, R. L., A. J. COULOMBRE (1971): Morphogenesis of the collagenous stroma in the chick cornea. J. Cell Biol. *50:* 840 – 858.

TRELSTAD, R. L., K. HAYASHI, B. P. Toole (1974): Epithelial collagens and glycosaminoglycans in the embryonic cornea. J. Cell Biol. *62:* 815 – 830.

VAN DER REST, M., R. MAYNE (1988): Type IX collagen proteoglycan from cartilage is covalently cross-linked to type II collagen. J. Biol. Chem. *263:* 1615 – 1618.

VAN DER REST, M., R. GARRONE (1991): Collagen family of proteins. The FASEB Journal *5:* 2814 – 2823.

VAN DER REST, M., R. MAYNE, Y. NINOMIYA, N. G. SEIDAH, M. CHRETIEN, B. R. OLSEN (1985): The structure of type IX collagen. J. Biol. Chem. *260:* 220 – 225.

VAUGHAN, L., M. MENDLER, S. HUBER, P. BRUCKNER, K. H. WINTERHALTER, M. I. IRWIN, R. MAYNE (1988): D-periodic distribution of collagen type IX along cartilage fibrils. J. Cell Biol. *106:* 991–997.

VON DER MARK, H., K. VON DER MARK, S. GAY (1976): Study of differential collagen synthesis during development of the chick embryo by immunofluorescence. I. Preparation of collagen type I and type II specific antibodies and their application to early stages of the chick embryo. Develop. Biol. *48:* 237–249.

VON DER MARK, H., M. AUMAILLEY, G. WICK, R. FLEISCHMAJER, R. TIMPL (1984): Immunochemistry, genuine size and tissue localization of collagen VI. Eur. J. Biochem. *142:* 493–502.

VON DER MARK, K. (1981): Localization of collagen types in tissue (Review) Int. Res. Conn. Tissue Res. *9:* 265–324.

VON DER MARK, K., M. ÖCALAN (1982): Immunofluorescent localization of type V collagen in the chick embryo with monoclonal antibodies. Collag. Rel. Res. *2:* 541–555.

VON DER MARK, K., H. VON DER MARK, R. TIMPL, R. L. TRELSTAD (1977): Immunofluorescent localization of collagen types I, II and III in the embryonic chick eye. Develop. Biol. *59:* 75–85.

YAMAGUCHI, N., P. D. BENYA, M. VAN DER REST, Y. NINOMIYA (1989): The cloning and sequencing of α1(VIII) collagen cDNAs demonstrate that type VIII collagen is a short chain collagen and contains triple-helical and carboxyl-terminal non-triple-helical domains similar to those of type X collagen. J. Biol. Chem. *264:* 16022–16029.

YASUI, N., P. D. BENYA, M. E. NIMNI (1984): Identification of a large interrupted helical domain of disulfide-bonded cartilage collagen. J. Biol. Chem. *259:* 14175–14179.

YURCHENCO, P. D., J. C. SCHITTNY (1990): Molecular architecture of basement membranes. FASEB J. *4:* 1577–1590.

ZIMMERMANN, D. R., B. TRÜEB, K. H. WINTERHALTER, R. WITMER, R. W. FISCHER (1986): Type VI collagen is a major component of the human cornea. FEBS Lett. *197:* 55–58.

*Eye Research Institute and Department of Ophthalmology,*
*Harvard Medical School, Bosten, MA*

# Age-related changes in corneal basement membranes

I. K. GIPSON

Professor Johannes Rohen has made significant, well documented and beauti-fully illustrated contributions in the field of age-related changes in the extracellular matrix of the aqueous outflow system. Therefore, on the occasion of his seventieth birthday, it is very appropriate to consider the topic of age-related changes in the extracellular matrix of other tissues of the eye.

Two of the major morphologically distinguishable changes which occur in the cornea with increasing age occur where a cell layer of epithelium interfaces with the extracellular matrix. These two age-related changes are thickening and redupli-cation of the corneal epithelial basement membrane zone (Fig. 1) and general and localized thickenings of the corneal endothelial basement or Descement's mem-brane. The localized thickenings in Descemet's membrane have been termed gut-tata or Hassel-Henle warts.

Not only do these two age-related changes have the common feature of being reduplication of extracellular matrix in the basement membrane of an overlying epithelium, but they have a common developmental pattern. As ALVARADO et al. (1983) have so beautifully demonstrated, the age-related corneal epithelial base-ment membrane generally thickens, then reduplications begin as small discrete islands in the cornea which increase in size and finally in the later decades of life coalesce to form a rather uniformly reduplicated basement membrane zone. The corneal endothelial basement membrane generally thickens and the guttata have a similar island formation (KENYON 1983), but these islands remain as discrete islands perhaps due to the fact that unlike the corneal epithelium, the endothelium does not mitose and turnover.

To understand the nature of the age-related accrual of extracellular matrix in the basement membrane zone, we must understand the normal association between an epithelium and its underlying connective tissue. The basement membrane, a synthetic product of the overlying epithelium, has several functions. It serves in some epithelia as a filter and limiting border which isolates the epithelium from adjacent cells. Another major function of this limiting layer is in adhesion of the overlying epithelium to the stroma or connective tissue.

Two mechanisms of cell to basement membrane adhesion occur; one is through interaction between matrix receptors in the cell membranes and their extracellular matrix ligands, a second mechanism is through specialized adhesion junctions. This latter mechanism has been studied extensively, particularly in regard to the corneal epithelium. The cell-matrix adhesion junction of the corneal epithelium and all other stratified squamous epithelia is the hemidesmosome (Fig. 1). The hemidesmosome is structurally similar to half of a desmosome in that intermediate filaments insert into an electron-dense plaque along the membrane. The extracytoplasmic face of the junction as well as its molecular composition differs, however, from the desmosome. On the external side of the cell membrane at the hemidesmosome, an electron-dense line parallels the membrane, and from it, anchoring filaments extend through the lamina lucida to the lamina densa of the basement membrane. Opposite the lamina densa, anchoring fibrils insert from the stromal side. These fibrils form an intertwining network in the anterior 0.5–2 μm of the stroma. Distal from their insertions in the basement membrane, anchoring fibrils insert into anchoring plaques which structurally appear as small segments of basement membrane (Fig. 1). Collectively, all these structurally linked components including intermediate filaments, hemidesmosomes, anchoring filaments, basement membrane, anchoring fibrils, and anchoring plaques are termed the adhesion complex (GIPSON et al. 1987). The complex functions to hold corneal epithelium securely to the stroma.

There are two well characterized components of the hemidesmosome. The bullous pemphigoid antigen (BPA) is a 220-kD protein located in the electron-dense plaque of the junction. Recent sequence analysis of the BPA shows no membrane spanning region (TANAKA et al. 1990). The second component known to be present in the hemidesmosomes of corneal (STEPP et al. 1990), epidermal (SONNENBERG et al. 1991) and tongue epithelium (JONES et al. 1991) is the $\alpha_6\beta_4$ integrin heterodimer. This molecule spans the cell membrane of the hemidesmosome between the plaque region and the extracytoplasmic anchoring filaments. The extracellular matrix ligand of $\alpha_6\beta_4$ has yet to be determined. Recently a protein termed kalinin has been isolated, antibodies to which localize to the anchoring filament (ROUSELLE et al. 1991).

The other major known component of the adhesion complex is type VII collagen, the anchoring fibril collagen (SAKAI et al. 1986). The globular domain of type VII collagen is present in the lamina densa of the basement membrane and in anchoring plaques. The long helical domains of the molecule associate to from the unique cross-banded fibrils of the anchoring fibril network.

As a basal cell of the corneal epithelium divides, one daughter cell moves up to differentiate toward the apical surface where, 5–7 days later, it will be lost by desquamation. As the cells mitose, they round up and disassemble their hemidesmosomes. Thus cells along the basement membrane constantly make and break

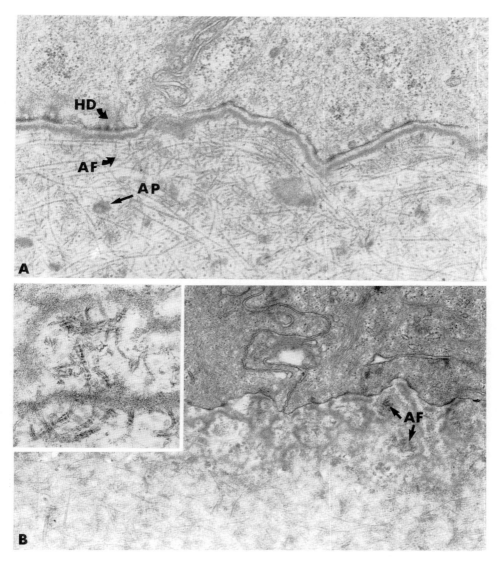

Fig. 1. Electron micrographs of the basement membrane zone of the human corneal epithelium from a 9-month-old infant (A), an 87-year-old (B), and a 77-year-old (inset in B). In A, hemidesmosomes (HD) are obvious along the basal cell membrane, anchoring fibrils (AF) extend from the basement membrane into the anterior stroma, and anchoring plaques (AP) are present. In B, reduplications of basement membrane can be seen in this section from an aged human. Pockets of anchoring fibrils (AF) are present in the reduplication areas at higher magnification (inset). The cross-banded nature of the anchoring fibrils present within pockets of basement membrane is obvious. (A x 42.000, B x 11.000, Inset x 63.000).

their hemidesmosomes. Data from an in vitro model for study of hemidesmosome formation has demonstrated that new hemidesmosomes form over sites on the basement membrane where anchoring fibrils insert from the stromal side (GIPSON et al. 1983). These studies suggest that as basal cells mitose and lose hemidesmosomes, the daughter cell remaining on the basement membrane reforms new hemidesmosomes on old sites on the basement membrane used by the prior mother cell.

The corneal endothelium's adhesion to Descemet's has been less well studied. No discernible specialized adhesion junctions have been described. One assumes that the adhesion of the corneal endothelium is brought about by cell membrane receptor (perhaps integrin heterodimers) and matrix interactions.

With regard to age-related changes in this interface zone between cells and basement membrane, several hypotheses have been proposed. ALVARADO et al. (1983) have proposed that basement membrane reduplication is in response to small focal wounds or injury to epithelium from rubbing or abrasions. This hypothesis may be unlikely since age-related basal membrane thickening occurs in inaccessible tissues in deeper regions of the body. A second hypothesis is that in the normal homeostatic processes of cells, regulation of turnover of matrix receptors within cell membranes is linked to matrix turnover and resynthesis. Finally, one could propose that low levels of metaloproteases secreted by cells, break down extracellular matrix ligands of receptors such that the matrix is no longer recognized by receptors. Lack of receptor ligand coupling could then induce new matrix production.

# References

ALVARADO, J., C. MURPHY, R. JUSTER (1983): Age-related changes in the basement membrane of the human corneal epithelium. Invest. Ophthalmol. Vis. Sci. *24:* 1015 – 1028.

GIPSON, I. K., S. M. GRILL, S. J. SPURR et al. (1983): Hemidesmosome formation in vitro. J. Cell Biol. *97:* 849 – 857.

GIPSON, I. K., S. J. SPURR-MICHAUD, A. S. TISDALE et al. (1987): Anchoring fibrils form a complex network in human and rabbit cornea. Invest. Ophthalmol. Vis. Sci. *28:* 212 – 220.

JONES, J. C. R., M. A. KURPAKUS, H. M. COOPER et al. (1991): A function for the integrin $\alpha_6\beta_4$ in the hemidesmosome. Cell Regul. *2:* 427 – 438.

KENYON, K. R. (1983): Morphology and Pathologic Responses of the Cornea. In: SMOLIN, G., R. A. Thoft (Eds): The Cornea, p. 43 – 75. Little, Brown and Co., Boston/Toronto.

ROUSELLE, P., G. P. LUNSTRUM, D. R. KEENE et al. (1991): Kalinin: an epithelium-specific basement membrane adhesion molecule that is a component of anchoring filaments. J. Cell Biol. *114:* 567 – 576.

SAKAI, L. Y., D. R. KEENE, N. P. MORRIS et al. (1986): Type VII collagen is a major structural component of anchoring fibrils. J. Cell Biol. *103:* 1577 – 1586.

SONNENBERG, A., J. CALAFAT, H. JANSSEN et al. (1991): Integrin $\alpha_6\beta_4$ complex is located in hemidesmosomes, suggesting a major role in epidermal cell-basement membrane adhesion. J. Cell Biol. *113:* 907 – 917.

Stepp, M. A., S. Spurr-Michaud, A. Tisdale et al. (1990): $\alpha_6\beta_4$ integrin heterodimer is a component of hemidesmosomes. Proc. Natl. Acad. Sci. USA *87:* 8970–8974.

Tanaka, T., N. J. Korman, H. Shimizu et al. (1990): Production of rabbit antibodies against carboxy-terminal epitopes encoded by bullous pemphigoid cDNA. J. Invest. Dermatol. *94:* 617–623.

*Biochemistry & Molecular Biology Laboratory*
*Department of Ophthalmology*
*College of Physicians & Surgeons of Columbia University, New York*

# Lens epithelial cell DNA-effect of oxidative stress, disease and aging

A. Spector and N. J. Kleiman

It is generally accepted that oxidative insult is an initiating or early event in cataractogenesis (Spector and Roy 1978; Augusteyn 1981; Spector 1984; Varma et al. 1984). This is based on numerous reports of oxidative damage to lens components including protein (Dische and Zil 1951; Harding 1972; Spector and Roy 1978; Anderson and Spector 1978; Lou et al. 1986), lipid (Bhuyan and Bhuyan 1983 a & b) and DNA (Spector et al. 1989; Kleiman et al. 1990 a & b) as well as epidemiological and clinical studies examining the relationship between physiological levels of various antioxidants or biochemical markers of oxidative insult and cataract (Bellows 1936; Spector and Garner 1981; Bhuyan et al. 1986; Costagliola et al. 1988; Jaques et al. 1988; Robertson 1989; Reddy 1990). The hypothesis that oxidative stress is intimately associated with the development of human cataract is further supported by 1) the unique morphology of the lens itself, 2) its potential for photooxidation due to continual exposure to light and 3) the reportedly high levels of reactive species in the aqueous humor bathing this tissue (Spector and Garner 1981; Bhuyan et al. 1986; Huang and Hu 1990; Ramachandran et al. 1991).

Oxidative stress can be defined as an increase in the concentration(s) of a number of oxygen derived species, including, but not limited to superoxide $O_2^{\cdot-}$, hydroxyl radical $OH^{\cdot}$, singlet oxygen $^1O_2$, $H_2O_2$, and various lipid oxidation products. All of these intermediates are directly or indirectly produced from reaction of divalent oxygen ($O_2$). Although the oxygen tension at the surface of the avascular lens is lower than in many tissues ($\approx 10$ mm) (Kwan et al. 1972), diffusion of oxygen from either the highly vascularized retina or through the cornea is more than sufficient to support the formation of significant and damaging levels of these compounds. While all reactive oxygen intermediates are potentially damaging, it is likely that $H_2O_2$, due to its stability and potential for further reaction, is the most critical of these species in the aqueous humopr and lens.

$H_2O_2$ can be produced by univalent reductions of $O_2$ yielding first $O_2^{\cdot-}$ and then $H_2O_2$: $O_2 \rightarrow O_2^{\cdot-} \rightarrow H_2O_2$. Under certain conditions, namely in the presence of reduced metals ($M^n$), hydroxyl ion is produced: $H_2O_2 + M^n \rightarrow OH^{\cdot} + OH^- + M^{n+1}$.

It is theorized that many of the damaging effects attributed to elevation in $H_2O_2$ are in fact mediated through the formation of short lived but very reactive hydroxyl radicals.

Measurement of the normal level of $H_2O_2$ in the aqueous humor of a number of animals, including humans, indicate a physiological range from $10-35$ μm (PIRIE 1965; BHUYAN and BHUYAN 1977; SPECTOR and GARNER 1981; MATSUDA et al. 1981; GIBLIN et al. 1984; RAMACHANDRAN et al. 1991). It is likely that the high concentration of ascorbate in the aqueous humor ($\approx$ 1 mM) contributes to these relatively elevated levels (GIBLIN et al. 1984). In human patients undergoing cataract surgery, however, concentrations as high as 600 μM have been reported (SPECTOR and GARNER 1981; BHUYAN and BHYAN 1986; HUANG and HU 1990; RAMACHANDRAN et al. 1991). These extraordinarily high and potentially damaging levels of $H_2O_2$ cannot be produced by alteration in ascorbate concentration and may be the result of photochemical reactions (ZIGMAN 1985) or pathological conditions elsewhere in the eye. Further evidence for the involvement of $H_2O_2$ in caractogenesis comes from experiments demonstrating a direct relationship between elevations in $H_2O_2$ and the formation of lens opacities in organ culture (GARNER et al. 1982; GIBLIN et al. 1987) and experiments in which $H_2O_2$ detoxifying systems were altered *in vivo* (BHUYAN and BHUYAN 1977; GIBLIN et al. 1981). Furthermore, exposure of cultured lenses to $H_2O_2$ causes a pattern of oxidative damage similar to that observed in cataractous lenses (ZIGLER et al. 1989).

It is well known that exposure of cells to $H_2O_2$ causes a spectrum of DNA damage including single strand breaks, ring saturated thymines and protein-DNA and DNA-DNA crosslinks (HOFFMAN & MENEGHINI 1979; BRADLEY and ERICKSON 1981; LEWIS and ADAMS 1985; SZMIGIERO and STUDZIAN 1988; IMLAY and LINN 1988). Evidence suggest that OH˙, formed via a Fenton reaction involving $H_2O_2$ and reduced metals (FENTON 1894), is the actual DNA damaging agent (MELLO FILHO and MENEGHINI 1984; IMLAY et al. 1988). It has been further demonstrated that the rate limiting step in OH˙ production is the reformation of reduced metal by superoxide: $O_2^{\cdot-} + M^{+1} \rightarrow M + O_2$ (MELLO FILHO and MENEGHINI 1984). The overall reaction, termed the Haber-Weiss Reaction (HABER and WEISS 1934); $O_2^{\cdot-} + H_2O_2 \rightarrow O_2 + OH^- + OH˙$, is believed to result in DNA damage.

Utilizing bovine lens epithelial cell cultures, this laboratory reported that relatively low levels of $H_2O_2$ ($50-200$ μM) caused large numbers of DNA single strand breaks in a short period of time (KLEIMAN et al. 1990a). Although repair was rapid ($< 30$ min) (SPECTOR et al. 1989), the low levels of oxidant required suggests that DNA is much more sensitive to slight elevations in $H_2O_2$ than either protein or lipid. As will be dicussed below, this finding has profound implications for the relationship between oxidative stress and cataractogenesis in the human lens. Additional experiments, utilizing various scavengers, metal chelators and inhibitors of superoxide dismutase, demonstrated that the actual DNA damaging species in lens epithelial cells was the hydroxyl radical, formed in close proximity to the DNA in what is probably a Haber-Weiss reaction.

Other studies in this laboratory were designed to assess the potential DNA damaging effect of ultraviolet light in cultured lens epithelial cells (KLEIMAN et al. 1990 b). Fluences similar to those found in sunlight were utilized. As the cornea effectively absorbs all light below 295 nm (BOETNER and WOLTER 1962), only UV-B (290 – 320 nm) and UV-A (320 – 380 nm) irradiation was used. As expected, pyrimidine dimers were the predominant form of DNA damage induced by UV-B exposure although some thymine glycols and DNA-DNA crosslinks could be detected. UV-A irradiation, even at high fluences, did not cause any detectable DNA damage. Curiously, when the kinetics of DNA repair were measured, UV-B induced lesions were found to be repaired at a ten fold slower rate than $H_2O_2$ induced lesions. The implications of this finding on cataractogenesis is unclear.

The evidence presented in this manuscript strongly suggests that it is $H_2O_2$, normally present in the range of 10 – 30 $\mu M$ in the human aqueous humor, that may be responsible for much of the oxidative damage reported in the aged and cataractous lens. This hypothesis is based on the ability of $H_2O_2$ or its reaction products to cause a spectrum of damage in lens epithelial cell and organ cultures similar to that found in cataract and to cause cataract in organ culture. It is further supported by studies demonstrating an elevation in $H_2O_2$ in the aqueous of patients with cataract and epidemiological studies linking levels of various antioxidants and protective enzyme system to cataract development. The role of light in $H_2O_2$ and free radical production has also been described. One of the remaining questions concerning the mechanism of cataract formation involves the contribution of oxidized DNA to the overall process of cataract development. In the following paragraphs support for the hypothesis that oxidative damage to DNA is one of the earliest events in cataractogenesis is described.

The lens is composed of specialized anuclear cells called lens fibers. Throughout life, a single layer of epithelial cells on the anterior surface provide fiber cell progenitors and transport nutrients into and wastes out of the lens (KUCK 1970). In the central region of the epithelium (along the visual axis) the mitotic index is very low (<0.001) (VON SALLMAN et al. 1962; MCAVOY 1978) while in the germinative region, cells begin to divide and, eventually, at the lens equator, differentiate into mature lens fibers. As a result of this structural arrangement, the consequences of unrepaired DNA damage in the lens epithelium may by quite severe. Damage to critical housekeeping genes in the central region of the epithelium (e. g., membrane pumps) may have profound effects on fiber cells whose metabolism is dependent on these overlying cells. Damage to genes expressed during mitosis or differentiation may result in aberrant lens fibers. Either pathway has the potential for forming lens opacities. Support for this hypothesis is provided by preliminary studies of DNA damage in human lens epithelium *in vivo* (KLEIMAN and SPECTOR 1992), and a report suggesting that cataractous lens epithelium contains increased numbers of micronuclei (Worgul et al. 1991). Unfortunately, the limited availability of normal human lenses hampers analysis of DNA in non-cataractous lenses. In addition, available methodologies for assaying DNA damage *in vivo* are limited by their sensitivity as estimates of the number of cells in a young, normal human lens epithelium range from 350000 – 750000 cells (KARIM et al. 1987; KUSZAK and BROWN, 1992) and there is some evidence of decreased cell density accompanying both aging and cataractogenesis (KARIM et al. 1987; KONOFSKY et al. 1987; HARA and HARA 1988; GUGGENMOOS-HOLZMANN et al., 1989). Modifications made to a recently developed single cell gel electrophoresis assay (SCG) (SINGH et al. 1988), however, are beginning to provide new data regarding the extent and distribution of DNA damage in human cataractous and normal lens epithelium. Preliminary studies from this laboratory suggest that with appropriate utilization of specific DNA repair enzymes, the SCG technique can be utilzed to measure single strand breaks, pyrimidine dimers and thymine glycols in lens epithelial cells. As the spectrum of DNA damage induced by $H_2O_2$ or UV light, the two most likely lens damaging agents, is quite different, this technique also offers a way to compare the relative contribution of each insult to DNA damage in the human lens epithelium. Early results from this laboratory indicate that significant number of cells containing DNA single strand breaks are found in lens epithelia from patients with cataract as compared to the absence of such damage in non-cataractous human Eye Bank lenses. In some individuals, almost 30% of the lens epithelial cell population contained some degree of DNA single strand breakage. No correlation between aging and DNA damage was noted.

To summarize, available data suggest that the development of maturity onset cataract is closely related to oxidative stress in the lens, mediated in some situations through elevation in $H_2O_2$ and its reaction products. Evidence suggest that protein, lipid and DNA is oxidized although the relative contribution of each to the onset of cataractogenesis is unclear. Studies of DNA damage in the lens epithelium, both in cell culture and *in vivo,* have provided important new evidence for lens oxidative insult and suggest alternative pathways for cataractogenesis that require far lower levels of potential oxidants than in situations where protein or lipid is involved.

# References

ANDERSON, E. I., A. SPECTOR (1978): Exp. Eye Res. *26:* 407–417.

AUGUSTEYN, R. C. (1981): In: Mechanisms of Cataract Formation in the Human Lens. G. DUNCAN (Ed.) Academic Press, New York. Pp. 72–111.

BELLOWS, J. (1936): Arch. Ophthalmol. *15:* 78–83.

BHUYAN, K. C., D. K. BHUYAN (1977): Biochim. Biophys. Acta. *497:* 641–651.

BHUYAN, K. C., D. K. BHUYAN (1983a): Curr. Eye Res. *2:* 597–606.

BHYAN, K. C., D. K. BHUYAN (1983b): In: Oxy Radicals and Their Scavengers Systeme Vol. II: Cellular and Medical Aspects. R. A. GREENWALD, G. COHEN (eds.) Elsevier, New York Pp. 349–355.

BHUYAN, K. C., D. K. BHUYAN, S. M. PODOS (1986): Life Sci. *38:* 1463–1471.

BOETTNER, E. A., J. R. WOLTER (1962): Invest. Ophthalmol. *1:* 776–783.

BRADLEY, M. O., L. C. ERICKSON (1981): Biochim. Biophys. Acta *654:* 135–141.

COSTAGLIOLA, C., G. IULIANO, M. MENZIONE, A. NESTI, F. SIMONELLI, E. RINALDI (1988): Ophthalmol. Res. *20:* 308–316.

DISCHE, Z., H. ZIL (1951): Amer. J. Ophthalmol. *34:* 104–113.

FENTON, H. J. M. (1894): J. Chem. Soc. *65:* 899–910.

GARNER, M. H., W. H. GARNER, A. SPECTOR (1982): Invest. Ophthalmol. Vis. Sci. *22 (Suppl.):* 34.

GIBLIN, F. J., J. P. MCCREADY, L. SCHRIMSCHER, V. N. REDDY (1987): Exp. Eye Res. *45:* 77–91.

GIBLIN, F. J., J. P. MCCREADY, T. KODAMA, V. N. REDDY (1984): Exp. Eye Res. *38:* 87–93.

GIBLIN, F. J., D. E. NEIS, V. N. REDDY (1981): Exp. Eye Res. *33:* 289–298.

GUGGENMOOS-HOLZMANN, I., V. ENGEL, V. HENKE, O. H. NAUMANN (1989): Invest. Ophthalmol. Vis. Sci. *30:* 330–332.

HABER, F., J. WEISS (1934): Proc. R. Soc. London Ser. A. *147:* 332–351.

HARA, T., T. HARA (1988): Arch. Ophthalmol. *106:* 1683–1687.

HARDING, J. J. (1972): Exp. Eye Res. *13:* 33–40.

HOFFMAN, E. M., R. MENEGHINI (1979): Photochem. Photobiol. *30:* 151–155.

HUANG, Q.-L., T.-S. HU (1990): Invest. Ophthalmol. Vis. Sci *31 (Suppl.):* 350.

IMLAY, J. A., S. M. CHIN, S. LINN (1988): Science *240:* 640–642.

IMLAY, J. A., S. LINN (1988): Science. *240:* 1302–1309.

JACQUES, P. F., L. T. CHYLACK, R. B. MCGANDY, S. C. HARTZ (1988): Arch. Ophthalmol. *106:* 337–340.

KARIM, A. K. A., T. J. C. JACOB, G. M. THOMPSON (1987): Exp. Eye Res. *45:* 865–874.

KLEIMAN, N. J., A. SPECTOR (1992): Invest. Ophthalmol. Vis. Sci. *33 (Suppl.):* 799.

KLEIMAN, N. J., R.-R. WANG, A. SPECTOR (1990a): Mut. Res. *240:* 35–45.

KLEIMAN, N. J., R.-R. WANG, A. SPECTOR (1990b): Curr. Eye Res. *9:* 1185–1193.

KONOFSKY, K., G. O. H. NAUMANN, I. GUGGENMOOS-HOLZMAN (1987): Ophthalmol. *94:* 875–880.

KUCK, J. (1970): In: Biochemistry of the Eye. C. N. GRAYMORE (Ed.), Academic Press, New York Pp. 261–318.

KUSZAK, J. R., H. G. BROWN (1992): In: Priciples and Practice of Ophthalmology. ALBERT, D. M., F. A. JACOBIEC (eds.) W. B. Saunders Co., Philadelphia, in press.

KWAN, M., J. NIINIKOSKI, T. K. HUNT (1972): Invest. Ophthalmol. Vis. Sci. *11:* 108–114.

LEWIS, J. G., D. O. ADAMS (1985): Cancer Res. *45:* 1270–1275.

LOU, M. F., R. MCKELLAR, O. CHYAN (1986): Exp. Eye Res. *42:* 607–616.

MATSUDA, H., F. J. GIBLIN, V. N. REDDY (1981): Exp. Eye Res. *33:* 253–265.

MCAVOY, J. W. (1978): J. Embryol. Exp. Morph. *44:* 149–165.

MELLO FILHO, A. C., R. MENEGHINI (1984): Biochim. Biophys. Acta *781:* 56–63.

PIRIE, A. (1965): Biochem. J. *96:* 244–253.

RAMACHANDRAN, S., S. M. MORRIS, P. S. DEVAMANOHARAN, M. HENEIN, S. D. VARMA (1991): Exp. Eye Res. *53:* 503–506.

REDDY, V. N. (1990): Exp. Eye Res. *50:* 771–778.

ROBERTSON, J. M., A. P. DONNER, J. R. TREVITHICK (1989): Ann. NY Acad. Sci. *570:* 372–382.

SPECTOR, A. (1984): Invest. Ophthalmol. Vis. Sci. *25:* 130–146.

SPECTOR, A., W. H. GARNER (1981): Exp. Eye Res. *33:* 673 – 681.

SPECTOR, A., N. J. KLEIMAN, R.-R. C. HUANG, R.-R. WANG (1989): Exp. Eye Res. *49:* 685 – 698.

SPECTOR, A., D. ROY (1978): Proc. Natl. Acad. Sci. U.S.A. *75:* 3244 – 3248.

SZMIGIERO, L., K. STUDZIAN (1988): Anal. Biochem. *168:* 88 – 93.

VARMA, S. D., D. CHAND, Y. R. SHARMA, J. F. KUCK, R. D. RICHARDS (1984): Curr. Eye Res. *3:* 35 – 57.

VON SALLMAN, L., P. GRIMES, N. MCELVAIN (1962): Exp. Eye Res. *1:* 449 – 456.

WORGUL, B. V., J. DAVID, S. ODRICH, G. R. JR. MERRIAM, C. MEDVEDOVSKY, J. C. MERRIAM, S. L. TROKEL, C. R. GEARD (1991): Mutagenesis *6:* 495 – 499.

ZIGLER, J. S., Q.-L. HUANG, X.-Y. DU (1989): Free Radicals Biol. Med. *7:* 499 – 505.

ZIGMAN, S. (1985): In: The Ocular Lens. MAISEL, H. (Ed.) Marcel Dekker, Inc. New York. Pp. 301 – 347.

*Eye Research Institute, Oakland University, Rochester, Mi*

# Changes in cell polarity of human lens epithelium in tissue culture

V. N. Reddy

## Introduction

Recent studies from our laboratory have shown[1-4] that human lens epithelium (HLE) can be successfully cultured through several passages in which the cells retain their lens specific characteristics. Furthermore, it was demonstrated that HLE cells when cultured on a non-haptotactic (non adhesive) substrate undergo differentiation consistently in a predictable manner. These studies on differentiation of epithelial cells into fiber-like structures (lentoids) suggested a possible reversal of cell polarity in which the basal side is inwards, leading to the accumulation of basement-like membrane at the center of the lentoid (Fig. 1). In order to examine the changes in cell polarity we have investigated the spatial distribution of Na, K-ATPase in the *in situ* lens and in the cultured HLE cells as well as in lentoids.

Although the localization of Na, K-ATPase in the lens has been studied histologically by several investigators,[5-7] the results have been inconsistent and controversial. We, therefore, developed an immunohistochemical method at the ultrastructural level which has the potential for detection of this enzyme with a higher resolution and greater specificity than the histochemical procedures. The details of this method have been described in a recent publication.[8]

Initial studies with rat lens revealed that immunolocalization of the enzyme was observed on the basal plasma membrane of the epithelial cells facing the capsule. Lateral and apical plasma membranes as well as the control sections demonstrated an absence of the enzyme activity. These findings are in contrast to earlier reports that the enzyme is localized in the apical and lateral plasma membrane of the lens epithelial cells.

Studies with surgical specimen of human lens capsule-epithelium with attached cortical fibers showed immunolabeling for Na, K-ATPase only in the basal plasma membrane, with no immunoreaction in the apical or lateral plasma membrane (Fig. 2). Also there was no detectable immunoreaction in the lens fibers. These findings indicate that the polarized distribution of Na, K-ATPhase in the plasma membranes of human lens epithelium is similar to that in the rat lens.

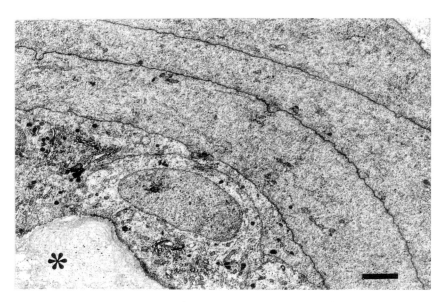

Fig. 1. Ultrastructure of lentoid derived from human lens epithelium. Outer layers show regularly arranged elongated cells. The basement membrane-like material is observed in the center of the lentoid (*). The scale line indicates 2 μm.

In order to investigate the possible change in cell polarity during cell culture the distribution of Na, K-ATPase was examined in monolayer cultures and in the explants of capsule-epithelium before the cells migrated on to the culture dish. Monolayer cultures showed that the enzyme was localized on the cell surface facing the culture medium with complete absence on the plasma membrane attached to the culture dish (basal surface; data not shown). In contrast to the *in situ* lens, when the explants of the capsule-epithelium were cultured, the enzyme was localized in the apical surface (facing the media) (Fig. 2). These results show that the transport enzyme was translocated from the basal side to the plasma membrane in contact with the culture medium. Surprisingly, the translocation of the enzyme occurred within 3 hrs of culture.

Studies on the distribution of Na, K-ATPase in lentoids also showed that the immunolabeling of the enzyme was restricted to the surface plasma membrane in contact with the culture medium; no immunoreaction was observed in the intercellular plasma membranes within the lentiod (Fig. 3). Thus, in cultured cells the localization of Na, K-ATPase in the cell surface appeared to be related to the accessibility of the plasma membrane to the culture medium. It was, therefore, of interest to study the distribution of the enzyme in cultured cells in which both surfaces have access to the culture medium. The characteristics of biopore membranes as substrate in tissue culture are that they allow the basal plasma membrane as well as

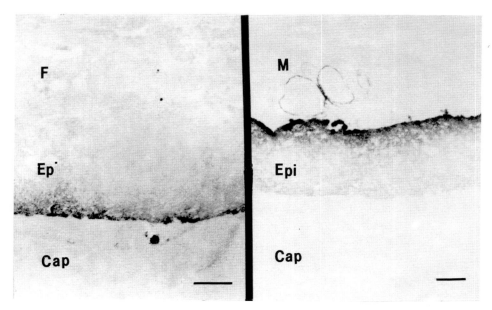

Fig. 2. Immunohistochemical localization of Na, K-ATPase in human lens epithelium *in situ* and in tissue culture. In the *in situ* lens (left) the enzyme is localized on the basal surface adjacent to the capsule. The apical surface and lens fibers (F) show no reaction. When the explant of capsule epithelium was cultured for 3 days (right) the enzyme translocated to the apical surface was facing the medium (M). Note the absence of enzyme activity on the basal surface. The scale lines indicate 1 μm.

the apical membrane to contact the growth media. Thus when monolayers of the epithelial cells were established on biopore membrane filters the distribution of Na, K-ATPase was no longer restricted to a single plasma membrane domain but the enzyme reaction was observable in both the apical and basal plasma membrane (facing the biopore membrane surface) (Fig. 3).

A summary of these findings is presented in the schematic diagram shown in Fig. 4. In the *in situ* lens, Na, K-ATPase is localized in the basal surface of the epithelium. This polarized distribution of the enzyme is translocated to the apical side of the epithelium facing the media when capsule-epithelium is cultured as an explant with the capsule attached to the culture dish. The monolayer cultures which are established on a regular culture dish, in which a single cell surface is exposed to the medium, the enzyme is localized on the surface facing the medium (not shown in the diagram). Similarly, the other surface of lentoids facing the medium showed enzyme activity. On the other hand monolayer cultures grown on millipore membranes showed enzyme reaction on both cell surfaces.

The common phenomenon in our studies on cultured HLE cells and lentoids, with regard to the distribution of Na, K-ATPase, is that the enzyme is located in

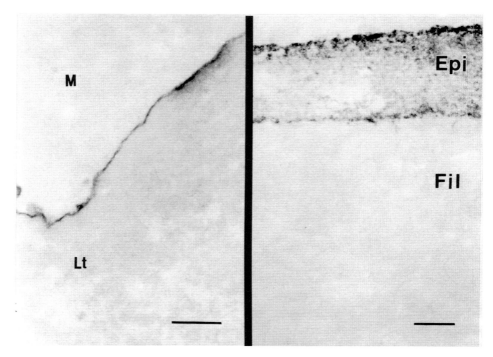

Fig. 3. Immunohistochemical localization of Na, K-ATPase on the surface of lentoid (left) facing the medium and in human lens epithelial cells grown on biopore filter (right) in which both cell surface are accessible to the medium. Note that the enzyme activity is observed on both apical and basal surfaces of the epithelium. The scale lines indicate 1 μm.

the plasma membrane which is in direct contact with the growth medium. These morphological data might indicate that Na, K-ATPase participates in exchanging the ions between growth media and cytoplasm of these culture cells. Also of interest is the finding that Na, K-ATPase was detected in the apical plasma membrane in the HLE cells on the capsule after only 3 hr of culture, indicating the rapidity with which polarization of Na, K-ATPase distribution occurs when HLE cells are cultured. The precise mechanisms involved in the change of Na, K-ATPase distribution in these cells are not clear, but it is likely that cell-media contact acts as an exogenous trigger for the Na, K-ATPase to distribute along the plasma membrane facing the growth media.

In contrast to lens fiber *in situ*, there was a positive reaction of Na, K-ATPase in the surface plasma membrane of lentoids. The change in cell polarity was also confirmed in unpublished studies on long-term cultures of monolayers. Extracellular matrix similar to lens capsule was synthesized which formed a continuous sheet between the monolayers and the culture dish. In this preparation also, the Na, K-

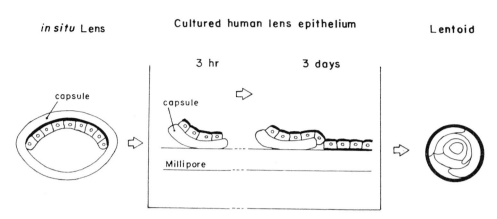

Fig. 4. A schematic drawing showing the distribution of Na, K-ATPase in *in situ* lens, cultured epithelia and differentiated lentoid. While the enzyme is localized on the basal surface of the epithelium *in situ* it was translocated to the apical side when capsule-epithelium explant was cultured for 3 hrs on the millipore filter. However, when the cells migrate onto the millipore after 3 days the enzyme reaction was observable on both cell surfaces. In the lentoid, immunolabeling of Na, K-ATPase was restricted to the surface plasma membrane.

ATPase was localized in the plasma membrane facing the culture medium but not in the cell surface in contact with the extracellular matrix expressed by the cultured epithelia. In a previous study,[3] lens fiber characteristics of the lentoids were presented by showing both ultrastructural and biochemical markers for the differentiated lens fiber cells, such as loss of cytoplasmic organelles, gap junction formation, and the expression of gamma-crystallin and $MP_{26}$. However, the present findings indicate that the similarity of lentoids with lens fiber does not extend to the distribution of Na, K-ATPase in the plasma membrane. When the structure of lentoids is compared to that of the *in situ* lens, there are several differences. One of these is that lentoids lack epithelial cells, whereby lentoid cell is in direct contact with the environment. In the *in situ* lens, the exchange of ions and metabolites between lens and its enviroment takes place in the epithelial cells, whereas in lentoids, their exchange should occur through the surface plasma membrane. To respond to these demands, it is likely that in lentoids the synthesis of Na, K-ATPase is induced during the process of lentoid formation *in vitro*, resulting in the increased levels of the enzyme in the surface plasma membrane.

It is of interest to comment on the localization of Na, K-ATPase in the lens *in situ* in relation to the aqueous humor. In intact ocular tissue, aqueous humor, which bathes crystalline lens, serves as growth medium for the lens epithelial cells. Among plasma membrane domains of the *in situ* lens epithelium, basal plasma membrane, which exhibited Na, K-ATPase reaction, can be regarded to have the most direct relation with the aqueous humor. It has been postulated that the Na, K-

ATPase in the lens epithelium plays a key role in the exchange of ions between lens and its environment.[9] According to the pump leak hypothesis,[9] Na ions enter the lens through the posterior capsule and diffuse along the fiber layer anteriorly to the epithelium, where the ions are actively extruded into the anterior chamber. On the other hand, K ions are actively pumped by the Na, K-ATPase system in the epithelium into the lens. They diffuse posteriorly and leave the lens through the posterior capsule. As a result of this mechanism, lens can maintain a high concentration of K ions and a low concentration of Na ions. Our data show that that Na, K-ATPase enzyme in the lens epithelial cells is localized primarily in the basal plasma membrane where Na-ions are extruded into the aqueous humor for maintaining ion homeostasis in the lens.

## Summary

The possible change in cell polarity in lens epithelium in tissue culture was studied by immunohistochemical localization of Na, K-ATPase. Contrary to previous reports Na, K-ATPase was localized in the basal plasma membrane but not in the apical and lateral plasma membrane of both rat and human lens epithelium *in situ*. Upon culturing the explants of human lens capsule-epithelium, the immunoreaction for the enzyme was observed on the apical surface of the epithelium. Similarly, monolayers of the cultured cells showed Na, K-ATPase activity in the apical surface (facing the media). However, the enzyme activity was found in both the apical and basal plasma membrane of lens epithelium cultured on biopore membrane filters in which both cell surfaces have access to the culture medium. The findings indicate that the change in polarity of Na, K-ATPase distribution in cultured lens epithelium may be dictated by the need to maintain ion homeostasis by extrusion of sodium ions across the cell membrane facing the medium.

## Acknowledgment

I wish to gratefully acknowledge the contributions of my colleagues Drs.: T. Arita, L-R Lin, Y. Murata and T. Tsuji who collaborated in the studies summarized in this presentation. This work was supported in part by the National Eye Institute Grants EY-00484 and EY-05025 (Core Grant for Vision Research).

# References

1. REDDY, V. N., L.-R. LIN, T. ARITA, J. S. Jr. ZIGLER, Q. L. HUANG (1988): Crystallins and their Synthesis in Human Lens Epithelial Cells in Tissue Culture. Exp. Eye Res. *47:* 465 – 78.

2. ARITA, T., L.-R. LIN, V. N. REDDY (1988): Differentiation of Human Lens Epithelial Cells in Tissue Culture. Exp. Eye Res. *47:* 905 – 910.

3. ARITA, T., L.-R. LIN, S. R. SUSAN, V. N. REDDY (1990): Enhacement of Differentiation of Human Lens Epithelium in Tissue Culture by Changes in Cell-Substrate Adhesion. Invest. Ophthalmol. Vis. Sci. *31:* 2395 – 404.

4. REDDY, V. N., H. KATSURA, T. ARITA, L.-R. LIN, G. EGUCHI, K. AGATA, K. SAWADA (1991): Study of Crystallin Expression in Human Lens Epithelial Cells During Differentiation in Culture and in Non-lenticular Tissues. Exp. Eye Res. *53:* 367 – 374.

5. PALVA, M., A. PALKAMA (1974): Histochemically Demonstrable Sodium-Potassium-activated Adenosine Triphosphatase (Na-K-ATPase) Activity in the Rat Lens. Exp. Eye Res. *19:* 117 – 23.

6. PALVA, M., A. PALKAMA (1976): Electronmicroscopical, Histochemical and Biochemical Findings on the Na-K-ATPase Activity in the Epithelium of the Rat Lens. Exp. Eye Res. *22:* 229 – 36.

7. UNAKAR, N. J., J. Y. TSUI (1980): Sodium-postassium-dependent ATPase 1. Cytochemical localization in normal and cataractous rat lenses. Invest. Ophthalmol. Vis. Sci. *19:* 630 – 41.

8. TSUJI, T., L.-R. LIN, Y. MURATA, V. N. REDDY (1992): Immunohistochemical Localization of Na, K-ATPase in the *in Situ* Lens, Cultured Human Lens Epithelium and Lentoid. Exp. Eye Res. *55:* 469 – 478.

9. KINSEY, V. E., D. V. N. REDDY (1965): Studies on the crystalline lens XI. The relative role of the epithelium and capsule in transport. Invest. Ophthalmol. *4:* 104 – 116.

Department of Ophthalmology,
University of Missouri School of Medicine,
Columbia, Missouri

# Age-related alterations in the retina

M. L. KATZ

## Introduction

The world is presently experiencing an unprecedented increase in the proportion of the human population that is elderly. This expansion of the aged population has engendered a growing interest in the aging process as a predisposing factor in many types of pathology. Senescence is almost certainly involved in many of the most common pathologies of the eye including cataract, glaucoma, and macular degeneration. In fact, it is likely that these pathologies result directly from normal age-related changes occurring in the affected tissues. Thus, prevention of the most common eye diseases is likely to depend on development of a better understanding of how aging affects the various tissues that compose this organ.

Senescence not only underlies the development of visual impairment severe enough to be classified as pathological, but also more mild decrements in visual performance. For example, it has been reported that visual acuity and light sensitivity both decrease in the general population during aging (PITTS 1982). Understanding the basis for these milder forms of visual deficit is important both because they adversely affect the quality of life and because they probably represent early stages in a process that could lead to more pronounced visual loss.

The purpose of this chapter will be to briefly summarize current knowledge about the influence of senescence on the structure and function of the retina. Possible mechanisms for some of these age-related changes will be discussed. Changes in visual performance that might be related to retinal senescence will be reviewed. Finally, the potential role of senescent changes in the retina in age-related macular degeneration, the most common retinal disease, will be considered.

## Vascular changes of the retina

The human retina is a highly vascularized tissue served by two distinct networks of blood vessels. One set of large vessels enters the eye through the optic nerve head and branches to form capillary networks in two layers of the neural retina: the ganglion cell layer and the inner nuclear layer. These capillary beds within the neural retina provide support for all of the retinal neurons other than the photoreceptor cells. A second set of ocular blood vessels penetrates the sclera at a distance from the optic disc and branches to form the choroidal capillary network beneath the retinal pigment epithelium (RPE). The metabolic requirements of the photoreceptor cells and RPE are satisfied primarily by the choroidal circulation. In light of the extremely high metabolic rate of the retina, it is obvious that even minor disturbances in the delivery of oxygen and nutrients to this tissue by the retinal or choroidal vessels can have detrimental effects on retinal function. Any primary age-related changes in the ocular vasculature are likely to contribute to the deterioration of retinal function during senescence.

Retinal blood vessels, particularly capillaries, have been found to undergo a number of changes during the aging process that are likely to be detrimental. The walls of retinal capillaries contain two cell types: endothelial cells, which surround the capillary lumina; and mural cells, which lie within the capillary wall external to the endothelial cells (Fig. 1). During senescence, there is a progressive loss of both cell types from the retinal capillaries, with endothelial cell loss apparently preceding the disappearance of mural cells (KUWABARA and COGAN 1965). Eventually, many retinal capillaries become totally acellular and their lumina lose their patency. The acellular capillary remnants are composed of the basal lamina that had once surrounded the endothelial and mural cells. Muller cell processes often insinuate into what had been the lumina of these degenerated capillaries (KUWABARA and COGAN 1965). In subjects with age-related macular degeneration, the number of retinal capillaries that have become acellular and occluded is considerably higher than in individuals of the same ages who have healthy retinas, suggesting that loss of functional retinal capillaries may play a role in the development of this disease (KORNZWEIG, ELIASOPH and FELDSTEIN 1966).

A more subtle change that occurs in retinal capillaries during senescence is a progressive increase in the thickness of the basement membranes that represent major components of the vessel walls (LEUENBERGER 1973; NAGATA, KATZ and ROBISON 1986). The significance of this increased basement membrane thickness for capillary function is not known. However, a similar increase in capillary basement thickness occurs early in diabetes, and could be involved in the retinopathy that develops in this disease (FISCHER and GARTNER 1983).

## Influence of aging on the choroid and Bruch's membrane

The choroid is a pigmented and heavily vascularized layer of tissue lying between the fibrous outer wall of the eye (the sclera) and the retina. It contains a layer of relatively large vessels, mostly veins, in its outer portions, and a single layer of large capillaries, the choriocapillaris, just beneath the RPE. The portions of the endothelial cells lining the retinal side of the choriocapillaris are extremely thin and fenestrated, whereas the endothelial cytoplasm on the scleral side of these capillaries is thick. Pericytes are present only on the scleral side of the choriocapillaris. The endothelial cells of the choriocapillaris apparently do not act as a barrier to the exchange of large molecules, such as proteins, between the blood in these capillaries and the overlying RPE (BOK and HELLER 1976). Bruch's membrane forms the

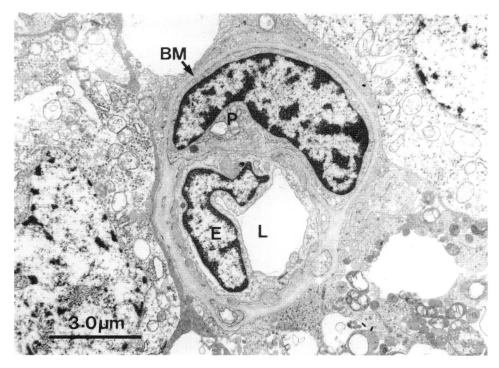

Fig. 1. Electron micrograph showing the structure of a human retinal capillary. The capillary lumen (L) is surrounded by endothelial cells (E). Pericytes (P) partially surround the endothelial cells. A continuous basement membrane (BM) forms the external wall of the capillary and also separates the endothelial cells and pericytes from one another. The micrograph was provided by DR.W. Gerald Robinson, Jr. of the National Institutes of Health.

inner boundary of the choroid. It consists of the basement membrane of the RPE as its inner limit, the basement membranes of the choroidal capillaries and the intercapillary pillars as its outer limit, and internally contains two collagenous layers separated by an elastic zone. As indicated earlier, the choroidal vessels support the RPE and photoreceptor cells, so age-related changes in the choroid are likely to affect the retina.

The region of the choroid that has been most extensively studied with respect to aging is Bruch's membrane. Numerous alterations have been reported to occur in this region of the choroid during senescence. Among these is an increase in overall thickness, due primarily to thickening of the collagenous zones (HOGAN and ALVARADO 1967; SARKS 1976; NEWSOME, HUH and GREEN 1987). The RPE basal lamina also increases in thickness during the aging process, and in eyes from elderly subjects, the basal lamina often protrudes into the RPE basal infoldings (NEWSOME, HUH and GREEN, 1987). Accompanying this thickening is a deposition of heterogeneous-appearing material within Bruch's membrane, particularly in the collagenous zones (FEENEY-BURNS and ELLERSIECK 1985). Ultrastructurally, these deposits are seen to include vesicular, tubular, membranous, and amorphous components (HOGAN and ALVARADO 1967; MISHIMA, HASEBE and KONDO 1978; FEENEY-BURNS and ELLERSIECK 1985) (Fig. 2). Often these extracellular deposits form focal

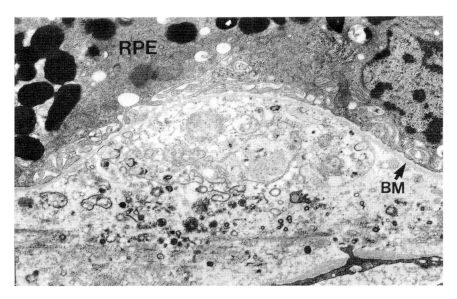

Fig. 2. Electron micrograph illustrating the polymorphous material that accumulates in Bruch's membrane beneath the RPE basement membrane (BM) of elderly human subjects. Micrograph provided by Dr. Lynette Feeney-Burns.

aggregates beneath the RPE basal lamina large enough to cause an elevation and thinning of the overlying RPE cells. Those localized accumulations of material that are large enough to be seen clinically constitute a major type of drusen. Both the numbers and average size of drusen increase during senescence (COFFEY and BROWNSTEIN 1986). Accompanying drusen formation, there is a mineralization of Bruch's membrane (BURNS and FEENEY-BURNS 1980; FEENEY-BURNS and ELLER-SIECK 1985), apparently due to calcium deposition (NEWSOME, HUH and GREEN 1987). These mineral deposits are often associated with drusen.

Extracellular material accumulates not only within Bruch's membrane during senescence, but also often extends more deeply into the choroidal stroma around the capillaries (FEENEY-BURNS and ELLERSIECK 1985). During aging, additional extracellular material is often deposited on the inner surface of Bruch's membrane, adjacent to the RPE basal plasma membranes (SARKS, 1976; FEENEY-BURNS and ELLERSIECK 1985) (Fig. 3). This material, which was designated as the basal linear deposit by Sarks, consists mainly of spindle-shaped structures with a unique and distinct banded appearance. Degeneration of the overlying RPE and photoreceptor cells appears to be closely related to the presence of basal linear deposit material adjacent to Bruch's membrane (SARKS 1976). The molecular composition of this material is not known, although it has been proposed that it may represent collagen aggregated in an abnormal manner (SARKS 1976).

In addition to the age-related changes in Bruch's membrane, the choroid has been reported to undergo a number of other alterations during senescence. The most prominent of these is a thinning or atrophy of the choroid, with selective loss of smaller vessels (SARKS 1976; FEENEY-BURNS and GAO 1990). As in the retinal capillaries, the walls of the choroidal vessels apparently become thickened during senescence, and some vessels become occluded (SARKS 1976). The thickness of the intercapillary connective tissue zones also increases during aging (HOGAN and ALVARADO 1967). In some elderly individuals focal areas of new vessel growth from the choroid into the area beneath the retina take place (SARKS 1973; BERKOW 1984). This new vessel growth is almost always associated with retinal degeneration. Besides affecting the choroidal vessels, senescence is also accompanied by altera-tions in the stromal melanocytes of the choroid. The melanin granules of these cells become aggregated and vacuolized during senescence (HU and MAH 1979), apparently leading to partial depigmentation of the choroid (WEITER, DELORI, WING and FITCH 1986). Low levels of choroidal pigmentation are associated with an increased risk for age-related macular degeneration (WEITER, DELORI, WING and FITCH 1985), suggesting that this age-related depigmentation may be detrimen-tal.

It is likely that the connective tissue stroma of the choroid undergoes most of the same age-related changes that have been reported to occur in connective tissue elsewhere in the body. For example, collagen, the major extracellular matrix pro-tein of the choroid, as well as of most tissues, is known to undergo a progressive crosslinking during senescence (BORNSTEIN 1976). The significance of collagen

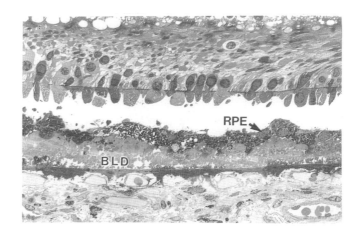

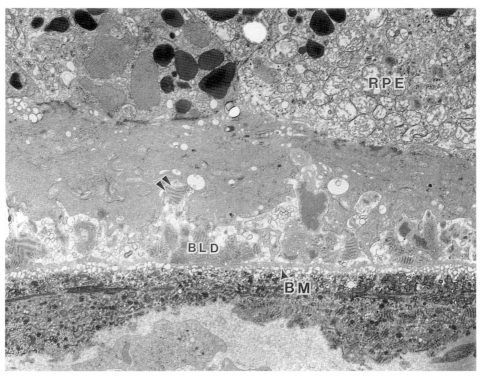

Fig. 3. Light micrograph (top) and electron micrograph (bottom) showing the basal linear deposit (BLD) often found between the basal sides of the RPE cells and the RPE basement membrane (BM) of elderly human subjects. The BLD contains large amounts of a distinctive banded material (double arrowheads). Micrograph provided by Dr. Lynette Fenney-Burns.

crosslinking for tissue function is not known in most cases. It is possible that formation of crosslinks between the functional groups of connective tissue proteins could affect the transport of various substances through the connective tissue stroma. Thus, it is possible that the accumulation of material in Bruch's membrane during aging is due, at least in part, to crosslinking between the connective tissue proteins of the choroid.

## Loss of neuronal elements from the retina

The first stages of visual processing are carried out by several types of neurons within the retina. The photoreceptor cells transduce light into neural impulses. These impulses are transmitted to neurons with nuclei in the inner nuclear layer. The neurons of this layer are distinguished from one another by their positions within the neural circuitry of the retina. The last retinal neurons are the ganglion cells that receive inputs from the inner nuclear layer neurons and transmit the processed visual information to the brain via their axons, which form the optic nerve. Obviously, age-related alterations in any of these cells are likely to affect visual performance.

During senescence, there appears to be a progressive loss of cells from all layers of the retina. In the retinal periphery, neuronal elements virtually disappear from sizable patches of retina, leaving large cyst-like holes (WOLTER and WILSON 1959; FOOS, SPENCER and STRAATSMA 1969). Such severe degeneration does not usually occur in the macula. However, there does appear to be a progressive loss of macular photoreceptor cells during aging. GARTNER and HENKIND (1981) reported an obvious reduction in photoreceptor density in the macular zone in some individuals over age 40, although this cell loss was not quantitated. Recently FEENEY-BURNS and colleagues (1990), using morphometric techniques, quantitated photoreceptor cell densities in the maculas of eyes of human donors aged 49 to 101 years. A significant age-related loss of photoreceptors was found to occur over this age span, although some elderly individuals maintained a normal complement of macular photoreceptor cells. Loss of macular photoreceptors during senescene was also reported by DOREY and coworkers (1989), although the latter investigators reported that such cell loss was restricted to the eye donors in their sample who were black. The failure by DOREY et al. to observe photoreceptor cell loss in white donors may have been due to lack of consistency in the region of the macula that was sampled; photoreceptor density varies across the macula, and the region examined was not precisely defined. Evidence for age-related photorecptor cell loss has also been obtained in living human subjects (KEUNEN, VAN NORREN and VAN MEEL 1987); foveal cone pigment densities measured by retinal densitometry were found to decline significantly after age 60. This loss of cone pigment was attributed to a reduction in the number of foveal cones during senescence.

Age-related loss of photoreceptors apparently occurs by a process in which the nuclear and synaptic regions of specific cells become displaced from their normal positions in the retina into the zone between the outer limiting membrane and the RPE (LAI, MASUDA, MANGUM, LUG, MACRAE, FLETSCHER and LIU 1982). These displaced cells appear to degenerate and be removed from the retina by either macrophages or the RPE. The numbers of displaced photoreceptors increase during senescence (LAI et al. 1982), suggesting that with increasing age the factors responsible for maintaining retinal integrity are altered.

Age-related losses of photoreceptor cells have been reported not only in humans, but also in animals maintained under controlled conditions, suggesting that such cell loss is truely intrinsic to senescence. For example, ORDY and colleagues (1980) found that foveal cone density in captive Rhesus monkeys decreased significantly between 5 and 22 years of age. Age-related losses of photoreceptors have also been reported in pigmented (KATZ and ROBISON 1986) and albino rats (WEISSE, STOETZER and SEITZ 1974; LAI, JACOBY and JONAS 1978; SHINOWARA, LONDON and RAPOPORT 1982). In albino animals, light appears to accelerate this cell loss (WEISSE, STOETZER and SEITZ 1986; LAI, JACOBY and JONAS 1978).

The mechanisms underlying age-related decreases in photoreceptor cell densities have yet to be determined. However, in light of the importance of the RPE in supporting the photoreceptor cells, it is possible that primary aging changes in the RPE might in turn lead to photoreceptor cell death. Evidence that this might be the case is provided by the finding of DOREY et al. (1989) that photoreceptor densities were inversely correlated with lipofuscin (age pigment) concentrations in the adjacent RPE. A summary of age-related changes that have been identified in the RPE will be presented in the next section.

Accompanying the decrease in photoreceptor density in the central retina, and the generalized degeneration of the peripheral retina that occurs during senescence is a progressive loss of retinal ganglion cells. Retinal ganglion cell content can be estimated from the number of axons in the optic nerve. In humans, it has been reported that the number of optic nerve axons decreases with increasing age (BALAZSI, ROOTMAN, DRANCE, SCHULZER and DOUGLAS 1984; JOHNSON, MIAO and SADUN 1987; JONAS, MUELLER-BERGH, SCHOETZER-SCHREHARDT and NAUMANN 1990). Rats also show a decreased optic nerve axon population during senescence (RICCI, BRONZETTI and AMENTA 1988), and this is correlated with a decrease in the number of ganglion cell nuclei observed in sections of the retina (KATZ and ROBISON 1986). Age-related ganglion cell death could result from retrograde degeneration due to loss of brain neurons with which the ganglion cells form synapses (HOLLANDER, BISTI, MAFFEI and HEBEL 1984). Because each ganglion cell transmits visual information that has been processed by a number of preceeding neurons, loss of a single ganglion cell is likely to have a greater impact on visual performance than is the loss of a single photoreceptor cell.

Not only does the number of ganglion cells in the retina decline during senescence, but the pattern of axons and dendrites that determines how these cells are connected within the neural circuitry also changes (VRABEC 1965). In eyes from elderly individuals, ganglion cell axons are often truncated and fail to extend out of the retina through the optic nerve. These axons may have become shortened due to the loss of the cells with which they had synapsed in the brain. Changes in the dendritic arborization of the ganglion cells is suggestive of the loss of intraretinal neurons with which the ganglion cells normally form synapses.

## Changes in the retinal pigment epithelium

The RPE plays a critical role in photoreceptor cell maintenance and function. It forms a barrier between the photoreceptors and their supporting blood supply in the choroid. Almost all nutrient and waste exchange between the photoreceptors and the blood is mediated by the RPE. Separation of the retina from the RPE (retinal detachment) leads to photoreceptor degeneration (BENSON 1980), illustrating the importance of the RPE to photoreceptor function and survival. Even impairment of a single RPE function can result in photoreceptor cell death (BOK and HALL 1971). Thus, it is possible that the observed age-related loss of photoreceptors is secondary to primary senescent alterations in RPE function.

Several morphological changes have been reported to occur in the RPE during aging. One of the most prominent of these is the accumulation of autofluorescent pigment granules, lipofuscin, within the RPE cell cytoplasm (FEENEY 1978; WING, BLANCHARD and WEITER 1978; FEENEY-BURNS, HILDERBRAND and ELDRIDGE 1984) (Fig. 4). As this pigment accumulates, the amount of pigment-free cytoplasm in the RPE decreases (FEENEY-BURNS, HILDERBRAND, and ELDRIDGE 1984). Animal and cell culture experiments have demonstrated that the bulk of the lipofuscin granule contents are derived from phagocytosed photoreceptor outer segments (KATZ, DREA, ELDRED, HESS and ROBISON 1986; KATZ and ELDRED 1989; KATZ and SHANKER 1989; BOULTON, MCKECHNIE, BREDA and MARSHALL 1989). Although it has not been conclusively demonstrated that lipofuscin accumulation is detrimental to cell function, BOULTON and MARSHALL (1986) found that the phagocytosis of large numbers of nondegradable particles by cultured RPE can lead to cell death. In addition, the number of photoreceptors overlying RPE cells with high lipofuscin content are lower than those over areas of the RPE with less lipofuscin (DOREY WU, EBENSTEIN, GARSD and WEITER 1989), suggesting that lipofuscin impairs the ability of the RPE to support photorecptor survival. Thus it is likely that the presence of large amounts of lipofuscin in the RPE of aged individuals is detrimental.

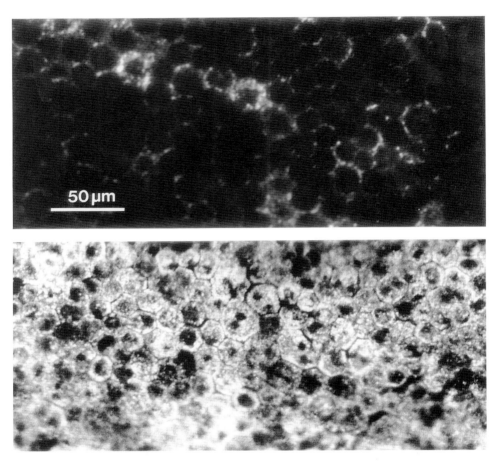

Fig. 4. Fluorescence micrographs of RPE cells from a 5-year-old human donor (top), and from a donor who was 78 years old (bottom). The RPE from the young donor contains very little autofluorescent pigment, whereas the RPE of the elderly donor is heavily packed with autofluorescent lipofuscin. Fluorescence photomicrography was performed as described by KATZ et al. 1986.

Along with lipofuscin, the RPE also apparently accumulates pure lipid inclusions during senescence (HOGAN 1972). The lipophilic nature of both types of inclusion apparently makes them reservoirs for the nonspecific deposition of lipidic compounds in the RPE. During aging, both the lipid-soluble vitamins E and A accumulate in the RPE of animals (KATZ and ROBISON 1987; KATZ, DREA and ROBISON 1987), and at least vitamin E accumulates in the human RPE (ORGANISCIAK, BERMAN, WANG and FEENEY-BURNS 1987). Vitamin A has been found to be a component of isolated lipofuscin granules from human eyes. The partitoning of vitamin A into the lipofuscin compartment of the RPE may make it less available for visual pigment synthesis. This could account for a slowing of cone pigment regeneration rates during senescence (KEUNEN et al 1987).

In addition to lipofuscin, RPE cells also contain another type of pigment granule, melanin. The nature of the RPE melanin is altered during senescence. In young individuals, most melanin granules are ellipsoid-shaped bodies that are filled with a uniform-appearing substance. In older subjects, melanin is often incorporated into complex granules that have a cortex of lipofuscin or lysosome-derived material (FEENEY, 1978).

Besides developing these pigmentary changes, RPE cells also become much more polymorphic during senescence. Cell size, shape, and height within an eye all become more variable with advancing age (FRIEDMAN and Ts'o 1968; MISHIMA, HASEBE and KONDO 1978). RPE cells overlying drusen become particularly shortened or flattened (FEENEY-BURNS and ELLERSIECK 1985). The infoldings along the basal side of the RPE also apparently become less regular during senescence. In localized areas of the RPE from elderly individuals these infoldings are greatly enlarged (MISHIMA, HASEBE and KONDO 1978). Similar focal proliferations of the RPE basal infoldings also occur in animals (KATZ and ROBISON 1985). In the peripheral regions of the human eye, the RPE becomes vacuolated during aging (FRIEDMAN and Ts'o 1968). This vacuolization is likely to be a sign of cell degeneration (HOGAN 1972).

One of the major functions of the RPE is to degrade phagocytosed components of the photoreceptor outer segments. While most of this degradation probably takes place intracellularly, it has been proposed that partially degraded material is externalized at the bases of the RPE cells by a process of evagination and pinching off of small fragments of the cell cytoplasm (BURNS and FEENEY-BURNS 1980). WILCOX (1988) reported that significant proprotions of the RPE lysosomal degradative enzymes are secreted from cultured RPE. These enzymes, if secreted at the bases of RPE cells in vivo, may help to complete the breakdown of materials that was initiated within the RPE. During aging, there is a significant decrease in the secretion of a major RPE protease at the base of the RPE (WILCOX 1988). This could contribute to the accumulation of polymorphous material that occurs in Bruch's membrane during senescence.

## Aging and visual performance

There is little doubt that some aspects of visual performance deteriorate as a consequence of aging. Since visual perception involves not only the retina and other parts of the eye, but also the central nervous system, it is often difficult to localize anatomically the lesions responsible for visual deterioration. However, it is likely that some of the age-related changes in the retina contribute to the visual impairment that develops during senescence.

Among the components of visual perception that show deterioration during aging are overall sensitivity (GUNKEL and GOURAS 1963; EISNER, FLEMING, KLEIN and MAULDIN 1987), visual acuity (GITTINGS and FOZZARD 1986), contrast sensitivity (PITTS 1982), chromatic discrimination (EISNER, FLEMING, KLEIN and MAULDIN 1987), temporal resolution (SEKULER, HUTMAN and OWSLEY 1980; KLINE and SCHIEBER 1982; WRIGHT and DRASDO 1985), and stereopsis (BELL, WOLF and BERN-HOLTZ 1972; PITTS 1982). Some of these decrements can be attributed at least partially to changes in the transmission characteristics of the parts of the eye through which light must pass before reaching the retina. For example, during senescence the lens develops opacities and pigmentation and loses the capacity for accommodation. In addition, the size of the pupil decreases with advancing age. These age-related changes in the optical characteristics of the eye reduce the intensity and quality of the retinal image. However, they do not appear to be sufficient to account for all of the visual deficits that develop during aging. A number of studies have been performed in attempts to anatomically localize the sites of the lesions responsible for age-related deterioration in visual performance. Some of these investigations have suggested that age-related changes in the retina at least contribute to the development of visual deficits.

Several techniques to assess the functional integrity of the retina in human subjects have been developed. One of these, the pattern reversal retinal potential measurement (PRRP), is a contrast-specific electrical potential across the eye that is correleated with the responses of the retinal ganglion cells to specific visual stimuli (HOLLANDER, BISTI, MAFFEI and HABEL 1984). TRICK and colleagues (1986) measured the PRRP in human subjects with good visual acuity between the ages of 20 and 80 years and found that the amplitude of this response was significantly reduced in the older individuals under a variety of stimulus conditions. The data was corrected for the effects of senile miosis on retinal illumination, so the reduction in PRRP amplitude is likely to reflect a reduction in retinal sensitivity. Age-related decreases in retinal responsiveness to light stimuli are also indicated by an observed decrease in ganzfeld electroretinogram amplitudes during senescence (WELEBER 1981), and by decreases in visual field sensitivities that cannot be attributed to lens changes (JOHNSON, ADAMS and LEWIS 1989). Sensitivities in different parts of the visual field decrease at different rates during aging (HAAS, FLAMMER and SCHNEIDER 1986), which would not be the case if loss of visual sensitivity were due primarily to changes in the eye tissues in front of the retina.

Longitudinal as well as cross-sectional studies have demonstrated a progressive decline in visual acuity during senescence, even in eyes that show no signs of pathology (PITTS 1982; GITTINGS and FOZARD 1986). This loss in acuity does not appear to be due primarily to age-related changes in the lens; the decline in acuity that occurs during aging was found to continue in individuals who had been aphakic for many years (JAY, MAMMO and ALLEN 1987). Thus, the age-related declines in acuity must be due to changes in the neural elements involved in vision. Acuity is obviously a function of the number of neurons involved in image processing. Therefore, the decline in acuity probably is attributable to the loss of retinal neurons and perhaps of extraocular neurons in the visual system as well. A direct relationship between the age-related decrease in visual acuity and the loss of foveal cones has been demonstrated in monkeys (ORDY, BRIZZEE and HANSCHE 1980).

One of the major changes that occurs in visual function during senescence is a decline in speed of performance, as reflected in a loss of temporal resolving power (KLINE and SCHIEBER 1982). Visual events that follow one another in rapid succession and are separable by young individuals are often seen as fused or single events by older subjects. The temporal resolving power of the visual system can be assessed by measuring the critical flicker frequency (CFF) threshold. The CFF is the minimum frequency of a pulsating light source at which the light appears to be constantly on and reflects the visual system's limited ability to temporally track rapid changes in illumination. During senescence, there is a well-documented decline in the CFF threshold (HUNTINGTON and SIMONSON 1965; FALK and KLINE 1978), which is at least partially attributable to neural elements of the visual system (KLINE and SCHIEBER 1982). The precise neural mechanism for this decrease in CFF threshold has not been determined. However, KEUNEN and colleagues (1987) reported that the time constant for cone pigment regeneration after bleaching increases substantially during aging in human subjects, suggesting that an increase in photoreceptor recovery times may contribute to the age-related decrease in CFF.

Clearly many aspects of visual performance deteriorate during senescence. Age-related changes throughout the visual system undoubtedly contribute to the development of these functional deficits. A variety of evidence, including that discussed above, strongly suggests that age-related alterations in the retina play a major role in the decline of at least some components of vision that accompanies aging.

## Aging and retinal pathology

It is somewhat difficult to clearly separate those age-related changes in the retina that might be detrimental, but are considered "normal", from alterations in this tissue that are considered pathological. Age-related visual deterioration occurs gradually over many years. In many individuals the progression of retinal changes occurs slowly enough that vision is never so severely impaired as to be incapacitating. In others, these changes may progress beyond a threshold where many visual tasks become impossible. Only in the cases of severe visual impairment is there generally agreement that pathology exists. However, if this pathology develops as a consequence of normal aging processes, it is probably most constructive to consider age-related retinal pathology as an end-stage of senescence rather than as a distinct entity.

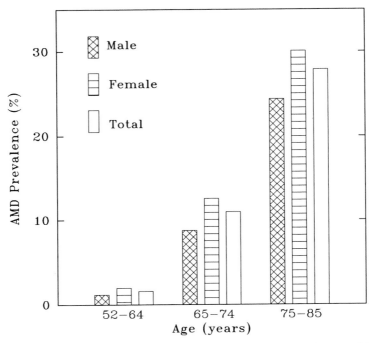

Fig. 5. Prevalence of age-related macular degeneration (AMD) in Americans between 52 and 85 years of age as determined in the Framingham Eye Study. Data from Kini et al. 1978.

Age-related retinal degeneration, particularly that affecting the macula, is one of the leading causes of severe visual impairment in developed countries (Marmion 1974; Kini, Leibowitz, Colton, Nickerson, Ganley and Dawber 1978; Ganley and Roberts 1983; Green, Bear, and Johnson 1986). There is no precise clinical definition of age-related macular degeneration (AMD) that is universally accepted in diagnosing this condition. However, when studies were designed with precise working definitions that were applied consistently, the prevalence of AMD was found to be as high as 11 % among Americans aged 65 to 74 years, and almost 28 % among those 75 to 85 years of age (Kini et al. 1978) (Fig. 5). Developing an understanding of the mechanisms underlying this disease, and idenitifying risk factors in addition to aging, have been greatly impeded by the lack of an animal model for AMD. However, some understanding of the nature of AMD has been developed from human studies.

Epidemiological studies have consistently identified light ocular pigmentation as a risk factor for AMD (Hyman, Lilienfeld, Ferris and Fine 1983; Weiter, Delori, Wing and Fitch 1985). This would suggest that light exposure of the retina may promote the development of this disease. The finding of Guyer et al

(1986) that aphakic eyes had a higher frequency of macular drusen than phakic eyes supports the possibility that ultraviolet light exposure of the retina promotes age-related macular disease. However, WEST and colleagues (1989) found that there was no correlation between the amount of long-term sunlight exposure to the eye and the risk of developing AMD in phakic individuals. Thus, it is not yet clear what role, if any, light may play in age-related retinal disease. Heredity may be an important factor in determining the risk for AMD, since this disease tends to run in families (HYMAN et al. 1983). There are racial differences in the incidence of AMD (GREGOR and JOFFE 1978; HOSHINO, MIZUNO and ICHIKAWA 1984), which is consistent with there being a genetic component to this disease. However, the presence of familial and race aggregations of this disease are not necessarily due to genetic factors.

Much of what is currently known of the morphological changes in the retina that correlate with clinical evidence of AMD comes from a study by Sarks (1976). This investigator performed histological studies of eyes from human subjects who had undergone clinical ophthalmological examinations an average of approximately 16 months before death. A primary conclusion of this study is that AMD appears to be the end stage of a normal aging process that results in the deposition of extracellular material (the basal linear deposit, BLD) beneath the RPE. The presence and severity of AMD were very closely correlated with the amount of BLD present in the eyes of the subjects examined. Although some BLD accumulation probably occurs during aging in everyone, there is a great deal of individual variability in the rate at which this material builds up. Only those with the greatest amounts of BLD showed severe signs of retinal degeneration. Thus, an understanding of the mechanisms involved in BLD accumulation is likely to suggest a way to decrease the incidence of age-related macular degeneration.

Sarks (1976) suggested that the accumulation of BLD is a manifestation of the gradual failure of the retinal pigment epithelium during aging. If this is the case, then prevention of AMD will depend on preserving RPE function in the elderly. One of the functions of the RPE that is essential to vision is the synthesis and delivery to the photoreceptor cells of the form of vitamin A required for visual pigment synthesis (LIOU, BRIDGES, FONG, ALVAREZ and GONZALEZ-FERNANDEZ 1982; DEIGNER, LAW, CANADA and RANDO 1989). EISNER and colleagues (1987) reported that recovery of sensitivity during dark adaptation was slower than normal in apparently healthy eyes of subjects whose other eye had suffered from exudative AMD. This could be indicative of impaired RPE function, and would be consistent with the hypothesis that RPE failure precedes macular degeneration. Identification of factors that cause age-related RPE failure to occur in some individuals and not others could form the basis for a rational approach to the prevention AMD.

Studies by NEWSOME and colleagues (1988) have suggested that dietary zinc may be effective slowing the progression of age-related macular degeneration. Whether this effect is due to enhancement of RPE function is not known. Zinc deficiency does have a dramatic effect on RPE morphology (LEURE-DUPREE and BRIDGES 1982), indicating that this element plays an important role in these cells. Additional studies will be required to determine whether dietary zinc retards AMD by improving RPE function.

Based on the studies of human subjects, it appears likely that age-related retinal pathology that results in severe visual impairment involves a deterioration in the function of the RPE. An animal model for AMD would be very useful for confirming the role of RPE decline in this disease. Such a model could be used to characterize age-related changes in the RPE, to determine the mechanisms for such changes, and to confirm the role of these changes in retinal degeneration. The effectiveness of potential therapies for preventing AMD could be adequately evaluated if such a model were available. Because retinal structure varies so much among mammalian species, an animal model for age-related degeneration of the retina is most likely to be found among the diurnal primates. There is limited evidence that at least some of the age-related changes in the eye that are associated with AMD occur in monkeys. For example, evidence for drusen formation from buds of RPE cytoplasm has been found in Macaca speciosa (ISHIBASHI, SORGENTE, PATTERSON and RYAN 1986).

## Summary and conclusions

During senescence, there is a progressive deterioration in a number of parameters of visual performance. Acuity, overall sensitivity, contrast sensitivity, color discrimination, and temporal resolution all decline somewhat during aging. Age-related changes in the retina are probably involved to some degree in the declines in most of these aspects of visual performance. In some individuals, visual deterioration progresses to a pathological stage that involves severe loss of central vision. One of the leading causes of incapacitating vision loss in the elderly is degeneration of the macular region of the retina that mediates central vision. This degeneration is probably an end stage of the normal age-related retinal changes that contribute to more mild vision loss in everyone.

Age-related changes affecting the retina that apparently contribute to declining visual performance include loss of retinal capillaries that support the inner retinal neurons, and changes in the choroid and retinal pigment epithelium that provide support for the photoreceptor cells. The alterations in these supporting tissues are accompanied by a progressive loss of neural elements, including photoreceptors, from the retina. Neuronal death and changes in the interactions between the retinal neurons and supporting tissues can explain at least some of the functional changes in vision that occur during senescence.

The ability to preserve healthy vision in the elderly, and in particular to prevent age-related macular degeneration, will depend on developing a better understanding of the mechanisms underlying deleterious changes in the retina that occur during senescence. Some progress in attaining such an understanding has been made in human and animal studies. Further significant advances will most likely be made if an adequate animal model for human retinal aging can be developed.

## Acknowledgements

I wish to express my gratitude to Dr. W. Gerald Robison, Jr. and to Dr. Lynette Fenney-Burns for providing me with the micrographs of human eye tissue used in this chapter. Support for the work of Dr. Katz was provided by the National Institutes of Health and Research to Prevent Blindness, Inc.

## References

BALAZSI, A. G., J. ROOTMAN, S. M. DRANCE, M. SCHULZER, G. R. DOUGLAS (1984): The effect of age on the nerve fiber population of the human optic nerve. Am. J. Ophthalmol. 97: 760–766.

BELL, B., E. WOLF, C. D. BERNHOLTZ (1972): Depth perception as a function of age. Aging Hum. Dev. 3: 77–81.

BENSON, W. E. (1980): Retina Detachment, Diagnosis and Treatment. Harper and Row Publishers, New York.

BOK, D., M. O. HALL (1971): The role of the pigment epithelium in the etiology of inherited retinal dystrophy in the rat. J. Cell Biol. 49: 664–682.

BOK, D., J. HELLER (1976): Transport of retinal from the blood to the retina: an autoradiographic study of the pigment epithelial cell surface receptor for plasma retinol-binding protein. Exp. Eye Res. 22: 395–042.

BORNSTEIN, P: (1976): Disorders of connective tissue function and the aging process: a synthesis and review of current concepts and findings. Mech. Age. Dev. 5: 305–314.

BOULTON, M., J. MARSHALL (1986): Effects of increasing numbers of phagocytic inclusions on human retinal pigment epithelial cells in culture: a model for aging. Br. J. Ophthalmol. 70: 808–815.

BOULTON, M., N. M. MCKECHNIE, J. BREDA, M. BAYLY, J. MARSHALL (1989): The formation of autofluorescent granules in cultured human RPE. Invest. Ophthalmol. Vis. Sci. 30: 82–88.

BURNS, R. P., L. FEENEY-BURNS (1980): Clinico-morphologic correlations of drusen in Bruch's membrane. Trans. Amer. Ophthalmol. Soc. LXXCVIII: 206–223.

COFFEY, A. J. H., S. BROWNSTEIN (1986): The prevalence of macular drusen in postmortem eyes. Am. J. Ophthalmol. 102: 164–171.

DEIGNER, P. S., W. C. LAW, F. J. CANADA, R. R. RANDO (1989): Membranes as the energy source in the endergonic transformation of vitamin A to 11-cis-retinol. Science 244: 968–971.

DOREY, C. K., G. WU, D. EBENSTEIN, A. GARSD, J. J. WEITER (1989): Cell loss in the aging retina: relationship to lipofuscin accumulation and macular degeneration. Invest. Ophthalmol. Vis. Sci. 30: 1641–1699.

EISNER, A., S. A. FLEMING, M. L. KLEIN, W. M. MAULDIN (1987): Sensitivities in older eyes with good acuity cross-sectional norms. Invest. Ophthalmol. Vis. Sci. 28: 1824–1831.

FALK, J., D. W. KLINE (1978): Stimulus persistence in CFF: underactivation or overarousal? Exp. Aging Res. 4: 109–123.

FEENEY, L. (1978): Lipofuscin and melanin of human retinal pigment epithelium. Invest. Ophthalmol. Visual Sci. *17:* 583 – 600.

FEENEY-BURNS, L., R. P. BURNS, C.-L. GAO (1990): Age-related macular changes in humans over 90 years old. Am. J. Ophthalmol. *109:* 265 – 278.

FEENEY-BURNS, L., M. R. ELLERSIECK (1985): Age-related changes in the ultrastructure of Bruch's membrane. Am. J. Ophthalmol. *100:* 686 – 697.

FEENEY-BURNS, L., E. S. HILDERBRAND, J. ELDRIDGE (1984): Aging human RPE: Morphometric analysis of macular, equitorial, peripheral cells. Invest. Ophthalmol. Vis. Sci. *25:* 195 – 200.

FISHER, F., J. GARTNER (1983): Morphometric analysis of basal laminae in rats with longterm streptozotocin diabetes. II. Retinal capillaries. Exp. Eye Res. *37:* 55 – 64.

FOOS, R. Y., L. M. SPEMCER, B. R. STRAATSMA (1969): Trophic degenerations in the peripheral retina. In: Symposium on Retina and Retinal Surgery. Transactions of the New Orleans Academy of Ophthalmology, pp. 19 – 120. C.V. Mosby Co., St. Louis.

FRIEDMAN, E., M. TS'O (1968): The Retinal Pigment Epithelium. II. Histologic Changes Associated with Age. Arch. Ophthalmol. *79:* 315 – 320.

GANLEY, J. P., J. ROBERTS (1983): Eye conditions and related need for medical care among persons 1-74 years of age: United States 1971-72. U.S. Government Printing Office. DHHS Pub. No. (PHS) 83 – 1678.

GARTNER, S., P. HENKIND (1981): Aging and degeneration of the human macula. 1. Outer nuclear layer and photoreceptors. Br. J. Ophthalmol. *65:* 23 – 28.

GITTINGS, N. S., J. L. FOZARD (1986): Age-related changes in visual acuity. Exp. Gerontol. *21:* 423 – 433.

GREEN, J. S., J. C. BEAR, G. J. JOHNSON (1986): The burden of genetically determined eye disease. Br. J. Ophthalmol. *70:* 696 – 699.

GREGOR, Z., L. JOFFE (1978): Senile macular changes in the black African. Br. J. Ophthalmol. *62:* 547 – 550.

GUERIN, C. J., D. H. ANDERSON, R. N. FARRISS, S. K. FISHER (1989): Retinal reattachment of the primate macula. Photoreceptor recovery after short-term detachment. Invest. Ophthalmol. Vis. Sci. *30:* 1708 – 1725.

GUNKEL, R. D., P. GOURAS (1963): Changes in scotopic visibility thresholds with age. Arch. Ophthalmol. *69:* 4 – 9.

GUYER, D. R., M. F. ALEXANDER, C. L. AUER, M. B. HAMILL, J. A. CHAMBERLIN, S. L. FINE (1986): A comparison of the frequency and severity of macular drusen in phakic and non-phakic eyes. Invest. Ophthalmol. Vis. Sci. (ARVO Suppl.) *27:* 20.

HAAS, A., J. FLAMMER, U. SCHNEIDER (1986): Influence of age on the visual fields of normal subjects. Am. J. Ophthalmol. *101:* 199 – 203.

HOGAN, M. J. (1972): Role of the retinal pigment epithelium in macular disease. Trans. Am. Acad. Ophthalmol. Otolaryngol. *76:* 64 – 80.

HOGAN, M. J., J. ALVARADO (1967): Studies on the human macula. IV. Aging changes in Bruch's membrane. Arch. Ophthalmol. *77:* 410 – 420.

HOLLANDER, H., S. BISTI, L., MAFFEI, R. HEBEL (1984): Electroretinographic responses and retrograde changes of retinal morphology after intracranial optic nerve section. A quantitative analysis in the cat. Exp. Brain Res. *55:* 483 – 493.

HOSHINO, M., K. MIZUNO, H. ICHIKAWA (1984): Aging alterations of retina and choroid of Japanese: light microscopic study of macular region of 176 eyes. Jpn. J. Ophthalmol. *38:* 89 – 102.

HU, F., K. MAH (1979): Choroidal melanocytes – a model for studying the aging process in nonreplicative differential cells. Mech. Age. Dev. *11:* 227 – 235.

HUNTINGTON, J. M., E. SIMONSON (1965): Critical flicker fusion frequency as a function of exposure time in two different age groups. J. Gerontol. *20:* 527 – 529.

HYMAN, L. G., A. M. LILIEN, F. L. FERRIS III, S. L. FINE (1983): Senile macular degeneration: a case control study. Am. J. Epidemiol. *118:* 213 – 217.

ISHIBASHI, T., N. SORGENTE, R. PATTERSON, S. J. RYAN (1986): Pathogenesis of drusen in the primate. Invest. Ophthalmol. Vis. Sci. *27:* 184 – 193.

JAY, J. L., R. B. MAMMO, D. ALLAN (1987): Effect of age on visual acuity after cataract extraction. Br. J. Ophthalmol. *71:* 112 – 115.

JOHNSON, B. M., M. MIAO, A. A. SADUN (1987): Age-related decline of human optic nerve axon populations. Age *10:* 5 – 9.

JOHNSON, C. A., A. J. ADAMS, R. A. LEWIS (1989): Evidence for a neural basis of age-related visual field loss in normal observers. Invest. Ophthalmol. Vis. Sci. *30:* 2056 – 2064.

JONAS, J. B., J. A. MULLER-BERGH, U. M. SCHLOTZER-SCHREHARDT, G. O. H. NAUMANN (1990): Histomorphometry of the human optic nerve. Invest. Ophthalmol. Vis. Sci. *31:* 736 – 744.

KATZ, M. L., C. M. DREA, G. E. ELDRED, H. H. HESS, W. G. ROBISON, JR. (1986): Influence of early photoreceptor degeneration on lipofuscin in the retinal pigment epithelium. Exp. Eye Res. *43:* 561 – 573.

KATZ, M. L., C. M. DREA, W. G. ROBISON, JR. (1987): Dietary vitamins A and E influence retinyl ester content and composition in the retinal pigment epithelium. Biochim. Biophys. Acta *924:* 432 – 441.

KATZ, M. L., G. E. ELDRED (1989): Retinal light damage reduces autofluorescent pigment deposition in the retinal pigment epithelium. Invest. Ophthalmol. Vis. Sci. *30:* 37 – 43.

KATZ, M. L., W. G. ROBISON JR. (1985): Senescence and the retinal pigment epithelium: alterations in basal plasma membrane morphology. Mech. Age. Dev. *30:* 99 – 105.

KATZ, M. L., W. G. ROBISON JR. (1986): Evidence of cell loss from the rat retina during senescence. Exp. Eye Res. *42:* 293 – 304.

KATZ, M. L., W. G. ROBISON JR. (1987): Light and aging effects on vitamin E in the retina and retinal pigment epithelium. Vision Res. *27:* 1875 – 1879.

KATZ, M. L., M. J. SHANKER (1989): Development of lipofuscin-like fluorescence in the retinal pigment epithelium in response to protease inhibitor treatment. Mech. Age. Dev. *49:* 23 – 40.

KEUNEN, J. E. E., D. VAN NORREN, G. J. VAN MEEL (1987): Density of foveal cone pigments at older age. Invest. Ophthalmol. Vis. Sci. *28:* 985 – 991.

KINI, M. M., M. M. LIEBOWITZ, T. COLTON, R. J. NICKERSON, J. GANLEY, T. R. DAWBER (1978): Prevalence of senile cataract, diabetic retinopathy, senile macular degeneration, and glaucoma in the Framingham eye study. Am. J. Ophthalmol. *85:* 28 – 34.

KLINE, D. W., F. J. SCHIEBER: Visual persistence and temporal resolution. In: Aging and Human Visual Function, pp. 231 – 244 (R. Sekuler, D. Kline and K. Dismukes, Eds.). Alan R. Liss, New York 1982.

KORNZWEIG, A. L., I. ELIASOPH, M. FELDSTEIN (1966): The retinal vasculature in macular degeneration. Arch. Ophthalmol. *75:* 326 – 333.

KUWABARA, T., D. G. COGAN (1965): Retinal vascular patterns. VII. A cellular change. Invest. Ophthalmol. *4:* 1049 – 1058.

LAI, Y., R. O. JACOBY, A. M. JONAS (1978): Age-related and light-associated retinal changes in Fischer rats. Invest. Ophthalmol. Vis. Sci. *17:* 634 – 678.

LAI, Y., K. MASUDA, M. D. MANGUM, R. LUG, D. W. MACRAE, G. FLETCHER, Y. LIU (1982): Subretinal displacement of photoreceptor nuclei in human retina. Exp. Eye Res. *34:* 219 – 228.

LEUENBERGER, P. M. (1973): Ultrastructure of ageing retinal vascular system, with special reference to quantitative and qualitative changes of capillary basement membranes. Gerontologia *19:* 1 – 15.

LEURE-DUPREE, A. E., C. D. B. BRIDGES (1982): Changes in retinal morphology and vitamin A metabolism as a consequence of decreased zinc availability. Retina *2:* 294 – 302.

LIOU, G. I., C. D. B. BRIDGES, S.-L. FONG, R. A. ALVAREZ, F. GONZALES-FERNANDEZ (1982): Vitamin A transport between retina and pigment epithelium – an interstitial protein carrying endogenous retinol (interstitial retinol-binding protein). Vision Res. *22:* 1457 – 1467.

MARMION, V. J. (1974): Investigation of senile macular degeneration. Trans. Ophthalmol. Soc. U.K. *94:* 1033 – 1039.

MARMOR, M. F.: Aging and the retina. In: Aging and Human Visual Function, pp. 59 – 78 (R. Sekuler, D. Kline and K. Dismukes, Eds.). Alan R. Liss, Inc., New York 1982.

MISHIMA, H., H. HASEBE, K. KONDO (1978): Age changes in the five structure of the human retinal pigment epithelium. Jpn. J. Ophthalmol. *22:* 476 – 485.

NAGATA, M., M. L. KATZ, W. G. ROBISON JR. (1986): Age-related thickening of retinal capillary basement membranes. Invest. Ophthalmol. Vis. Sci. *27:* 437 – 440.

NEWSOME, D. A., W. HUH, W. R. GREEN: Bruch's membrane age-related changes vary by region. Curr. Eye Res. *6:* 1211 – 1221.

NEWSOME, D. A., M. SWARTZ, N. C. LEONE, R. C. ELSTON, E. MILLER (1988): Oral zinc in macular degeneration. Arch. Ophthalmol. *106:* 192 – 198.

ORDY, J. M., K. R. BRIZZEE, J. HANSCHE (1980): Visual acuity and foveal cone density in the retina of the aged rhesus monkey. Neurobiol. Aging *1:* 133 – 140.

ORGANISCIAK, D. T., E. R. BERMAN, H. WANG, L. FEENEY-BURNS (1987): Vitamin E in neuronal retina and retinal pigment epithelium: Effect of age. Curr. Eye Res. *6:* 1051 – 1055.

PITTS, D. G.: The effects of aging on selected visual functions: dark adaptation, visual acuity, stereopsis, and brightness contrast. In: Aging and Human Visual Function, pp. 131 – 159 (R. Sekuler, D. Kline and K. Dismukes, Eds.). Alan R. Liss, New York 1982.

RICCI, A., E. BRONZETTI, F. AMENTA (1988): Effect of ageing on the nerve fibre population of rat optic nerve. Gerontol. *34:* 231 – 235.

SARKS, S. H. (1973): New vessel formation beneath the retinal pigment epithelium in senile ages. Br. J. Ophthalmol. *57:* 951 – 965.

SARKS, S. H. (1976): Aging and degeneration in the macular region: a clinico-pathological study. Br. J. Ophthalmol. *60:* 324 – 41.

SEKULAR, R., L. P. HUTMAN, C. OWSLEY (1980): Human aging and vision. Science *209:* 1255 – 1256.

SHINOWARA, N. L., E. D. LONDON, S. I. RAPOPORT (1982): Changes in retinal morphology and glucose utilization in aging albino rats. Exp. Eye Res. *34:* 517 – 530.

TRICK, G. L., L. R. TRICK, K. M. HAYWOOD (1986): Altered pattern evoked retinal and cortical potentials associated with human senescence. Curr. Eye Res. *5:* 717 – 724.

VRABEC, F. (1965): Senile changes in the ganglion cells of the human retina. Br. J. Ophthalmol. *49:* 561 – 572.

WEISSE, I., H. STOTZER, R. SEITZ (1974): Age- and light dependent changes in the rat eye. Virchows Arch. A Path. Anat. and Histol. *362:* 145 – 156.

WEITER, J. J., F. C. DELORI, G. L. WING, K. A. FITCH (1985): Relationship of senile macular degeneration to ocular pigmentation. Am. J. Ophthalmol. *99:* 185 – 187.

WEITER, J. J., F. C. DELORI, G. L. WING, K. A. FITCH (1986): Retinal pigment epithelial lipofuscin and melanin and choroidal melanin in human eyes. Invest. Ophthalmol. Vis. Sci. *27:* 145 – 152.

WELEBER, R. G. (1981): The effect of age on human cone and rod ganzfeld electroretinograms. Invest. Ophthalmol. Vis. Sci. *20:* 392 – 399.

WEST, S. K., F. S. ROSENTHAL, N. M. BRESSLER, S. B. BRESSLER, B. MUNOZ, S. L. FINE, H. R. TAYLOR (1989): Exposure to sunlight and other risk factors for age-related macular degeneration. Arch. Ophthalmol. *107:* 875 – 879.

WILCOX, D. K. (1988): Vectorial accumulation of cathepsin D in retinal pigmented epithelium: effects of age. Invest. Ophthalmol. Vis. Sci. *29:* 1205 – 1212.

WING, G. L., G. C. BLANCHARD, J. J. WEITER (1978): The topography and age relationship of lipofuscin concentration in the retinal pigment epithelium. Invest Ophthalmol. Vis. Sci. *17:* 601 – 607.

WOLTER, R. J., W. W. WILSON (1959): Degeneration of the peripheral retina. Am. J. Ophthalmol. *47:* 153 – 166.

WRIGHT, C. E., N. DRASDO (1985): The influence of age on the spatial and temporal contrast sensitivity function. Doc. Ophthalmol. *59:* 385 – 195.

*Cullen Eye Institute, Division of Neuroscience, Baylor College of Medicine, Houston, Texas*

# Cell loss during aging of the human retina

H. Gao and J. G. Hollyfield

## Introduction

The human retina undergoes a variety of structural and physiological changes during aging (Ordy and Brizze 1979; Kilbride et al., 1986; Marshall 1987; Feeny-Burns et al. 1984; Feeney-Burns et al. 1990). Despite extensive research, controversy still surrounds the question as to whether loss of retinal cells is a characteristic of the aging human retina (Gartner and Henkind 1981; Dorey et al., 1989; Balazsi et al. 1984; Repka and Quigley 1989). Quantitative data describing senescent changes in human retinal cell density remain limited. Although age related loss of photoreceptors, retinal pigment epithelium cells (RPE), and ganglion cell axons have been separately reported, no systematic analysis of rods, cones, ganglion cells and RPE cells in the same retina has been made. To establish the pattern of change in the densities of these retinal cells, we have analyzed the cell density of the normal human retina over a 78 year period covering the second to ninth decade of life using donor tissue with no previous history of eye disease. Our study indicates that rods, cones and cells in the ganglion cell layer (GCL) are lost at different rates during aging: equatorial rods and the GCL cells show the greatest decrease in cell number, whereas loss of foveal cones could not be detected; photoreceptor and RPE cell density changes closely parallel each other at the equator and in the fovea. Thus the pattern of retinal cell loss during aging is cell and site specific.

## Methods and procedures

The thirty-five human eyes used in this study were acquired by the Lions Eyes of Texas Eye Bank, Houston, over a 7 year period from 1984 to 1990. Details regarding donor tissue, processing and analysis are described elsewhere (Gao and Holly-field 1992). In the discussion to follow, only the overall highlights of this quantitative study are presented.

## Results

**The retinal equator.** Photoreceptors and RPE cells were counted in serial tangential sections through the photoreceptor inner segments, a level where the large
circular profiles of cone inner segments can easily be distinguished from the smaller profiles of rods. Linear regression analysis yields a highly significant negative
slope of rod densities (P=0.001) from the 2nd to 9th decade which reflects a total
average rod loss of about 570 rods/mm$^2$ per year (Fig. 1 – A, Table 1). The data are
replotted as a function of age with the best fit curves or lines (least squares). The
rod data are best fit with logarithmic plotting (Fig. 1 – B), which suggests a nonuniform rate of rod loss with age. Rod loss is very pronounced between the 2nd and
4th decades, with a gradual decline after that time. Logarithmic plotting model
indicates that from the 2nd decade, rod density is reduced by 15 % at the 4th decade
to 32 % by the 9th decade (decreasing from 131,500 rods/mm$^2$ at the 2nd decade to
89,400 rods/mm$^2$ by the 9th decade), with about 46 % of the total rod loss occuring
by the 4th decade. Linear regression analysis indicates that cone density is also sig-

Table 1: Simple linear regression analysis (one-factor) of the retinal and RPE cells from the 6 age groups studied

| Cells | Counts | r$^2$ | F-test | Probability | Level of significance |
|---|---|---|---|---|---|
| **Equator:** | | | | | |
| Rods | 29 | 0.33 | 13.5 | 0.001 | P=0.001 |
| Cones | 28 | 0.24 | 7.96 | 0.009 | P<0.01 |
| RPE | 29 | 0.18 | 5.97 | 0.021 | P<0.03 |
| GCL cells* | 29 | 0.45 | 21.72 | 0.0001 | P=0.0001 |
| Rods/RPE | 29 | 0.056 | 1.61 | 0.216 | P>0.2 |
| **Fovea:** | | | | | |
| Cones | 28. | 0.016 | 0.43 | 0.516 | P>0.5 |
| RPE | 22 | 0.06 | 1.44 | 0.245 | P>0.2 |
| Cones/RPE | 22 | 0.04 | 0.93 | 0.347 | P>0.3 |

\*    Cells in the GCL which include the ganglion cells and any displaced amacrine cells.

Fig. 1. Graphic representation of equatorial retinal cell densities as a function of age. Linear regression
analysis is applied for the retinal cell and RPE data and yields significant negative slopes (A, C, D and
E). Logarithmic plotting is used to best fit the rod and GCL cell data (B and F). A summary of the data
illustrated in these graphs are as follows (see detailed linear regression parameters in Table 1):
A: Linear regression: number of rods = 138,110 – 571 x age (years). The total average rate of loss is
about 570 rods/mm$^2$ per year.

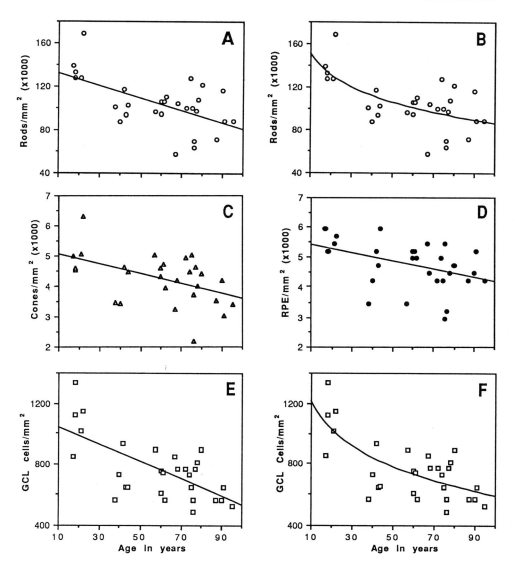

B: Logarithmic plot: number of rods = 215.4 – 64.5 x Log(age) (years), $r^2 = 0.4$ (N = 29). Notice the different cell loss rates at different periods of time with age.

C: Linear regression: number of cones = 5,218 – 16 x age (years). The total average rate of loss is 16 cones/mm$^2$ per year.

D: Linear regression: number of RPE = 5,531 – 14 x age (years). The total average rate of loss is 14 RPE cells/mm$^2$ per year.

E: Linear regression: number of GCL cells = 1,097 – 5,65 x age (years). The total average rate of loss is 6 GCL cells/mm$^2$ per year.

F: Logarithmic plot: number of GCL cells = 1,841 – 625.8 x Log (age) (years), $r^2 = 0.51$. (N = 29). Notice the different cell loss rates at different periods of time during aging.

nificantly reduced (Fig. 1 – C, Table 1), reflecting an average rate of cone loss at 16 cones/mm$^2$ per year. The cone data are best fit with a straight line (Fig. 1 – C), suggesting a uniform rate of cone loss. Cones are reduced by 6.7 % at the 4th decade and 23 % by the 9th decade (from 4,900 cones/mm$^2$ at the 2nd decade to 3,760 cones/mm$^2$ by the 9th decade). Thus, rod loss during aging is more pronounced and occurs much earlier than cone loss.

Linear regression analysis yields a significant negative slope of RPE densities (Fig. 1 – D, Table 1), suggesting that approximately 14 RPE/mm$^2$ are lost per year. The RPE data are also best fit with a straight line (Fig. 1 – D) which reflects a uniform rate of equatorial RPE loss during aging. The average photoreceptor density from all our data indicated 22 rods and 1 cone were subtended by each RPE cell in the equatorial retina (Table 2).

Cell densities in the GCL (ganglion cells and displaced amacrine cells) were determined on tangential sections in the equatorial GCL. Linear regression analysis shows a highly significant decline during aging (P = 0.0001), with a total average loss rate of 5.6 cells/mm$^2$ per year (Fig. 1 – E, Table 1). The GCL cell data are also best fit by logarithmic plotting (Fig. 1 – F) which indicates a nonuniform rate of cell loss. The GLC cell loss is rapid from the 2nd to 4th decade, with a slower loss rate after the 4th decade. From the logarithmic model, about 18.4 % of GCL cell loss occurs between the 2nd and 4th decades, and by the 9th decade nearly 40 % of the GCL cells are lost (from 1,030 cells/mm$^2$ at the 2nd decade to 620 cells/mm$^2$ at the 9th decade). This indicates that about 46 % of total GCL cell loss occurs between the 2nd to 4th decade.

**The fovea.** Peak cone density was determined by counting hexagonal and/or circular profiles at the level of the inner or outer segments in the foveal center. Linear regression analysis of foveal cone density (Fig.2 – A) does not indicate a significant negative slope (P=0.516, Table 1). Further, the data from the 2nd, 4th, and 6th decade groups were combined to form an "early age group" and these data were compared separately with the individual values from the 7th, 8th, and 9th decade groups, respectively. The Mann-Witney test reveals no significant difference between any of these comparisons. These findings suggest that foveal cone density does not show a significant decrease with aging by the 9th decade. The stability of cone density in the fovea is also evident in some of the data from the individual samples. The high variability of the foveal cone density not withstanding, it is noteworthy that the oldest donor tissue sampled (95 years) had approximately the same foveal cone density as one of the youngest samples (19 years).

To measure RPE density change in the fovea, we counted RPE cells at the foveal center and in areas around the center along two radii that were at right angle to each other. Twelve eyes from the six decade groups are evaluated and in each sample the RPE at the foveal center shows the highest density. The PRE density is reduced by 9.7 % 60 μm away from the foveal center, and by 16.3 % 120 μm away from the center

Table 2: RPE density and photoreceptor/RPE ratios in the retinal equator

| Decade | RPE (mm$^2$) | Photoreceptor/RPE | Rod/RPE | Cone/RPE |
|--------|-------------|-------------------|---------|----------|
| 2nd | 5,490±320 | 26.28 | 25.35 | 0.93 |
| 4th | 4,700±940 | 22.22 | 21.38 | 0.85 |
| 6th | 4,750±730 | 22.66 | 21.70 | 0.95 |
| 7th | 4,650±530 | 22.02 | 22.01 | 0.94 |
| 8th | 4,155±1,040 | 23.07 | 22.15 | 0.91 |
| 9th | 4,510±460 | 21.00 | 20.21 | 0.78 |
| Mean | 4,710±670 | 22.88 | 22.13 | 0.89 |

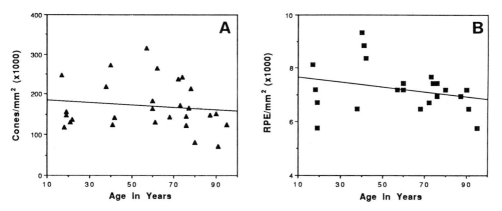

Fig.2. Graphic representation of cone and RPE cell densities at the foveal center as a function of age. Linear regression and ANOVA analyses did not reveal any significant differences in cell densities among the six age groups studied.
A. Peak cone density as a function of age. The slight decline with age is not significant (P=0.516). Note the marked variability among donors of similar age. (N=28)
B. Fovea RPE density as a function of age. No significant density changes are observed (P=0.245). Note that the density shows a slight increase from the 2nd to 4th decade, and a slight decrease from the 6th through to the 9th decade. (N=22).

(Fig. 3) with only 0–2 RPE cell difference at two directions per counting window (57 x 61 μm), resulting in circular isodensity contours; whereas peak cone density declines faster along the vertical than the horizontal meridian according to previous report, resulting in horizontal elliptical isodensity contours (CURCIO et al. 1990 b). From the data of ØSTERBERG (1935) and CURCIO et al. (1990 b), peak cone density decreases about 23 % to 26 % within 60 μm from the foveal center along the nasal and temporal meridian, and about 44 % to 49 % at 120 μm from the center (Fig. 3). Thus, the area in which RPE density is maximal is usually larger than the area in which foveal cones are present in the highest density. While the foveal cone and RPE cell densities are highest in the foveal center and both decrease from that point toward the perifovea, a more pronounced decrease occurs in the foveal cone population than was observed in the RPE cell density which occurs over the same distance (Fig. 3). The RPE densities at the foveal center for each age group are shown in Table 3. Linear regression analysis (Fig. 2 – B) does not show a significant negative slope of foveal RPE density (P = 0.245, Table 1). Further, the data of the 2nd, 4th, and 6th decade, when grouped together as an "early age group" and compared with Mann-Witney test with the RPE density values from the 7th, 8th, or 9th decades, respectively, show no significant difference. All of these comparisons support the interpretation that foveal RPE density is relatively stable from the 2nd through the 9th decade.

Table 3: Foveal cone and RPE cell densities ($mm^2$)

| Decade | Cone density range | Cones (mean) | RPE | Cones/RPE |
|---|---|---|---|---|
| 2nd | 121,678 - 255,227 | 161,047 | 7,170±1,033 | 22.46 |
| 4th | 127,613 - 281.936 | 195,378 | 8,534±1,302 | 22.89 |
| 6th | 135,775 - 325,464 | 218,583 | 7,501±145 | 29.14 |
| 7th | 148.882 - 251.024 | 205,637 | 7,294±589 | 28.19 |
| 8th | 83,592 - 253,249 | 171,192 | 7,418±248 | 23.08 |
| 9th | 74,193 - 156,550 | 127,800 | 6,798±651 | 18.80 |
| Mean | 74,193 - 325,464* | 179,940 | 7,452±661 | 24.09 |

* The range of foveal cone density of six decade groups.

RPE cell density from the foveal center was also compared with RPE density at the equator. The Mann-Witney test shows a significantly higher RPE density at the foveal center than at the equator in each age group studied. The RPE density at the foveal center is about 63 % higher than at the equator based on paired t-test. The equatorial photoreceptors/RPE ratio and the cones/RPE ratio at the foveal center were also compared since the latter was reported higher than the former in a recent study (DOREY et al. 1989). We noted no significant difference between equatorial photoreceptors/RPE ratio and foveal cones/RPE ratio in any decade group studied.

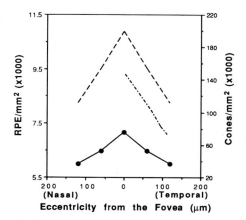

Fig. 3. Eccentricity of foveal RPE density based on an analysis of 12 eyes from six age groups. The RPE density decreases by 9.7% and 16.3%, at positions 60 μm and 120 μm away from the foveal center, respectively. The data from ØSTERBERG (1935, dot-dashed line) and CURCIO et al. (1990b, dashed line) indicate that peak cone density decreases about 23% to 26% 60 μm and 44% to 49% 120 μm away from the foveal center along the nasal and temporal meridian. Thus the change in RPE density from the fovea to perifovea is less pronounced than the density decrease that occurs in the foveal cone population over the same distance. Additionally, the area in which RPE density is maximal, is usually larger than the area over which foveal cones are present in the highest density.

Two sample paired t-test shows that photoreceptors/RPE ratio at the equator was not different from the cones/RPE ratio at the foveal center.

## Discussion

**The retinal equator.** Since the initial report by ØSTERBERG (1935), several studies have been published which evaluate cell density in tangentially sectioned retinas or in retinal whole mounts using a small number of eyes (CURCIO et al. 1990b; FARBER et al. 1985). Unlike topographic studies, cone and rod photoreceptors densities have not generally been differentially assessed in aging studies of human retina; instead photoreceptor densities have been evaluated in radial sectioned retinas without distinguishing rods or cones (GARTNER and HENKIND 1981; DOREY et al. 1989). Reduction in thickness of the outer nuclear layer and displacement of photoreceptor nuclei into the interphotoreceptor matrix were reported to occur more often in older eyes, (GARTNER and HENKIND 1981) although the latter was not considered as an age-related phenomenon by other authors (DOREY et al. 1989). We have evaluated equatorial cone and rod densities separately. Our rod density values are higher than previous topographic studies of corresponding age groups (Table 4). The rod density from CURCIO et al. (1990b) study was underestimated since the tis-

Table 4: Equatorial and foveal photoreceptor and the GCL cell densities (mm$^2$)

| Data | Age (Years) | Equatorial | | | Foveal | |
|------|-------------|-------|-------|-----|------------|-----|
|      |             | Rods  | Cones | GCL | Peak cones | GCL |
| Østerberg (1935) | 16 | 78,731* | 4,262* | | 147,300 | |
| Curcio et al (1990b) | 35±4.5 (27-44) | 87,000† | 4,000† | | 98,200- 324,100 | |
| Stone & Johnston (1981) | NA | | | 500⊕ | | |
| Curcio & Allen (1990) | 33.8±4 (27-37) | | | 400§ | | 35,100§ |
| This report | 18.9±1.8 (17-22) | 131,500 | 4,900 | 1,030 | 121,678- 255,227 | 34,000 |
|  | 41.3±2.2 (38-44) | 112,100 | 4,570 | 840 | 127,613- 281.936 | 28,500¶ |

* The data were taken from the temporal retina 12 mm from the fovea and were corrected for tissue shrinkage.

† The data were taken from the temporal retina 13 mm from the fovea and were not corrected for tissue expansion which was 2-12%. Thus the data were underestimated to a certain extent.

⊕ This data reflects cell counts in the GCL from temporal retinal 13 mm away from the fovea and was not corrected for tissue shrinkage.

§ These data reflect ganglion cell counts from the temporal retina 13 mm away from the fovea and 1 mm around the fovea, respectively. Counts were not corrected for tissue expansion (2-6% areal expansion).

Our data from the 2nd, 4th (photoreceptors and equatorial GCL cells) and 6th decades (foveal GCL cells¶) are chosen for comparison with results from other authors in corresponding age groups. Notice that our equatorial rod and the GCL cell densities are higher than those from other authors, see text for explanation.

sue expansion (up to 12%) was not corrected; and the density from Østerberg's 1935 study was from only one eye. Equatorial cone densities from our study are in agreement with the densities reported by ØSTERBERG (1935) and CURCIO et al. (1990 b). Our data indicate that from the 2nd decade, equatorial cones decrease at a uniform rate of 16/mm$^2$ per year (Fig. 1 – C); whereas equatorial rods demonstrate a nonuniform rate, 970/mm$^2$ per year between the 2nd and 4th decades and 570 – 330/mm$^2$ per year thereafter (Fig. 1 – B). Our analysis indicates that by the 4th decade rod density is already significantly reduced by approximately 15%, whereas cone density is only 7% lower at this decade. Thus, rods appear to be more vulnerable to loss during aging than are cones. No previous report of rod loss during aging has appeared, although increased rod outer segment membrane convolutions have been reported as an age related change (MARSHALL et al. 1979). Our data are the first to clearly indicate that rod loss occurs during aging and that the rod population is significantly reduced relatively early in life. A reduction of rod density may in part explain why an age related elevation in dark adaptation threshold has been observed (MCFARLAND et al. 1960). Our finding of significant age related rod loss is compatible with the interpretation that at least a part of the reduction in rod threshold sensitivity which occurs during aging could be due to the loss of rods.

Reports on RPE cell density changes in the peripheral retina with age have been inconsistent. Previous studies, using a variety of methods, report that equatorial RPE density increases (TSO and FRIEDMAN 1968), decreases (Streeten 1969), or does not change (DOREY et al. 1989) with age. Our data indicate that equatorial RPE density decreases at a rate of about 14 RPE cells/mm$^2$ per year from the 2nd to 9th decade (Fig. 1-D). The discrepancy between our findings and previous reports (DOREY et al. 1989; Tso and Friedman, 1968) may be related to the relatively small number of eyes analyzed by these investigators. In contrast Streeten used a large sample size (35 eyes) and the results she reported are similar to our findings (STREETEN 1969). Thus, RPE cell loss from the peripheral retina during aging is evident if adequate numbers of tissues are analyzed.

Previous studies on ganglion cell density changes with age utilized ganglion cell axon counts taken from cross sections of the optic nerve. Most reports indicated that ganglion cell axon density decreased significantly with age (BALAZSI et al. 1984; DOLMAN et al. 1980; JOHNSON et al. 1987), while others observed that axon density was not significantly altered during aging (REPKA and QUIGLEY 1989; QUIGLEY et al. 1982). Our ganglion cell density data, taken from nuclear counts in the GCL within the retina, indicate that significant loss of GCL cells occurs during aging, with 40% loss at the equator from the 2nd to 9th decade (Fig. 1 – E and F), and 16% loss around the fovea from the 2nd to 6th decade. A recent study, using retinal whole mounts, reports that the total number of ganglion cells in the central 44° of the retina in eyes from older donors (aged 66 – 86 years) overlaps the lower end of the range of young eyes (aged 27 – 37 years), suggesting some decline in ganglion cell density with age (DRUCKER and CURCIO 1990). It should be noted, however, that with the histological method used in our study, ganglion cells could not be distinguished from the displaced amacrine cells in the GCL, which may represent 3% of the total cells at the central retina and 60% or more at the equator in the GCL (WASSLE et al. 1989; CURCIO and ALLEN 1990). Thus, our foveal GCL cell density is in good agreement with the foveal ganglion cell density of a recent study on human ganglion cell topography (CURCIO and ALLEN 1990); whereas our equatorial GCL cell density is higher than the ganglion cell density at comparable eccentricity in their study (CURCIO and ALLEN 1990; STONE and JOHNSTON, 1981; see Table 4).

Additional techniques will be required to clarify the true ganglion cell loss during aging in the GCL.

**The fovea.** Cone density in the fovea has been extensively studied in monkey (CURCIO et al. 1987; YOUNG 1971; ADAMS et al. 1974; ORDY et al. 1980; WIKLER et al. 1990) and human eyes (Curcio et al. 1990 b; Øsertberg 1935; Curcio et al. 1987; FARBER et al. 1985; YUODELIS and HENDRICKSON 1986; AHNELT et al. 1987). However, only a few reports describe the density of foveal cones during aging and the conclusions reached in these studies are far from consistent (GARTNER and HENKIND 1981; DOREY et al. 1989; CURCIO et al. 1990 a). Gartner and Henkind (GARTNER and HENKIND 1981) performed a qualitative study of nuclei in the ONL around the fovea of 104 eyes aged 3 to 96 years. Based on subjective criteria, eyes were separated into one of three categories defined as showing either "marked", "moderate" or "no" foveal cone loss. They reported that 30% of the eyes (24/81) above 40 years of age had marked or moderate loss of foveal cone nuclei. Since no numerical data were taken in this study, no statistical analysis was performed to support their conclusions and the authors failed to appreciate the wide ranges of cone densities which characterize the human fovea, their claims that a substantial loss of foveal cones occurs during the course of aging is not supported by any objective data. Because of the shortcomings of the Gartner and Henkind (GARTNER and HENKIND 1981) study, the conclusions reached in this paper cannot be accepted.

In contrast to the above referenced study, a recent report by Dorey et al. (DOREY et al. 1989) using quantitative analysis and statistical comparisons reports that no significant changes were observed in the foveal cone density of 18 donor eyes at ages spanning the 1st to 8th decade of life. Our data indicate that cone density at the foveal center is not significantly altered between the 2nd to the 9th decade of life, although the density tends to decline slightly between the 6th to the 9th decade (Fig. 2 – A). One additional recent abstract (CURCIO et al. 1990 a) employing flat mounted retina for the analysis of foveal cone density, also reported that no significant loss of foveal cones occurs during aging.

Based on linear regression analysis, we estimate from our data an average loss of 10 – 20 cones per year from the rod-free zone in the fovea, an area of 260 – 350 μm in diameter (CURCIO et al. 1990 b; ØSTERBERG 1935). Because the variability of cone density in each age group was quite large, up to 3 fold (Table 3), one might argue that the high variability would limit our ability to detect foveal cone loss during aging. Linear regression analysis indicates that from the 2nd to 9th decade at least $20 \pm 3\%$ of total cone population or 30 – 50 cones per year, would have to be lost from the rod-free zone before a significant difference could be demonstrated; whereas our data reflect only a $7 \pm 1\%$ loss of the cone population in the region. We must conclude from these analyses that foveal cones are relatively stable, although wide ranges in foveal cone density are present among the various samples evaluated.

Curcio et al. (CURCIO et al. 1990 b) recently analyzed photoreceptor topography in retinal flat mounts from 8 human eyes aged 27 to 44 years, viewed with Nomarski differential interference contrast microscopy. Her methodology allows for optical sections to be evaluated at various retinal depths along tangential planes identical to the orientation of the microtome sections of retinas used in our analysis. They also observed large individual variability in foveal cone density, up to 3.3 fold. The fovea from a 44 year old donor had the highest cone density, whereas the fovea from a 27 year donor had the lowest cone density (CURCIO et al. 1990 b). Thus, the variability in the density of foveal cones between individuals does not appear to be due to cell loss during aging, but may instead be related to individual variability in the number of cones which are incorporated into the fovea during maturation of this specialized region during late fetal and early postnatal life. The high individual variability which we and others have observed in foveal cone density may in part be due to a difference in rate, timing or extent of cone recruitment into the fovea during histogenesis (CURCIO et al. 1987; YUODELIS and HENDRICKSON 1986; PACKER et al 1990). Thus, our data are consistent with the interpretation that foveal cone density is very stable through the 9th decade of life although variability among the individual samples is quite large. While our studies did not extend beyond the 9th decade, a recent report by Feeny-Burns et al. demontrated a significant loss of foveal cones by 36 % by comparing foveal photoreceptor densities in 8 eyes from 49 to 68 years of age with 14 eyes from 90 to 101 years of age taken from radial sections (FEENEY-BURNS et al. 1990). Thus, beyond the 9th decade, it is very likely that the foveal cone density declines as Feeny-Burns et al. have reported (FEENEY-BURNS et al. 1990)

Earlier reports (TSO and FRIEDMAN 1968; STREETEN 1969) indicated that foveal RPE density increases from the 2nd to 4th decade. A casual view of our data from this period would tend to support these previous reports, however, the statistical analysis of our data does not support this interpretation. None of the methods we employed revealed any significant change in foveal RPE cell density from the 2nd to 9th decade (Fig. 2 – B).

It is generally held that age-related macular degeneration (AMD) is associated with cone photoreceptor loss in the fovea and its prevalence increases with age (MARSHALL 1987; MARSHALL 1985; YOUNG 1987; YOUNG 1988). Some authors suggested that AMD may be due to accelerated aging in human retina (MARMOR 1982). Accelerated aging should follow the same pattern of cell loss that occurs in normal aging, but this is not the pattern observed in the present study. Our findings indicate that rods and ganglion cells show a more accelerated loss during aging than do cones, and the loss of foveal cones is less pronounced than loss of rods or cones in the periphery. Thus, AMD must be due to some unique defect specific to the macula, which may be age related but not necessarily due to an accelerated aging process throughout the retina.

Above all, our study shows that equatorial rods, cones and RPE cells decrease in density from the 2nd to 9th decade of life; whereas cone and RPE cells in the fovea appear to be more stable over this same period. These results suggest that cell loss during aging at the fovea and equator are distinctly different. The reasons for these different patterns of cell loss remain to be determined.

## Summary

Cell loss from the human retina was examined in foveal and temporal equatorial regions in eyes from 35 donors with ages spanning a 78 year period, from the second into the ninth decade of life. At the equator, cones and retinal pigment epithelial cells (RPE) are lost at relatively uniform rates (16 and 14 cells/mm$^2$/year, respectively). In contrast, rods and cells in the ganglion cell layer (GCL) decrease at non-uniform rates. Between the 2nd to 4th decades, rods and the GCL cells are lost at rates of 970 and 9 cells/mm$^2$/year, respectively, which slows to 570-330 and 6-3 cells/mm$^2$/year, respectively, thereafter. In the fovea, no significant decrease in cone or RPE cell density was detected at the foveal center from the 2nd to 9th decade, suggesting that these cells are stable throughout this period. Foveal RPE density was significantly higher than equatorial RPE density in each age group. Cells in the GCL surrounding the fovea decrease by about 16% from the 2nd to 6th decade. Our results indicate that rod photoreceptors and cells in the GCL are more vulnerable to loss during aging than are cones and that photoreceptor loss accompanying aging is less pronounced in the fovea than in the peripheral retina.

## Acknowledgments

This study was supported by grants from the National Eye Institute, National Institute of Health, Bethesda, MD; The Retinitis Pigmentosa Foundation Fighting Blindness, Baltimore, MD; the Retina Research Foundation, Houston, TX; Research to Prevent Blindnes, New York, NY and the Chatlos Foundation, Longwood, FL. JGH is a recipient of the Alcon Research Institute Award.

## References

ADAMS, C. K., J. M. PEREZ, M. N. HAWTHORNE (1974): Rod and cone densities in the rhesus. Invest. Ophthalmol. *13:* 885 – 888.

AHNELT, P. K., H. KOLB, R. PELUG (1987): Identification of a subtype of cone photoreceptor, likely to be blue sensitive, in the human retina. J. Comp. Neurol. *255:* 18 – 34.

BALAZSI, A. G., J. ROOTMAN, S. M. DRANCE, M. SCHULZER, G. R. DOUGLAS (1984): The effect of age on the nerve fiber population of the human optic nerve. Am J. Ophthalmol. *97:* 760 – 772.

CURCIO, C. A., K. R. SLOAN, O. PACKER, A. E. HENDRICKSON, R. E. KALINA (1987): Distribution of cones in human and monkey retina: individual variability and radial asymmetry. Science *236:* 579 – 581.

CURCIO, C. A., K. A. ALLEN (1990): Topopgraphy of Ganglion cells in human retina. J. Comp. Neurol. *300:* 5 – 25.

CURCIO, C. A., K. A. ALLEN, R. E. KALINA (1990 a): Reorganization of the human photoreceptor mosaic following age related rod loss. Invest. Ophthalmol. Vis. Sci. *31:* (suppl): 38 – 38.

CURCIO, C. A., K. R. SLOAN, R. E. KALINA, A. E. HENDRICKSON (1990 b): Human photoreceptor topography. J. Comp. Neurol. *292:* 497 – 523.

DOLMAN, C. L., A. Q. MCCORMICK, S. M. DRANCE (1980): Aging of the optic nerve. Arch. Ophthalmol. *98:* 2053 – 2058.

DOREY, C. K., G. WU, D. EBENSTEIN, A. GARSD, J. J. WEITER (1989): Cell loss in the aging retina: Relationship to lipofuscin accumulation and macular degeneration. Invest. Ophthalmol. Vis. Sci. *30:* 1691 – 1699.

DRUCKER, D. N., C. C. A. (1990): Retinal ganglion cells are lost with aging but not in Alzheimer's disease. Invest. Ophthalmol. Vis. Sci. *31* (suppl): 356 – 356.

FARBER, D. B., J. G. FLANNERY, R. N. LOLLEY, D. BOK (1985): Distribution patterns of photoreceptors, protein, and cyclic nucleotides in the human retina. Invest. Ophthalmol. Vis. Sci. *26:* 1558 – 1568.

FEENY-BURNS, L., R. P. BURNS, C. GAO (1990): Age-related macular changes in humans over 90 years old. Am. J. Ophthalmol. *109:* 265 – 278.

FEENEY-BURNS, L., E. S. HILDERBRAND, S. ELDRIDGE (1984): Aging human RPE: Morphometric analysis of macular, equitorial, and peripheral cells. Invest. Ophthalmol. Vis. Sci. *25:* 195 – 200.

GAO, H., J. G. HOLLYFIELD (1992): Aging of the human retina: Differential loss of neurons and retinal pigment epithelial cells. Invest. Ophthalmol. Vis. Sci. *33:* 1 – 17.

GARTNER, S., P. HENKIND (1981): Aging and degeneration of the human macula. 1. Outer nuclear layer and photoreceptors. Br. J. Ophthalmol. *65:* 23 – 28.

JOHNSON, B. M., M. MIAO, A. A. SADUN (1987): Age-related decline of human optic nerve axon populations. Age *10:* 5 – 9.

KILBRIDE, P. E., L. P. HUTMAN, M. FISHMAN, J. S. READ (1986): Foveal cone pigment density difference in the aging human eye. Vis. Res. *26:* 321 – 325.

MARMOR, M. F. (1982): Aging and the retina. *In:* Aging and Human Visual Function, R. SEKULER, D. KLINE, K. DISMUKES, New York: Alan R. Liss, Inc., pp. 59 – 78.

MARSHALL, J. (1985): Light damage and ageing in the human macula. Res. Clin. For. *7:* 27 – 43.

MARSHALL, J. (1987): The ageing retina: Physiology or pathology. Eye *1:* 282 – 290.

MARSHALL, J., J. GRINDLE, P. ANSELL, B. BORWEIN (1979): Convolution in human rods: an ageing process. Br. J. Ophthalmol. *63:* 181 – 187.

MCFARLAND, R. A., R. G. DOMEY, A. B. WARREN, D. C. WARD (1960): Dark adaptation as a function of age: I. A. statistical analysis. J. Gerontol. *15:* 149 – 154.

ORDY, J., K. BRIZZEE (1979): Functional and structural age differences in the visual system of man and nonhuman primate models. In: KR, O. J. a. B. (Eds): Sensory systems and communication in the elderly (Aging). New York: Raven Press, pp. 13 – 50.

ORDY, J. M., K. R. BRIZZEE, J. HANSCHE (1980): Visual acuity and foveal cone density in the retina of the aged rhesus monkey. Neurobiol. Aging *1:* 133 – 140.

ØSTERBERG, G. A. (1935): Topopgraphy of the layer of rods and cones in the human retina. Acta. Ophthalmol. *13:* (suppl 6): 1 – 103.

PACKER, O., A. E. HENDRICKSON, C. A. CURCIO (1990): Developmental redistribution of photoreceptors across the *Macaca Nemestrina* (Pigtail Macaque) retina. J. Comp. Neurol. *298:* 472 – 493.

QUIGLEY, H. A., E. M. ADDICKS, W. R. GREEN (1982): Optic nerve damage in human glaucoma III. Quantitative correlation of nerve fiber loss and visual field defect in glaucoma, ischemic neuropathy, papilledema, and toxic neuropathy. Arch. Ophthalmol. *100:* 135 – 146.

REPKA, M. X., H. A. QUIGLEY (1989): The effect of age on normal human optic nerve fiber number and diameter. Ophthalmol. *96:* 26 – 31.

STONE, J., E. JOHNSTON (1981): The topography of primate retina: A study of the human, bushbaby, and new- and old-world monkeys. J. Comp. Neurol. *196:* 205 – 223.

STREETEN, B.W. (1969): Development of the human retinal pigment epithelium and the posterior segment. Arch. Ophthalmol. *81:* 383 – 394.

TSO, M. O. M., E. FRIEDMAN (1968): The retinal pigment epithelium. III. Growth and development. Arch. Ophthalmol. *80:* 214 – 216.

WASSLE, H., U. GRUNERT, J. ROHRENBECK, B. B. BOYCOTT (1989): Cortical magnification factor and the ganglion cell density of the primate Nature *341:* 643 – 646.

WIKLER, K. C., R. W. WILLIAMS, P. RAKIC (1990): Photoreceptor mosaic: Number and distribution of rods and cones in the rhesus monkey retina. J. Comp. Neurol. *297:* 499 – 508.

YOUNG, R.W. (1971): The renewal of rod and cone outer segments in the rhesus monkey. J. Cell. Biol. *49:* 303 – 318.

YOUNG, R.W. (1987): Pathophysiology of Age-related Macular Degeneration. Surv. Ophthalmol. *31:* 291 – 306.

YOUNG, R.W. (1988): Solar Radiation and Age-related Macular Degeneration. Surv. Ophthalmol. *32:* 252 – 269.

YOUDELIS, C., A. E. HENDRICKSON (1986): A qualitavtive and quantitative analysis of the human fovea during development. Vision Res. *26:* 847 – 855.

*Department of Physiology and Medical Biophysics, Uppsala University, Uppsala, Schweden*

# Blood supply and nutrition
# of the retina in rabbits: Effects of light

L. WANG, A. BILL and G. O. SPERBER

## Introduction

The nutrition of the retina is unusually complex and the solution of the problem of supplying the retina with nutrients and elimination of metabolites differs between species. In primates and many other species such as cats, dogs and pigs there is supply both by diffusion from the choroid and from the blood vessels in the retina itself. In rabbits, however, the so called retinal vessels are only distributed within two wing-shaped regions characterized by myelinated nerve fibers. These vessels may thus be regarded as an extension of the blood vessels of the optic nerve (ROHEN 1954) and are likely to take little or no part in the nutrition of the retina proper. In birds, finally, there are no retinal blood vessels (see KREBS 1972).

The metabolic rate of the retina is unusually high with both oxygen and glucose being required for normal function in mammals. WARBURG, POSENER and NEGELEIN (1924) were the first to observe that even under conditions of ample oxygen supply isolated retinal tissue produces lactate. They suspected this to be an artifact caused by the in vitro environment. A number of later investigators also studying isolated retinas have confirmed the observation of Warburg et al. but regarded the lactate formation to be an effect of aerobic glycolysis, which is lactate formation despite the presence of oxygen (see WINKLER 1988).

KREBS (1972) studied retinal metabolism both in vitro and in vivo. He found that under in vitro conditions the avian retina had a low respiration and a very high production of lactic acid when compared to rats and rabbits. In experiments with rabbits the problem of retinal lactate formation in vivo was approached and KREBS was able to demonstrate that blood collected from an opened vortex vein contained more lactate than blood from an artery. Calculations of lactate productions based on flow values previously given and a comparison with data for lactate production in the lens, cornea, sclera and anterior uvea, indicated that most of the lactate formed within the eye originated in the retina. The relative role of aerobic glycolysis and oxidative metabolism could not be determined since no data were presented for the oxygen consumption.

It could be argued that the observations by Krebs were proof of physiological lactate formation rather than aerobic glycolysis since there might be regions of the retina that were anoxic due to the lack of retinal vessels as discussed above. However, recent studies on the oxygen tension in the vitreous body close to the retina have shown that it is about 9 mmHg (TILLIS et al, 1988). Such observations suggest that there are significant amounts of oxygen present even in the inner layers of the rabbit retina and that the experiments of Krebs in fact demonstrated aerobic glycolysis under conditions with oxygen available throughout the whole retina.

Lactate production in the tissues drained by the vortex vein was observed during experiments using pigs also by TÖRNQUIST and ALM (1979). In an experiment in which blood was collected from a vortex vein under conditions with normal laboratory light and with minimal trauma to the eye they found a small negative arteriovenous concentration difference of −100 μmol/l. Calculations of oxygen and glucose consumptions indicated that 63% of the glucose extracted by the retina was not oxidized.

Most previous in vivo studies of retinal metabolism have been carried out under ordinary laboratory light conditions. Recent studies with the $^{14}$C-deoxyglucose method described by SOKOLOFF (1985) on the glucose metabolism under different light conditions have indicated that, at least in monkeys, retinal metabolism is lower under conditions of constant light than in darkness or flickering light (BILL and SPERBER 1990). Choroidal blood flow has been reported to be unaffected by switching from darkness to light in rabbits (MARIMOTO 1991) but the oxygen tension in the vitreous body increased about 2 mmHg under such conditions (TILLIS et al 1988). This observation suggests that even in darkness oxygen is available in all parts of the rabbit retina.

The enhanced $^{14}$C-deoxyglucose uptake which was observed in monkey eye under conditions of darkness was located in the outer retina and might be explained by a higher energy requirement in darkness caused by stimulation of the active transport of sodium out of the photoreceptors; in darkness the sodium permeability of the outer segments of the rods is higher than in light and the sodium "pumps" have to be more active than in light. This makes the dark-adapted retina very sensitive to alterations in arterial oxygen tension (STEINBERG 1987). Likewise the reason for a lower oxygen tension of the inner retina in rabbits in darkness than in light might be enhanced oxygen consumption by the photoreceptors. Such enhancement will lower the oxygen tension in all parts of the retina inside the region with enhanced metabolism.

Previous studies have indicated that the oxygen extraction from choroidal blood is little affected by moderate reductions in uveal blood flow (ALM and BILL 1970). We report here that the situation is similar in rabbits. This is of importance since a fall in blood pressure and uveal blood flow could not be avoided in the experiments with dark adaptation.

## Methods and results

In rabbits the uvea is drained by four vortex veins and usually one of these veins can be quite easily cannulated. Total uveal blood flow can be calculated as four times the flow observed. However, the cannulation seems to cause a longlasting vasodilatation due to the release of arachidonic acid metabolites. If the animal is pretreated with indomethacin this problem can be avoided (NILSSON and BILL 1984).

The experiments were performed in pigmented rabbits under urethan or pentobarbital anesthesia. Intravenous heparin used to prevent coagulation and indomethacin, 20 mg/kg body weight, were injected. One of the two upper vortex veins was cannulated with a tapered tubing and blood was sampled quantitatively from the tubing into glass capillaries. An ABL 300 Acid-Base analyzer (Radiometer, Copenhagen) was used to determine the oxygen content of arterial and venous blood. Glucose concentrations were determined with the GOD-PAP method and lactate with an enzymatic method (Sigma lactate diagnostic kit, Sigma 735).

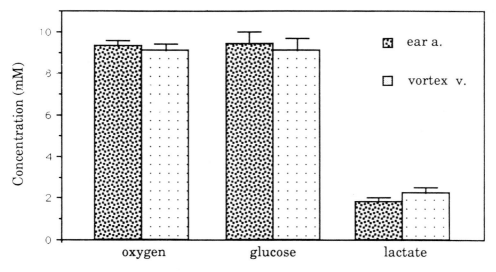

Fig. 1. Concentrations of oxygen, glucose and lactate in blood from an ear artery and a vortex vein in rabbits under urethan anesthesia. Mean ± SEM.

Fig. 1 shows arterial and venous concentrations of oxygen, glucose and lactate. The calculations of arteriovenous concentration differences were complicated by the fact that arterial and venous concentrations of oxygen and glucose were very similar. Table 1 shows data for oxygen and glucose consumptions and lactate formation. The mean arterial blood pressure was $134 \pm 18$ cm $H_2O$. The uveal blood flow was 1.09 ± 0.22 ml/min. Fig. 2 shows the ATP productions calculated on the assumption that aerobic metabolism of glucose resulted in 38 moles ATP/mol glucose, and glucose used in glycolysis with lactate formation resulted in 2 moles ATP/mol glucose used. Glycolysis with lactate formation accounted for about 30 % of the total.

Table 1: Oxygen and glucose consumption and lactate production in the rabbit uvea in laboratory light.

Mean values ± SEM, (n=6)

| | |
|---|---|
| Oxygen consumption | 0.145 ± 0.019 µmol/min |
| Glucose consumption | 0.242 ± 0.035 µmol/min |
| Lactate production | 0.388 ± 0.054 µmol/min |

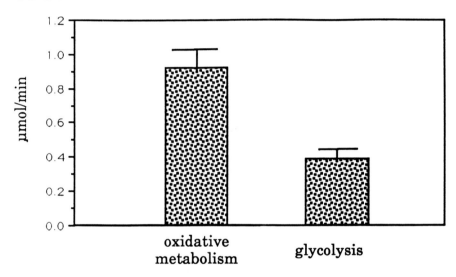

Fig. 2. ATP production from oxidative metabolism and glycolysis with lactate formation in rabbits under urethan anesthesia. Mean ± SEM.

In animals in which there was no replacement of the blood collected there was a fall in blood pressure and also in uveal blood flow. In other experiments the uveal blood flow was changed by increasing the intraocular pressure. The arterio-venous oxygen concentration difference which was very small at high blood flow rates increased with falling flow rates, Fig. 3. However, the oxygen extraction from uveal blood was essentially constant within a wide range of blood flow rates, Fig. 4. These experiments were performed with the animals under urethan anesthesia. It was found that the glucose concentration started to increase rapidly after about an hour even if net blood loss was avoided.

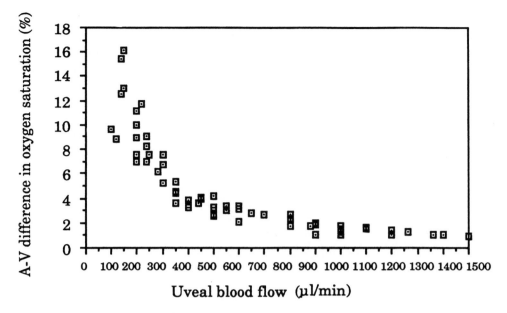

Fig. 3. The arterio-venous difference in oxygen saturation at different uveal blood flow rates in rabbits under urethan anesthesia. Data shown for five animals.

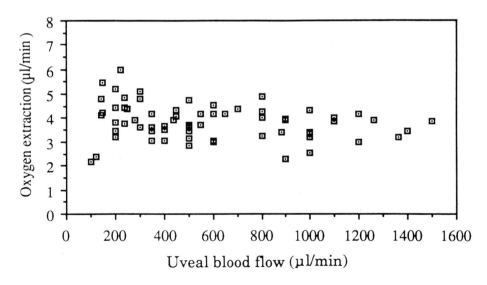

Fig. 4. The oxygen extraction from blood passing through the uvea was relatively constant within a wide range of uveal blood flow rates. Data from the same animals as in fig. 3.

Table 2: Oxygen and glucose consumption and lactate production in the rabbit uvea in darkness and light.

Mean values $\pm$ SEM, (n=5)

|  | Darkness | Light |
|---|---|---|
| Oxygen consumption | 0.067 $\pm$ 0.018 | 0.045 $\pm$ 0.011 µmol/min |
| Glucose consumption | 0.116 $\pm$ 0.019 | 0.106 $\pm$ 0.021 µmol/min |
| Lactate production | 0.19 $\pm$ 0.041 | 0.167 $\pm$ 0.035 µmol/min |
| Uveal blood flow | 0.37 $\pm$ 0.08 | 0.35 $\pm$ 0.10 ml/min |
| MAP | 116 $\pm$ 2.9 | 113 $\pm$ 3.0 cm H$_2$O |

In the experiments with different light conditions we used pentobarbital anesthesia in order to avoid the unstable glucose concentrations found with urethan. In these experiments the animals were first dark-adapted for at least 45 min and then exposed to laboratory light for 5 min. There was no statistically significant effect of

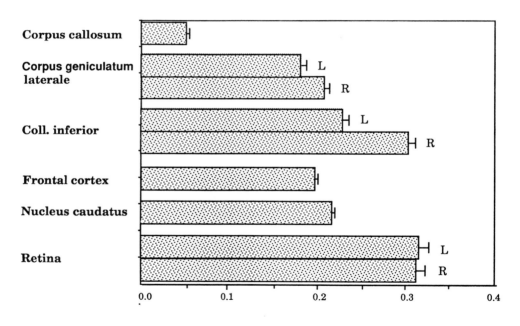

**Optical density**

Fig. 5. The optical density in autoradiographs was determined. The figure shows values for the dark-adapted right retina, R, and the left retina exposed to constant light, L, and for different parts of the rabbit brain. The optical densities of the right lateral geniculate body and the right inferior collicle were significantly higher than on of the left side. Means of at least 10 sections $\pm$ SEM.

this change on uveal blood flow, oxygen extraction, glucose extraction or lactate formation (Table 2). The mean values in light were about half those under urethan anesthesia.

An attempt was made in one pigmented rabbit using the [14]C-deoxyglucose method to find evidence for a change in retinal metabolism caused by constant light. A marginal vein was cannulated for injections of heparin and [14]C-deoxyglucose and an ear artery was cannulated under local anesthesia for blood sampling and measurements of the arterial blood pressure. The right eye was padded and the left eye exposed to white light reflected from a screen at some 8 cm distance resulting in 150 lux at the eye. After 90 min of dark adaptation of the right eye the [14]C-deoxyglucose was injected and blood samples were collected at different times for 40 min. The animal was killed with an overdose of pentobarbital sodium, the head was frozen and sectioned and autoradiographs were prepared as described elsewhere (SPERBER and BILL 1985). Concentrations of labelled material were determined with densitometry of the autoradiographs. Fig. 5 shows a comparison between the retina and different structures in the brain. The data shown for the retina are from a 18 mm long, 200 μm wide horizontal region located below the wing-shaped area containing the retinal blood vessels. There was no difference in optical

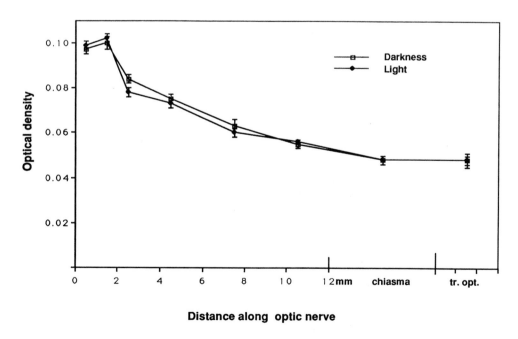

**Distance along optic nerve**

Fig. 6. The optical density in autoradiographs was determined. Values are shown for the optic nerves at different distances from the lamina cribrosa. Means of at least 10 sections ± SEM.

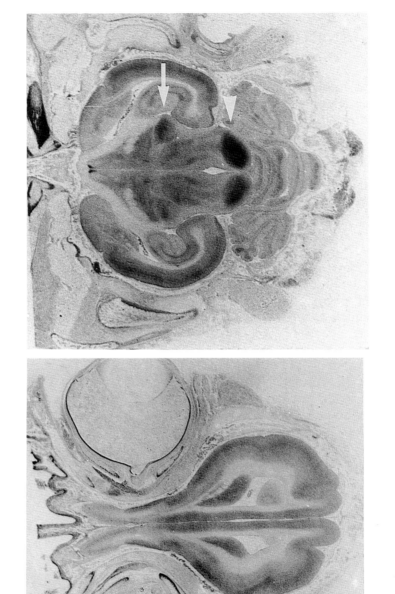

Fig. 7. Autoradiographs of horizontal sections through rabbit head. The concentrations of labelled material were higher in the right lateral geniculate body (arrow) and the right inferior collicle (arrow head) compared to the same structures on the left side. In the retina the concentrations were high on both sides. The left eye was exposed to light, the right was dark adapted.

density, which indicates that there was no difference in glucose consumption. The data for the optic nerve are shown in Fig. 6. There was a fall in optical density along both nerves but no major differences between the two sides. In the brain there were significantly higher concentrations of labelled material in the lateral geniculate body on the right side as compared to the left. The values for average optical density in 21 sections were $0.207 \pm 0.06$ and $0.180 \pm 0.005$ units on the right and left sides, respectively. There was also a significant difference in the inferior collicles with $0.302 \pm 0.008$ units on the right side and $0.228 \pm 0.007$ on the left. Fig. 7 shows an autoradiograph of the brain with these parts included. In the rabbit there is complete crossing of the nerve fibers from the eyes and the results thus indicate that constant light caused activation of the contralateral lateral geniculate body and inferior collicle.

## Discussion

In rabbits most parts of the retina have to be supplied by diffusion from the choroid, even the innermost layers, since there is no direct supply via retinal blood vessels and supply via the vitreous can be assumed to be very small. As mentioned, lactate production by the retina has been observed in many in vitro studies and in vivo studies in rabbits and pigs have shown that lactate is added to the blood on its way from the arteries to the vortex veins.

The results of our study confirm that in rabbits lactate is produced in the tissues drained by the vortex veins. The lactate production under urethan anesthesia was about twice that under pentobarbital anesthesia, which may be explained by the inhibitory effects of pentobarbital anesthesia on the metabolism of the retina (SPERBER and BILL 1985). The rates of lactate formation, 0.39 μmol/min under urethan and 0.18 μmol/min under pentobarbital anesthesia are lower than that of 0.65 μmol/min calculated by Krebs. According to Krebs the in vitro aerobic lactate formation in the retina is about 0.5 μmol/min and that of the other ocular structures about 0.17 μmol/min. Part of the lactate produced by the lens and the other tissues of the anterior segment leaves the eye with the aqueous humor. It seems likely therefore that about 50% of the lactate production observed in the experiments reported here performed with urethan anesthesia was due to lactate formation in the retina. However, under pentobarbital anesthesia most of the lactate produced may very well have originated in the non-retinal part of the eye.

Studies on the oxygen tension in different parts of the retina in cats have shown that there is a minimum tension in the region of the inner segments of the photoreceptors and higher values towards the choroid as well as towards the vascularized the part of the retina (LINSENMEIER 1986). During darkness there was a fall in oxygen tension to very low values. The increase in metabolism under conditions of darkness is probably the result of stimulation of the sodium transporting mechanism discussed above. Recent measurements of the pH in the subretinal space of the cat retina under different light conditions have shown a fall in pH in darkness (STEINBERG 1990). Preliminary observations in cats indicate that in this species there is indeed lactate production in the retina and that this production is enhanced in darkness which may explain the acidification.

At present we can only speculate about the reason for the difference in response to changes in illumination between cats, monkeys and rabbits. It seems likely, however, that in rabbits the oxygen tension of the photoreceptors is higher than in the other species. The whole retina has to be supplied with oxygen from the choroid and consequently there can be no intraretinal minimum in oxygen tension in the outer retina. As a result of a higher oxygen tension in the photoreceptors the extra energy required in darkness may be produced by oxidative phosphorylation. In our experiments the precision of the measurements of oxygen consumption was quite low due to the small arterio-venous concentration differences. The observation by TILLIS et al (1988) in which changes from darkness to light caused only a 2 mmHg change in preretinal oxygen tension indicates that any change in oxygen consumption was very small. Our result obtained with the $^{14}$C-deoxyglucose method support the notion that in rabbits the retinal metabolism in constant light is practically the same as that in darkness.

Our results suggest that in rabbits even under physiological conditions there is lactate formation in the retina and that this lactate production helps to maintain the oxygen tension of the inner retina above zero. The lactate formation appears to be little influenced by the presence of light or darkness but to be reduced by pentobarbital anesthesia.

## Acknowledgements

This study was supported by Grant no. 5 R 001 EY 00475 from the National Eye Institute, U. S. Public Health Service and by Grant no. B 91-04 X-00147 from the Swedish Medical Reasearch Council. We wish to thank Ms. Kristina Andersson and Mr. Alf Johansson for technical assistance.

# References

ALM, A., A. BILL (1970): Blood flow and oxygen extraction in the cat uvea at normal and high intraocular pressures. Acta Physiol. Scand. *80:* 19 – 28.

BILL, A., G. O. SPERBER (1990): Control of retinal and choroidal blood flow. Eye *4:* 319 – 325.

KREBS, H. A. (1972): The Pasteur effect and the relations between respiration and fermentation. In: Essays in Biochemistry, Vol. 8 Pp 1 – 34. Eds. DICKENS, F., P. N. CAMPBELL, Academic Press: New York.

LINSENMEIER, R. A. (1986): Effects of light and darkness on oxygen distribution and consumption in the cat retina. J. Gen. Physiol. *88:* 521 – 542.

MORIMOTO, N. (1991): Study on choroidal blood flow at dark and light adaptation. II. Choroidal blood flow at light adaptation. Nippon Ganka Gakkai Zasshi (Japan) *55:* 235 – 240.

NILSSON, S. F. E., A. BILL (1984): Vasoactive intestinal polypeptide (VIP): Effects in the eye and on regional blood flows. Acta Physiol. Scand. *121:* 385 – 392.

ROHEN, J. (1954): Über das Gefäßsystem der Retina beim Kaninchen. Ophthalmologica *128:* 307 – 317.

SOKOLOFF, L. (1985): Basic principles in imaging of regional cerebral metabolic rates. In: Brain imaging and brain function, 1 – 47 Ed. SOKOLOFF, L., Raven Press: New York.

SPERBER, G. O., A. BILL (1985): Blood flow and glucose consumption in the optic nerve, retina and brain; effects of high intraocular pressure. Exp. Eye Res. *41:* 639 – 653.

STEINBERG, R. H. (1987): Monitoring communications between photoreceptors and pigment epithelial cells: effects of "mild" systemic hypoxia. Invest. Ophthalmol. Vis. Sci 28: 188 – 204.

STEINBERG, R. H. (1990): Effects of light, dark and hypoxia on pH in the subretinal space of the cat. In: Proceedings of the International Society for Eye Research, Ridgefield, N. J., USA. Vol. VI, p. 163, Eds. UUSITALO, H., A. PALKAMA, K. MAHLBERG.

TILLIS, T. N., D. L. MURRAY, G. J. SCHMIDT, J. J. WEITER (1988): Preretinal oxygen changes in the rabbit under conditions of light and dark. Invest. Ophthalmol. Vis. Sci. *29:* 988 – 991.

TÖRNQUIST, P., A. ALM (1979): Retinal and choroidal contribution to retinal metabolism in vivo. A study in pigs. Acta Physiol. Scand. *106:* 315 – 357.

WARBURG, O., K. POSENER, E. NEGELEIN (1924): Über den Stoffwechsel der Carcinomzelle. Biochem. Z. *152:* 309 – 343.

WINKLER, B. S. (1989): Retinal aerobic glycolysis revisited. Invest. Ophthalmol. Vis. Sci. *30:* 1023.

*The Schepens Eye Research Institute and Department of Opthalmology Harvard Medical School Boston, MA*

# Extracellular matrix of the human optic nerve head: Age-related and glaucomatous changes

M. R. HERNANDEZ

Before 1985, there were few focused investigations into the extracellular matrix components of the connective tissue of the optic nerve head. A survey of scleral collagen types in bovine and human eyes gave a brief description of the lamina cribrosa. (KONOMI et al. 1983) In addition, a short report claimed an increase in the collagen content, and perhaps change in composition, in the lamina cribrosa of glaucomatous eyes compared to normal human eyes (TENGROTH and AMMITZBOLL 1984). Recent studies of the biology of the lamina cribrosa have characterized the extracellular matrix components; the cells that are present and their roles in the maintenance of the extracellular matrix materials; the age-related changes; and the response to elevated pressure as measured by biosynthetic parameters.

The extracellular matrix is the structural support that allows groups of cells to function as a tissue. The extracellular matrix is made up of specific macromolecules that are assembled in geometric relationships to provide strength, flexibility, elasticity and surfaces to the tissues that they serve. Study of the extracellular matrix has become a major objective in many laboratories because changes in this structure are related to changes in development, aging, disease, and various aspects of cellular behavior (HAY 1983).

The development of immunohistochemical techniques has allowed the study of the distribution of the macromolecules of the extracellular matrix in different tissues. Using this approach, a specific monoclonal or polyclonal antibody to the macromolecule is reacted with tissue sections or cells in tissue culture. The antibodies distinguish between the different types of collagens as well as the different types of attachment factors and other macromolecules present in the extracellular matrix. To visualize the antibody associated with the antigenic site in the tissue sections, a second antibody directed against the first antibody is tagged with fluorescent or enzyme label and is reacted with the tissue sections or cells in culture.

Using immunofluorescent staining for extracellular matrix components in the human lamina cribrosa, Hernandez and co-workers have provided new insights into the structure of this tissue. In the lamina cribrosa of young adults, the core of the cribriform plates contains substantial amounts of elastin in the form of long fibers (Fig. 1) (HERNANDEZ et al. 1987) which is consistent with the ultrastructural

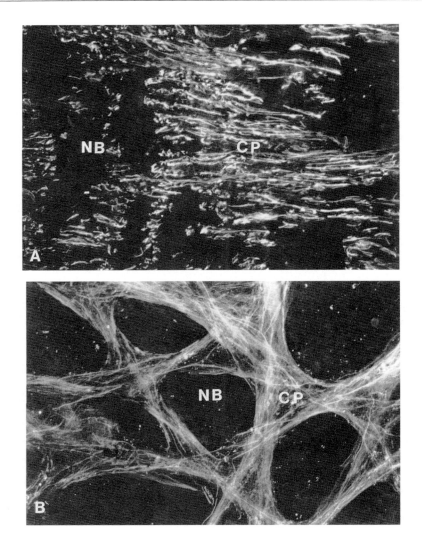

Fig. 1. Immunofluorescent staining for α-elastin in the lamina cribrosa. A, 36 year-old. Sagittal view of the cribriform plates showing fibers of elastin running across the lamina cribrosa. (x370). B, 20 year-old. Cross-sectional view of the cribriform plates showing fibers of eleastin running longitudinally in the core of the plates. NB: nerve bundles; CP; cribriform plates. (x405). (With permission: From HERNANDEZ M. R. et al. 1991).

demonstration of elastic fibers (ANDERSON 1969). Collagen type III co-distributes with elastin, appearing as patches within the core. Collagen type I is present, disposed transversely as fine fibrils in the core of the plates (HERNANDEZ et al. 1986, 1987). These immunohistochemical findings are consistent with the ultrastructural

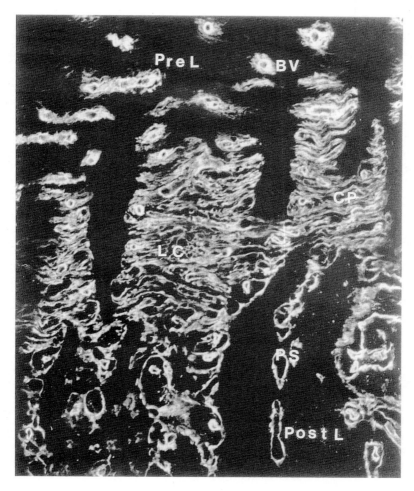

Fig. 2. Immunofluorescent staining for collagen type IV in a sagittal section of the optic nerve head, 49 year old. (x420). In the prelaminar region (PreL), only the blood vessels (BV) show positive staining. In the lamina cribrosa (LC), staining for collagen type IV forms lamellar structures corresponding to the cribriform plates (CP). In the post laminar region (Post L), staining for collagen type IV is observed lining the pial septa (PS) and around blood vessels. (With permission: From HERNANDEZ M. R. et al. 1991)

demonstration of striated collagen fibrils within this tissue (ANDERSON 1969). Within the core of the cribriform plates, the blood vessels are delimited by collagen type IV and laminin, consistent with the distribution of their basement membranes, and are also surrounded by collagen type III and fibronectin. Fibronectin does not appear elsewhere in the cribriform plates of the human lamina cribrosa (HERNANDEZ et al. 1986, 1987).

Separating the core of the cribriform plates from the surrounding astrocytes, there is a well defined continuous layer of collagen type IV and laminin. These lamellar structures of collagen type IV and laminin are apparently part of the basement membranes of the astrocytes and extend lenearly into the core of the cribriform plates forming a network of fibrillar material (Fig. 2) (HERNANDEZ et al. 1986, 1989). A recent report using immunohistochemistry and electron microscopy describes a "mesh-like web of astrocytes processes" piercing the connective tissue of the cribriform plates (ELKINGTON et al. 1990). This is consistent with the reported staining for collagen type IV inside the core of the cribriform plates (HERNANDEZ et al. 1987, 1989, GOLDBAUM et al. 1989).

Hernandez and co-workers (HERNANDEZ et al. 1987) concluded that the extracellular matrix of the lamina cribrosa is quite different than sclera. As an interstitial connective tissue, the extracellular matrix of the sclera is made up primarily of fibrillar forms of collagen, mostly collagen type I, surrounding fibroblasts. The sclera contains no collagen type IV and little elastin. In contrast, the core of the cribriform plates containing elastin, fibrils of collagen type IV, relatively little collagen types I and III and being surrounded by basement membrane macromolecules indicates that the lamina cribrosa is a specialized connective tissue of the centrtal nervous system.

The insertion of the lamina cribrosa in the sclera is a specialized structure. Concentric, circumferential, tightly packed elastin fibers surround the laminar and prelaminar region of the optic nerve head. Furthermore, the elastin fibers of the cribriform plates, running perpendicular to the nerve bundles, are continuous with, and appear to originate from, those of the insertion. In the adjacent sclera, the elastin fibers are short and sparse and do not show any special orientation. Glial cell processes, which are covered by basement membranes, form anchoring network through the bundles of elastin fibers in the insertion region; the basement membrane components extend beyond the glial cell processes into the sclera (HERNANDEZ et al. 1987, GOLDBAUM et al. 1989).

There are age-related changes in the ECM of the human optic nerve head in the lamina cribrosa. Observations with the fluorescence microscope suggest age-related increases in the amounts and densities of collagen types I, III, and IV and in elastin (HERNANDEZ et al. 1989). As the core of the cribriform plates enlarges with age, the apparent density of collagen types I and III increases markedly, indicating increases in interstitial collagen in the core of the cribriform plates. Thus, as the lamina cribrosa ages, there is a gradual increase in the fibrillar forms of collagen. In tissues such as the sclera and corneal stroma, these macromolecules provide structural support, strength, and rigidity. Furthermore, a network of filamentous material, which stains positive for collagen type IV within the cribriform plates in young eyes, also increases in density as the plates expand with age (Fig. 3). There is also a marked increase in the density of fibers of elastin in this tissue with age.

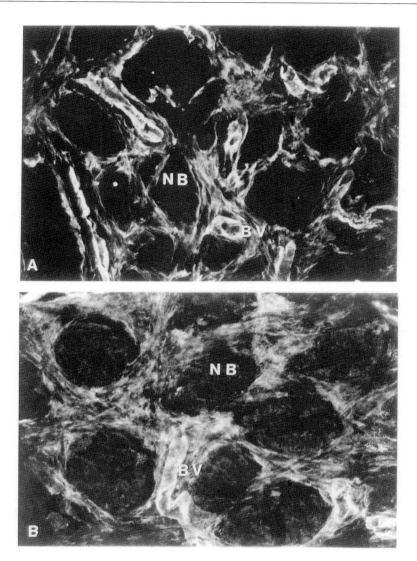

Fig. 3. Immunofluorescent staining for collagen type IV in cross sections of the lamina cribrosa, (x450). A, 31 year-old. B, 73 year-old. Collagen type IV is present inside the core of the cribriform plates. Note the increase with age in collagen type IV positive material. BV: blood vessels; NB: nerve bundles. (With permisssion: From HERNANDEZ M.R. et al. 1991)

The increased collagen and elastin presumably accounts for the increased area of connective tissue with age described by Ogden and associates (OGDEN et al. 1988). Thus, as gradual loss of axons of the optic nerve occurs with age (VRABEC 1977,

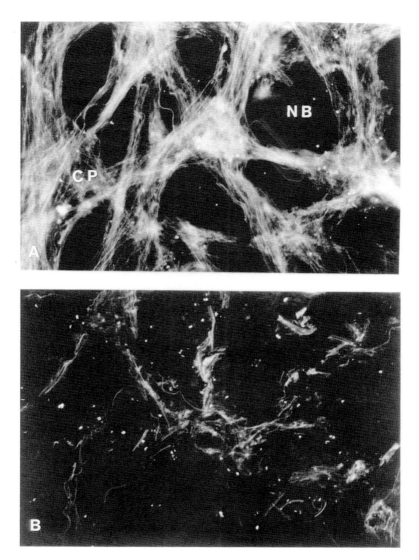

Fig. 4. Immunofluorescent staining for α-elastin in cross sections of the human lamina cribrosa (x405). A, 75 year-old, normal CP: Cribriform plate; NB: nerve bundle. B, 69 years old, POAG. In a region adjacent to the surface of the disk, note the loss of elastin fibers in the remaining cribriform plates. (With permission: From HERNANDEZ M.R. et al. 1991)

REPKA and QUIGLEY 1989), lost tissue is at least partially replaced with extracellular matrix material, including fibrillar forms of collagen and elastin. Therefore, little loss of volume of the optic nerve head may occur with age. Increases in extracellular matrix macromolecules like collagen types I and III may make the tissue more rigid and less resilient with age; whereas collagen type IV and elastin may allow the tissue to retain some flexibility and resiliency as it ages. Perhaps the normal aging process in this tissue increases the ratio of these macromolecules in a way that maintains normal function. However, in certain individuals, the aging process may alter the distribution of the macromolecules and thus alter function of the connective tissue of the optic nerve head.

Using immunofluorescence, Hernandez and co-workers examined the extracellular matrix components of the optic nerve head from eyes with diagnosis of primary open angle glaucoma and from age-matched normal eyes. They observed an increase in density and in the area occupied by basement membranes in the prelaminar region and in the lamina cribrosa of human glaucomatous eyes (HERNANDEZ et al. 1989). A similar observation was recently reported in experimental glaucoma in primates (MORRISON et al. 1989). Histopathological examination of glaucomatous human eyes in early or moderate stages of injury demonstrated glial hyperplasia in both the laminar and prelaminar regions (MINCKLER an SPAETH 1981). These proliferating glial cells are the most likely source of newly synthesized basement membranes and probably represent a response to injury and the loss of axons during the glaucomatous process.

In the cribiform plates of the glaucomatous lamina cribrosa, granular masses of elastin appear and the fibers of elastin are increasingly disorganized with the progression of the disease. In severe primary open angle glaucoma, there is marked loss of elastin from the cribriform plates immediately bordering the disk surface (Fig. 4).

Ultrastructural immunocytochemical analysis revealed marked abnormalities in the elastic fiber morphology. Fragmentation of elastic fibers, accumulation of masses of non-fibrillar elastic-like material and abundance of bundles of microfibrils are present throughout the core of the cribriform plates and in the insertion region in eyes with well documented POAG (Fig. 5). These changes in the elastic component of the lamina cribrosa are similar to those observed in other connective tissue diseases that are characterized by abnormal biosynthesis and/or enhanced degradation of elastic fibers.

Using laser Doppler velocimetry, Zeimer and Ogura have recently reported that optic nerve head compliance diminishes as the glaucomatous damage progresses (ZEIMER and OGURA 1989). The changes in the elastin fiber organization and decreases in density of elastin fibers that we have observed in the lamina cribrosa may explain the loss of compliance of the optic nerve head in primary open angle glaucoma.

Collagen type VI forms a filamentous network in the extracellular matrix. This form of collagen is found in most tissues interconnecting fibers of collagen types I and III and near basement membranes (KEENE et al. 1988). In the normal lamina

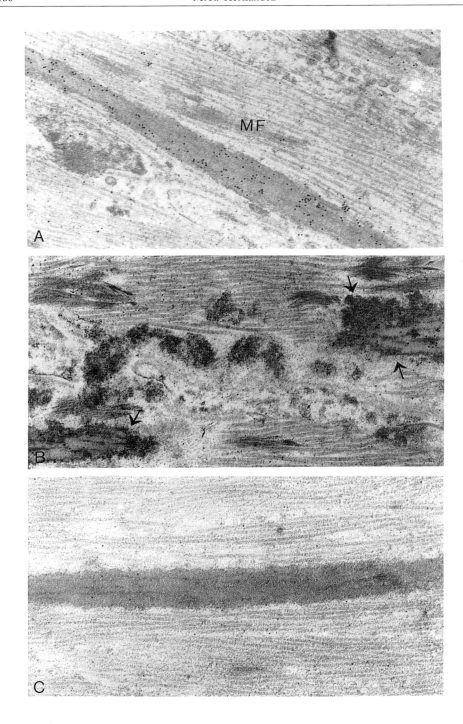

cribrosa, collagen type VI is localized at the edge, and as patches of staining in the core, of the cribriform plates. In glaucoma, collagen type VI appears to increase markedly in amount and density especially in the core of the plates. The increase in collagen type VI is apparent at all stages of the glaucomatous process (HERNANDEZ et al. 1990) and throughout the entire lamina cribrosa, suggesting that collagen type VI may be a reactional form of collagen in this tissue.

Unfortunately, it is not possible at this time to conclude whether the changes that are observed in glaucomatous eyes are the response to the loss of neural tissue and subsequent rearrangement of the cribriform plates due to elevated IOP or the changes imply a predisposing weakness in this connective tissue that permits the glaucomatous excavation of the optic nerve head to progress in response to elevated intraocular pressure.

The new techniques of molecular biology provide means to study gene expression and regulation of the synthesis of extracellular matrix macromolecules. Cloned human genes, as well as genomic and cDNA probes for collagen, elastin and attachment factor are now widely available from laboratories working in the field. Immunohistochemistry has identified and localized extracellular matrix macromolecules, but does not yield information on the metabolic activity of specific cells, nor distinguish newly synthesized from accumulated material. In situ hybridization allows the identification of mRNA within fixed tissue sections or cells in culture using radiolabelled cDNA or cRNA probes followed by autoradiography (SINGER et al. 1986).

Recently, Hernandez and co-workers have shown, using in situ hybridization, that cells of the lamina cribrosa express mRNA for both collagen types I and IV in individual human optic nerves at different ages (Fig. 6) (HERNANDEZ et al. 1991). Future work using this technique will allow the determination of whether the changes observed with age and in glaucoma are due to biosynthesis or degradation of extracellular matrix macromolecules.

Investigation into the extracellular matrix of the human lamina cribrosa are continuing to test the hypothesis that there is a connective tissue component in the glaucomatous changes causing optic nerve degeneration. Some weakness in this tissue, derived from the individual variability of age-related changes, may predispose certain individual's optic nerves to damage due to elevated intraocular pres-

◄ Fig. 5. Low magnification electronmicrographs of cross sectional views of cribriform plates. (A) Normal, 81 year-old. Tubular elastic fibers (E) run longitudinally in the core of the cribriform plates. Note the dense collagen matrix surrounding the fibers. Asterisks mark the position of basement membranes not clearly visible at this magnification (x4,200). (B) Mild POAG, 74 year-old. The extracellular matrix of the cribriform plates appears disorganized . Fragments of elastic fibers (E) are present in the markedly loose collagen matrix. Asterisks point to basement membranes that are thickened and serve as reference for the limits of the core of plates (x4,200). (With permission from HERNANDEZ M. R. 1991)

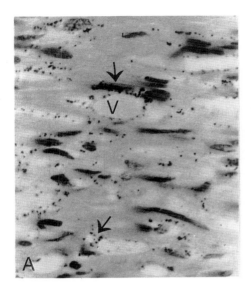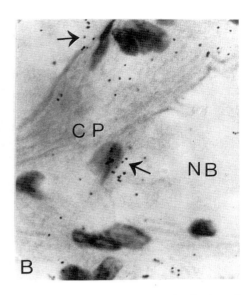

Fig. 6. Expression of collagen type IV mRNA in human optic nerve heads. In situ hybridization of human lamina cribrosa from normal eyes with [35]S-antisense RNA for collagen type IV. A normal 56 year-old. Sagittal view of the cribriform plates. Arrows point to labeled cells in the plates and in the blood vessels (V) (x450). B, normal 55 year-old. Cross sectional view of the cribriform plates. Arrows point to labaled cells lining the plates (CP) NB: Nerve bundle. (x890). (With permission: From HERNANDEZ M. R. et al.: Invest. Ophthalmol. Vis. Sci. *32:* 2169–2177, 1991)

sure. Furthermore, inherent defects or weaknesses in the extracellular matrix of the lamina cribrosa of certain individuals, which are due to slight changes, errors or imbalances of key macromolecular components, may produce an optic nerve head which will progressively cup at normal IOP, causing low tension glaucoma. Thus, the composition of an individual's extracellular matrix of the lamina cribrosa can provide the optic nerve head with a structure that has biophysical characteristics of more, or less, rigidity, that changes with age, and that is sensitive to IOP. Demonstration of the causative role that this connective tissue plays in the glaucomatous process awaits further investigation.

## References

ANDERSON, D. A. (1969): Ultrastructure of human and monkey lamina cribrosa and optic nerve head. Arch. Ophthalmol. *82:* 800.

ELKINGTON, A. R., C. B.E. INMAN, P. V. STEART, R. O. WELLER (1990): The structure of the lamina cribrosa of the human eye: An immunocytochemical and electron microscopical study. Eye *4:* 42.

GOLDBAUM, M. H., S. JENG, R. LOGEMANN, R. N. WEINREB (1989): The extracellular matrix of the human optic nerve. Arch. Ophthalmol. *107:* 1225.

HAY, E. D. (1983): Cell Biology of Extracellular matrix, 2nd ed. New York, Plenum Press.

HERNANDEZ, M. R., F. IGOE, A. H. NEUFELD (1986): Extracellular matrix of the human optic nerve head. Am. J. Ophthalmol. *102,2:* 139.

HERNANDEZ, M. R., X. X. LUO, F. IGOE, A. H. NEUFELD (1987): Extracellular matrix of the human lamina cribrosa. Am. J. Ophthalmol. *104:* 576.

HERNANDEZ, M. R., X. X. LUO, W. ANDRZEJEWSKA, A. H. NEUFELD (1989): Age-Related changes in the extracellular matrix of the human optic nerve head. Am. J. Ophthalmol. *107:* 476.

HERNANDEZ, M. R., W. M. ANDRZEJEWSKA, A. H. NEUFELD (1990): Changes in the extracellular matrix of the human optic nerve head in primary open angle glaucoma. Am. J. Ophthalmol. *109:* 180.

HERNANDEZ, M. R., N. M. HANLEY, A. H. NEUFELD (1991): Localization of collagen types I and IV mRNAs in human optic nerve head by in situ hybridization. Invest. Ophthalmol. Vis. Sci. *32:* 2169.

KEENE, D. R., E. ENGVALL, R. W. GLANVILLE (1988): Ultrastructure of type VI collagen in human skin and cartilage suggests an anchoring function for this filamentous network. J. Cell. Biol. *107:* 1995.

KONOMI, K., T. HAYASHI, J. SANO, K. TERATO, Y. NAGAI, M. ARIMA, K. NAKAYASU, M. TANAKA, A. NAKAJIMA (1983): Immunohistochemical localization of type I, III, and IV collagens in the sclera and choroid of bovine, rat and normal and pathological human eyes. Biomed. Res. *4:* 451.

MINCKLER, D. S., G. L. SPAETH (1981): Optic nerve damage in glaucoma. Surv. Ophthalmol. *26:* 128.

MORRISON, J., M. E. DORMAN, H. QUIGLEY (1989): Extracellular matrix changes in glaucomatous optic atrophy. Invest. Ophthalmol. Vis. Sci. (ARVO Suppl.) *30,3:* 301.

OGDEN, T. E., J. DUGGAN, K. DANLEY, M. WILCOX, D. S. MINCKLER (1988): Morphometry of nerve fiber bundle pores in the optic nerve head of the human. Exp. Eye Res. *46:* 559.

REPKA, M. X., H. A. QUIGLEY (1989): The effect of age on normal human optic nerve fiber number and diameter. Ophthalmol. *96:* 26.

SINGER, R. H., J. B. LAWRENCE, C. VILLNAVE (1986): Optimization of in situ hybridization using isotopic and non-isotopic detection methods. BioTechniques *4:* 230.

TENGROTH, B., T. AMMITZBOLL (1984): Changes in the content and composition of collagen in the glaucomatous eye-basis for a new hypothesis for the genesis of chronic open angle glaucoma. Acta Ophthalmol. *62:* 999.

VRABEC, F. (1977): Age changes of the human optic nerve. A neurohistologic study. Graefes Arch. Klin. Exp. Ophthalmol. *202:* 231.

ZEIMER, R. C., Y. OGURA (1989): The relation between glaucomatous damage and optic nerve head mechanical compliance. Arch. Ophthalmol. *107:* 1232.

*Department of Anatomy, University of Erlangen-Nürnberg, FRG*

# Ageing processes in the anterior segment of the eye

J.W. ROHEN and E. LÜTJEN-DRECOLL

In principle the various tissues of the anterior eye segment undergo the same general ageing processes as they take place in the organism itself. However, the time course of these processes differs considerably from tissue to tissue, so that one can distinguish between quickly and slowly ageing tissues. Some tissue-formations seem to keep a nearly normal structure and function until the last decade of life, whereas others show earlier age-related changes. These differences do not occur at random, but are rather differentiations within the particular systems which, by this mechanism, may retain most of their functional capacity.

Therefore, we have to concentrate on the functional systems as a whole in order to understand the ageing-processes of the individual cells or the related extracellular elements (cf. ROHEN and LÜTJEN-DRECOLL 1981). If there is a kind of inhibition of age-related degeneration in certain constituents of a functional system, an early dysfunction of that system may be effectively prevented. In such an important sensory organ as the eye, an age-induced dysfunction of certain parts as, e. g. the cornea, regarding transparency, the retina or the aqueous circulation system with respect to intraocular pressure maintenance may be more critical on the survival of the organism than comparable ageing processes in the skin or bones. The corneal transparency for example depends on a continuous process of dehydration as on the maintenance of both the regular pattern and thickness of the collageneous fibers. The diameter of corneal collagen seems to remain unchanged during the entire life; the number of corneal endothelial cells appears to be constant (cf. REIM 1984, SHERRARD et al. 1987, CHAN-LING et al. 1988), whereas the pump function begins to decrease slightly beyond the age of 65 (BERAN 1981, POLSE et al. 1989, O'NEAL et al. 1986). On the other hand, endothelial ionic permeability and bicarbonate pump activity does not change significantly with age (WIGHAM and HODSON 1987). There is a suggestion that the endothelial cells may even tighten up with ageing, thereby partially compensating for the suggested ageing diminution in metabolic pump capability. There is no obvious age threshold for endothelial deterioration (WIGHAM et al. 1987). The well-known age-related increase in the diameter of Descements membrane (ALVARADO and MURPHY 1982, WORMER et al. 1979) possibly is also a compensatory phenomenon with respect to the maintenance of corneal transparency (ROHEN and LÜTJEN-DRECOLL 1981, 1984). In this respect the constancy of diameter and structure of the collageneous fibers within the corneal stroma is of particular importance (see also the paper by von der Mark in this volume).

In our opinion, ageing is a complicated biological process consisting of either intense or moderate or even "non-ageing" components, whereby structural and functional changes in one tissue may compensate for age-changes occuring in a neighbouring tissue, so that the function of the entire system remains relatively unchanged throughout most of life. We are far from a real understanding of such interrelations and compensatory mechanisms in the field of ocular gerontology. The following descriptions should therefore be considered as preliminary.

## 1. Iris

The iris serves primarily as a shutter which protects the retina from strong illuminations and regulates the depth of focus. The stromal layer contains the blood ves-

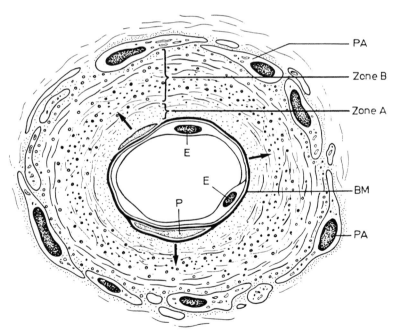

Fig. 1. Normal structure of the vessels in the human iris. Note the organization of the adventitial sheaths divided in an inner zone (A) and an outer zone (B) (according to R. Okamura and E. Lütjen-Drecoll, Graefes Arch. Klin. exp. Ophthalmol. *186*: 249 – 269, 1973) Arrows = Direction of fiber formation

BM = Basement membrane      E = Endothelial cells
P = Pericyt      PA = Periadventitial cells

sels which are embedded in a regularly arranged lattice-like network of collageneous fibers. The fiber lattice is capable of changing its angle according to the size of
the pupil (ROHEN 1951, 1964). Most vessels possess an adventitial sheath which is
several times larger than the vessel wall itself (Fig. 1). The sheaths consist of collageneous fibers embedded in a matrix rich in proteoglycans, mainly hyaluronan and
chondroitinsulfates. In older age, a decrease in hyaluronidase-resistant glycosaminoglycans within those adventitial sheaths has been observed (SAMES and ROHEN
1978, SAMES 1979). On the other hand, the periadventitial cellular layer which separates the adventitial sheaths from the iris stroma becomes thicker with increasing
age, so that around the vessels the number of cells seem to increase. Elastic fibers
are lacking within the iris stroma or within the vascular sheaths. The sheaths contain collageneous fibers of different size (Fig. 2). The inner zone of the adventitial
sheaths contains only thin fibers (diameter of 30 – 60 nm), whereas the outer zone
contains fibers with varying diameters (30 – 120 nm). It has been assumed that
there is a process of fiber formation and maturation within the adventitial sheaths
resulting in an increase in number and thickness of the collageneous fibers which
correlates with increasing age (OKAMURA and LÜTJEN-DRECOLL 1973).

Recently it has been shown by immunohistochemistry that the inner zone of the
adventitial sheaths consists mainly of type VI-collagen, whereas type IV-collagen
and laminin is present within the basement membranes of the vessels (Fig. 3).
Only fibronectin was found within the entire sheath (RITTIG et al. 1990). Both the
fixation of the endothelial tube within the adventitial sheath and the flexibility of
the vascular tube inside its sheaths during iris movements seem to depend on the
type-VI-collagen containing inner zone. With age the basement membrane of the
iris vessels thickens, the inner zone of their adventitial sheath increases and the
number and diameter of the collageneous fibers in the outer zone increases
(OKAMURA and LÜTJEN-DRECOLL 1973). These structural changes might be an
explanation for the increasing stiffness and rigidity of the iris with age.

In old age, the anterior border layer, particularly rich in glycoproteins, undergoes
a cellular densification, whereas the stroma layer becomes more and more atrophic. The crypts therefore appear shallower and the vessels more prominent. In the
adventitial sheaths of the ageing iris a decrease in hyaluronidase-resistant glycosaminoglycans, probably to a large extent keratan – or heparansulfate and a concomitant increase in these substances in the anterior border layer of the iris has been
observed (SAMES and ROHEN 1978). Thus, the main age-related change of the iris
concerns the stromal layer which becomes more and more atrophic whereas the
pericellular adventitial layer of the vessels and the anterior leaf develops an increasing cellularity. Interestingly, there is no significant obliteration of iris vessels,
although the mobility of the iris is markedly reduced with age. The adventitial
sheaths plays perhaps a major role in preventing vascular obliteration. Changes in
concentration and composition of proteoglycans surrounding the collageneous fib-

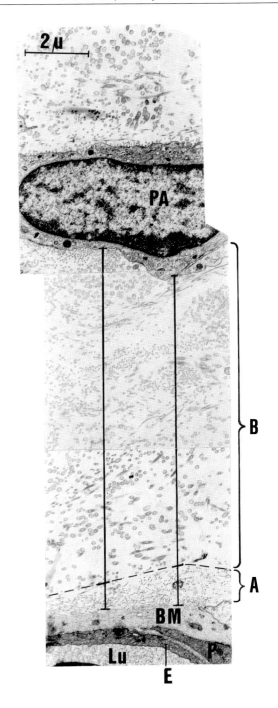

ers, particularly of the inner zone of the adventitial sheaths, may prevent collagen ageing in this region and may keep the vascular tubes functionally intact throughout life. What could be the reason for a possibly compensatory mechanism of this kind?

Recently, a new function of the iris was discovered, namely the capability of the iris vessels to deliver oxygen into the aqueous humor (HÖPER et al. 1989). It has been shown that the $PO_2$ in front of the pupil or in iridektomized eyes is substantially lower than in front of the anterior iris surface (Fig. 4). The $O_2$-supply of the anterior chamber by the iris vasculature seems to be important for the metabolism of the bradytrophic eye tissues, particularly the cornea and of the aqueos outflow pathways. Since the transparency of the cornea is greatly dependent on the pump activities of the endothelial lining, the $O_2$-supply of these cells is of high importance for the survival of the entire organism.

## 2. Trabecular meshwork

The trabecular meshwork serves as a filter which has to be passed by the aqueous humour before entering Schlemm's canal. The main portion of aqueous outflow resistance (75 – 90 %) is situated within the trabecular meshwork, most probably within the cribriform layer (BILL and SVEDBERG 1972, LÜTJEN-DRECOLL 1973, ROHEN 1982, MAPEÅ and BILL 1989). Any obstruction or blockage of outflow pathways of the mesh would result in an elevation of outflow resistance and possibly but not necessarily, also of intraocular pressure. It is, therefore, functionally of great importance, that the trabecular meshwork remains "clean" throughout life. The beauty of the system is indeed its great capability of self-cleaning, mainly by phagocytosis (ROHEN and VAN DER ZYPEN 1968, SHABO and MAXWELL 1972, GRIERSON and LEE 1973, 1978, SHERWOOD and RICHARDSON 1981). There is also some evidence that the trabecular cells possess lytic activities to prevent coagulation and obstruction of extracellular spaces.

With age the number of trabecular cells decreases, in average 0,58 % of cells per year (ALVARADO et al. 1981). The loss of cells in the endothelial lining of Schlemms canal was determined as being 430 cells per year (GRIERSON et al. 1984). Recent studies of cell numbers in the cynomolgus meshwork revealed that there is a continuous loss of trabecular cells with increasing age, although the degree of this decline differs within the various decades (Fig. 5).

◄ Fig. 2. Adventitial sheath of a human iris vessel (Electron micrograph, 62-years old patient, 10000x). Note the differences in the diameter of collagen fibers in zone A and B (according to R. OKAMURA and E. LÜTJEN-DRECOLL, Graefes Arch. Klin. exp. Ophthalmol. *186:* 1973).
BM = Basement membrane        E = Endothelial cell
Lu = Lumen of blood vessel        P = Pericyt
PA = Periadventitial cell

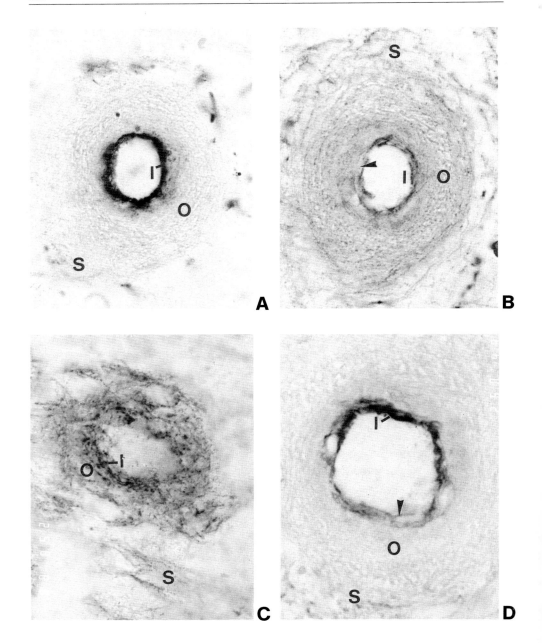

An interesting phenomenon is the increase in cell size with age, which might compensate for the cell loss, so that the trabecular lamellae remain covered by cytoplasmic processes throughout life. These cells contain great amount of endoplasmic reticulum, Golgi vesicles, ribosomes etc. In young eyes there are always trabecular cells which contain smooth muscle alpha-actin filaments indicating contractility. These cells disappear in higher age groups (FLÜGEL et al. 1992) Albeit we never found mitotic figures in the meshwork, a certain proliferative capacity seems nevertheless to exist. In monkey eyes we often found cell clusters in the nonfiltering part of the meshwork, which we called operculum. The operculum cells might be responsible for cell proliferation and regeneration in this region, but this has not been proven as yet. Nevertheless the continuous cell loss with age can not considered to be an absolute phenomenon, it indicates only the relative stage of the turnover in cell regeneration.

In organ cultures of both monkey and human trabecular meshwork a rapid degeneration of the uveal cells were observed whereas the cribriform cells began to proliferate and to produce extracellular material immediately after explantation (ROHEN et al. 1982). In monolayer cultures of trabecular cells a characteristic change in the pattern of secreted glycosaminoglycans was observed during the process of "in-vitro-ageing" in so far, as the production of hyaluronan decreases and that of heparansulfate concomitantly increases (SCHACHTSCHABEL et al. 1981, 1982, BINNINGER et al. 1987, ROHEN 1982).

It is possible that comparable changes in the composition of products formed by the meshwork cells in vivo are lastly responsible for the deposits of extracellular material ("plaque-material") found within the cribriform layer of the meshwork. Underneath the endothelial lining of Schlemm's canal irregularly arranged deposits of electron-dense, amorphous material was observe, the amount of which continuously increases with age. The same was found in the outer wall of Schlemm's canal (ROHEN et al. 1971, 1982, LÜTJEN-DRECOLL et al. 1986 a, b) (Fig. 6). The ultrahistochemical analysis has shown that this material is rich in chondroitinsulfate- and dermatansulfate and that it derives from the sheaths of the elastic-like fibers

Fig. 3A – D. Light micrographs of iris vessels, stained with antibodies against (A) type-VI collagen, (B) type-IV collagen, (C) fibronectin and (D) laminin, using the IGSS method. (x 1000), (according to M. RITTIG, E. LÜTJEN-DRECOLL et al., Cell and Tissue Res. 259: 305 – 312, 1990).
Fig. A) The inner zone (I) of the vascular sheath surrounding the endothelial tube is clearly stained, whereas the outer zone (O) and the iris stroma (S) remain unstained;
Fig. B) The basement membrane of the iris vessel (arrowhead) and some of the fibers in the iris stroma (S) are stained. The inner (I) and outer (O) zone of the vascular sheath show some positive fibrils;
Fig. C) Fibrillar and granular staining is seen in the inner (I) and outer (O) zones of the vascular sheath and in the iris stroma (S);
Fig. D) the endothelial basement membrane (arrowheads), the inner zone (I) of the vascular sheath and some fibrils in the iris stroma (S) are stained, whereas the outer zone (O) remains unstained.

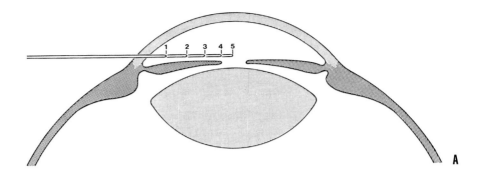

A

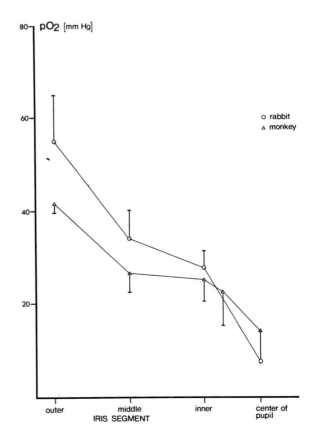

B

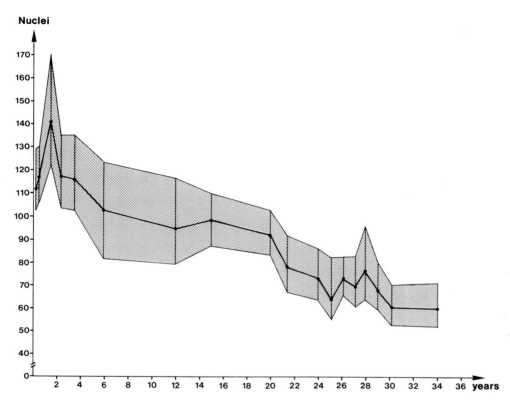

Fig. 5. Age-related changes in the number of trabecular cells in Rhesus monkeys. Note the continuous reduction of nuclei particularly after 20 years of age.

which form a dense network within the cribriform layer (ROHEN et al. 1981 a, LÜTJEN-DRECOLL et al. 1981). These deposits are therefore not "plaques" in the true sense of the word, so that we like to define them as "sheath-derived plaques" of the cribriform layer (Fig. 7). They often loose contact with the elastic-like fibers and form, at places, broad interlacing plates or sheets which can well be demonstrated in tangential sections (ROHEN et al. 1981 a). Recent immunocytochemical studies have shown that these plaques contain large amounts of short, small bundles of type VI collagen which were previously characterized as "long-spacing-collagen",

Fig. 4A). Anterior segment of the eye. Schematic drawing of the electrode position and points of measurement in the anterior chamber. 1 = outer segment of the iris; 2 = middle; 3 = inner segment of the iris; 4 = iris-pupil border; 5 = centre of the pupil (cf. Fig. 4B).
Fig. 4B). pO2-profiles measured in the anterior chamber of rabbit and cynomolgus monkey eye at the points indicated in Fig. 4A) (according to J. HÖPER et al., Current Eye Res. 8: 649–659, 1989).

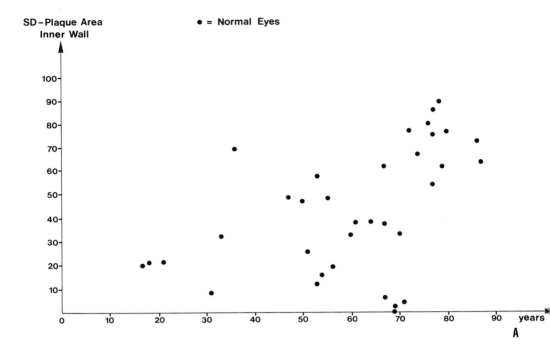

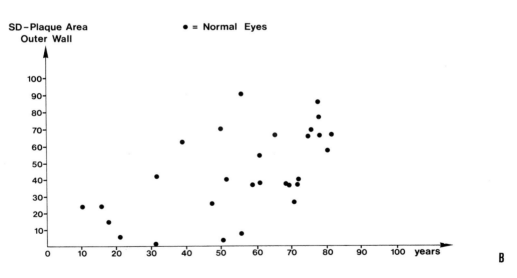

Fig. 6. Age-related changes in the amount of sheath-derived plaque-material in the inner wall (Fig. A) and outer wall (Fig. B) of Schlemm's canal of normal human eyes (according to E. LÜTJEN-DRECOLL et al., Exp. Eye Res. *42:* 443, 1986)

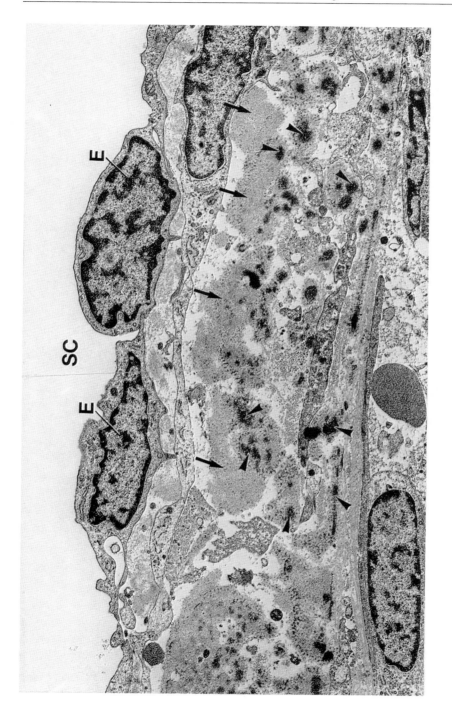

Fig. 7. Electron micrograph of the inner wall of Schlemm's canal in a 60-year old patient (x 12600). Note the deposits of sheath-derived plaque-material within the subendothelial layer (arrows). Arrowheads = elastic-like fibers. E = endothelium of Schlemm's canal (SC).

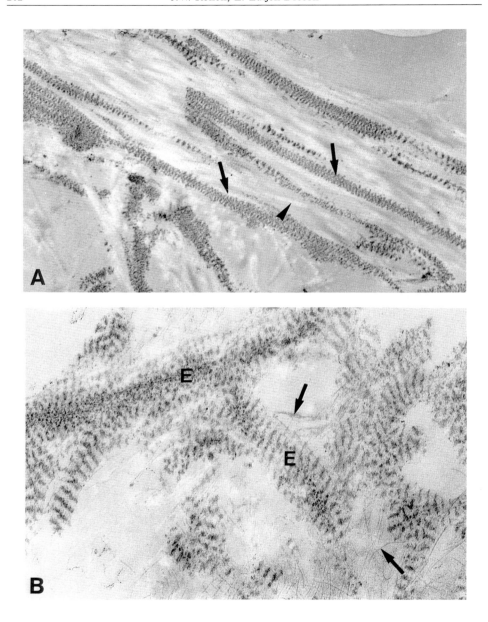

Fig. 8. Tangential sections through the trabecular meshwork of a normal human eye (female, 71 years old) after incubation with antibodies against type-VI collagen- and peroxidase-labelled goat anti-rabbit IgG as secondary antibody (60 min incubation). The sections were neither postfixed with osmium nor counterstained. Note the intense staining of type VI-collagen fibers in the elastic-like fiber sheaths.                                                                              ▶

curly or lattice-collagen (LÜTJEN-DRECOLL et al. 1989). The same material was also found within the sheaths of the elastic-like-fibers and the basement membranes of the trabecular beams. The so-called connecting fibrils of the subendothelial elastic network also contain type VI collagen (LÜTJEN-DRECOLL et al. 1989) (Fig. 8).

The elastic fiber material of the trabecular lamellae seem to be different in nature if compared with other elastic fibers of the body. Age changes of elastic fibers, e. g. in the skin, start after 30 years of age and begin with a decrease in the number of microfibrils surrounding the homogeneous matrix. Later a granular and finally a fibrillar degeneration of the matrix develops which shows more and more electron-dense inclusions and loss of elastin with the consequence that the laxity increases and the elasticity of these fibers decreases (see the paper by B. Streeten in this volume).

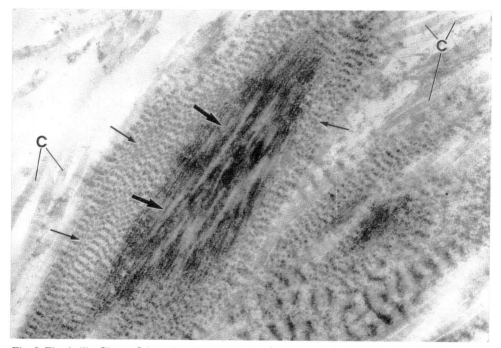

Fig. 9. Elastic-like fibers of the trabecular meshwork after incubation with alcian-blue (thick arrows); normal collagen fibers (C) and sheath material with regular banding (small, long arrows) can be seen (80000 x) (according to E. LÜTJEN-DRECOLL and J. W. ROHEN, Morphology of aqueous outflow pathways, in: The Glaucoma, by R. RITCH et al. (Eds.), C. V. Mosby Co., St. Louis, 1989).

(A) Transition area between scleral spur and trabecular lamellae (x 20000). Note the intense staining of the periodic sheath of the elastic-like fiber net (arrows). The elastic core of the fibers (arrowhead) as well as the thick collagen fibers are unstained.
(B) Central core of a trabecular lamellae (x 24000). Fine stained fibrils (arrows) lead into the sheath of the elastic-like fibers (E) (according to E. LÜTJEN-DRECOLL et al., Exp. Eye Res. 48: 139 – 147, 1989).

The elastic-like fibers situated within the core of the trabecular beams consist of an electron-dense core which can only partly be dissolved by pancreatic elastase (LÜTJEN-DRECOLL et al. 1981). These fibers are surrounded by a small sheath which contains elastic microfibrils (see the contribution by B. Streeten in this volume) and type VI collagen (LÜTJEN-DRECOLL et al. 1981). In contrast to the elastic fibers of the skin, the "elastic-like fibers" of trabecular meshwork do not loose their elastin-containing matrix with age, so that their diameter remains constant throughout life (LÜTJEN-DRECOLL et al. 1982). In contrast to the body fibers, the homogeneous sheaths of the elastic-like fibers become thicker with increasing age. Within the sheaths great amounts of long-spacing collagen develop which shows a periodicity of either 50 or 100 nm, probably the aggregated form of type VI-collagen (Fig. 9).

The elastic-like fiber net of the trabecular meshwork is an essential part of the trabecular meshwork and an important factor for the movements initiated by the ciliary muscle either directly or by pulling backward the scleral spur. An age-dependent increase in laxity of these fibers would be deleterious for the outflow mechanism because a breakdown of the elastic ring would result in a collaps of the canal and in an elevation of outflow resistance. One might speculate that the specific form of age-related changes in the elastic material of the meshwork may also reflect a compensatory mechanism to avoid relaxation and wrinkling of the entire system.

The ageing processes of the collageneous fibers of the trabecular meshwork also differ from that seen e. g. in the sclera (Fig. 10). In the sclera the collageneous fibers become thicker with increasing age often revealing atypical forms. The cross-linking between the peptide-chains increases and the fibers become stiffer. In the cribriform layer the diameter of the collageneous fibers remains relatively constant throughout life. On the other hand, the collageneous fibers of the corneoscleral lamellae show varying diameters in groups of higher age but without any signs of atypical formations (ROHEN et al. 1981 b). The degree of cross-links of the collagen in the trabecular meshwork is unknown. A characteristic event is, however, the development of long-spacing collagen (lattice-, curly collagen) within the central core or within the basement membranes of the trabecular beams. Here, again, this wide-banded material contains type VI-collagen (Fig. 11) The trabecular basement membranes becomes continuously thicker with age and contain more and more long-spacing material (Fig. 11, 12). A thickening often occurs only at the chamber side and not at the outer side (canal-side) of the trabecular lamellae; this might indicate that there is an exogeneous stimulation of these processes, but no details are known in this regard.

A biochemical analysis of the composition of proteins found within the human trabecular meshwork of different age groups has shown that with increasing age some of the protein-bound methionine is oxidized to methionine sulfoxide, reaching about 40 % of the total methionine content at the age of 80. It has been assumed

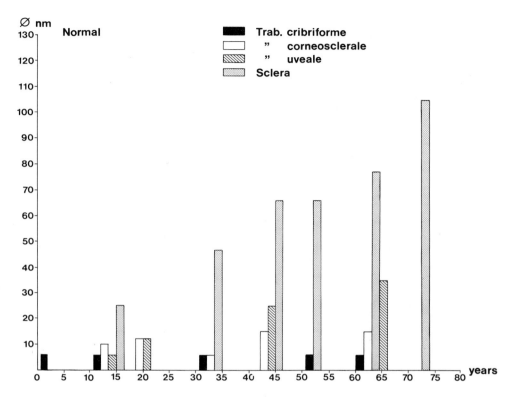

Fig. 10. Diameter of collageneous fibers within different parts of the trabecular meshwork of human eyes in comparison with collageneous fibers of the sclera. Notice the age-related increase in the scleral fibers whereas the diameter of the cribriform and corneoscleral fibers remains relatively constant throughout life.

that this age-related increase in methionin sulfoxide might be related to the development of longspacing collagen within the trabecular beams or their basement membranes (HORSTMANN et al. 1983).

With immunohistochemical methods it has recently been demonstrated that a number of trabecular cells contains contractile filaments because they can be stained with antibodies against alpha-smooth-muscle-actine. Beyond the age of 50 these contractile filaments in the meshwork disappear to a large extent (FLÜGEL et al. 1992) (Fig. 13). These findings indicate that in young eyes the trabecular cells may be able to contract thereby changing outflow resistance, whereas in old eyes functional changes of this kind would be reduced.

The main influence on outflow resistance comes however from the ciliary muscle. It is well established that the ciliary muscle is capable of moving the scleral spur slightly inwards and backwards, thereby expanding the system of interlacing

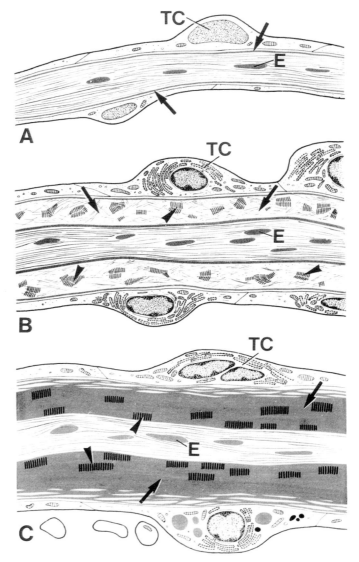

Fig. 11. Schematic diagram of trabecular beams demonstrating the increase in the diameter of the basement membranes (arrows) and in the amount of long spacing collagen (arrowheads) with age. A = young; B = middle; and C = older age groups. E = Elastic-like fibers; TC = Trabecular cells;

Fig. 12. Electron micrographs of trabecular lamellae of a 59 year old pat. (Fig. A) and a 89 year old pat. (Fig. B) (x 8500). Notice the increase in the diameter of the basement membranes (arrows) and the increasing amount of long-spacing material (arrowheads). C = Collagen fibers; EL = elastic-like fibers; T = Trabecular cells.                                                                          ▶

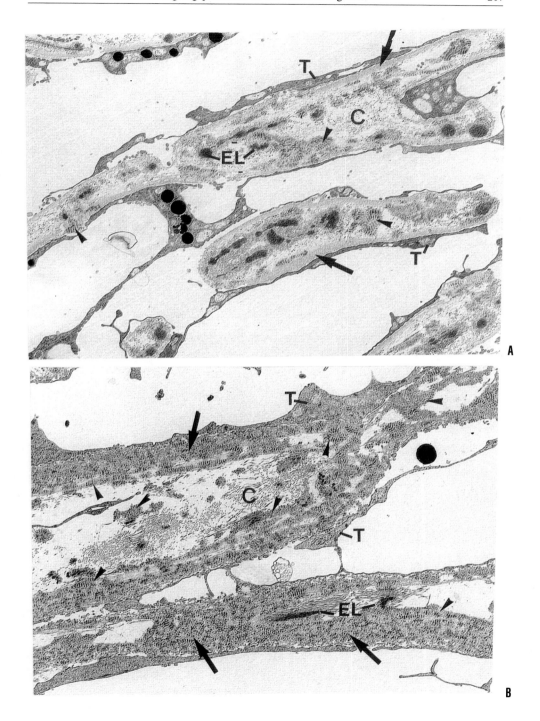

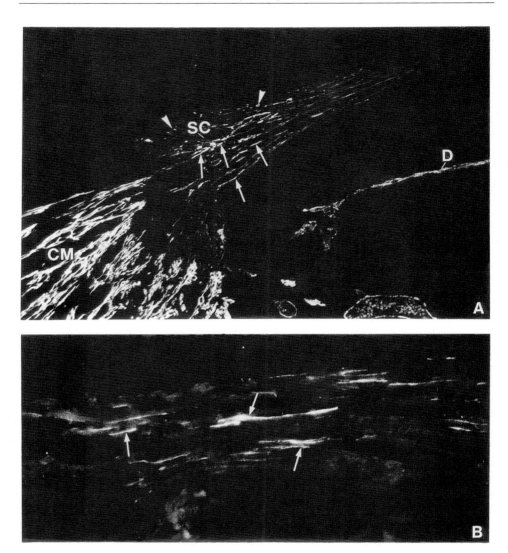

Fig. 13. Light micrographs of sagittal paraffin sections through the chamber angle of a 49-year old donor eye stained for alpha-smooth muscle actin (A = 100 x, B = 500 x). Positively stained trabecular cells are found within all regions of the trabecular meshwork (arrows) and in some cells next to the outer wall of Schlemm's canal (arrowheads) according to C. FLÜGEL, E. TAMM, E. LÜTJEN-DRECOLL and F. STEFANI, J. of Glaucoma 1992). CM = Ciliary muscle; D = Iris dilator; SC = Schlemm's canal.

trabecular lamellae. The diameter of the entire meshwork increases, e. g. after pilocarpine induced ciliary muscle contraction (ROHEN and UNGER 1959, ROHEN et al. 1967, GRIERSON et al. 1977, 1979). Spreading of the meshwork lamellae and opening of cribriform pathways are probably the cause for a decrease in outflow resistance (ROHEN et al. 1967, LÜTJEN-DRECOLL 1973, ROHEN 1982). After the decline of accommodation capacity in the age of 45–50, the movements of the meshwork may cease. The increase in stiffness of the tissue may thus be a compensatory change to prevent a collaps of the canal and an obstruction of the outflow pathways. In this regard, it seems particularly noteworthy, that the outer longitudinal portion of the ciliary muscle which is connected with the scleral spur does not show greater degenerative changes with increasing age. This muscle portion remains intact throughout life. There is little increase in intermuscular connective tissue and nearly no hyalinization of the interstitial tissue in this region. This longitudinal muscle portion might be specifically responsible for keeping some tension on the scleral spur, thus preventing a collaps of Schlemm's canal in old age.

Recently it was found that the scleral spur also contains contractile cells which possess smooth-muscle alpha-actin-filaments within their cytoplasma (TAMM et al. 1990). Interestingly these scleral spur cells do not disappear with increasing age. Contraction of these cells leading to an inward movement of the scleral spur might prevent a collaps of Schlemm's canal in old age when the contractiliy of the trabecular cells is lost.

## 3. Ciliary processes

Aqueous formation takes place within the ciliary processes. Aqueous outflow resistance increases with increasing age (cf. BECKER 1958). Beside this increase, aqueous production by the ciliary processes decreases so that the intraocular pressure normally does not become elevated with age. The decrease in aqueous production rate amounts to 0,006 µl/min/year, i. e. 2,4 % per decade (BECKER 1958, BRUBAKER et al. 1981, KAUFMAN 1986). In addition, a reduction of 33 % was determined in pseudofacility beyond the age of 50 (KUPFER 1973, GAASTERLAND et al. 1978). The morphological base for these changes is still unclear. Quantitative measurements of cell organelles and other structures in the ciliary processes of different age groups have shown that the number of mitochondria within the nonpigmented epithelium increases significantly with age. Furthermore, the number of fenestrations in the capillary endothelium adjacent to the ciliary epithelium increases (HARA et al. 1977, LÜTJEN- DRECOLL et al. 1982). The basal membrane infoldings of the nonpigmented epithelium are, however, reduced in number and in size and the adjacent basement membrane becomes thicker. in higher age groups a hyalinization of the ciliary process stroma develops. In the aged nonpigmented ciliary epithelium an increasing vacuolization of the cytoplasm and deposits of lipid granules, probably lipofuscine, was observed (GÄRTNER 1971). In addition, the pigmented epithelium gradually looses its pigment granules. The loss of pigment granules is most prominent at the tips of the pars plicata processes which in old eyes often appear nearly translucent. At the base of the nonpigmented ciliary epithelium, the internal limiting membrane also shows characteristic age-related changes such as a thickening of the entire membrane, inclusions of vesicles, lipids and granular material (VAN DER ZYPEN and RENTSCH 1971, GÄRTNER 1971).

The structural age-related changes in the ciliary processes described above result in that the distance between the capillary lumina and the posterior chamber becomes larger. This makes aqueous humor production more difficult. The increase in the number of mitochondria within the nonpigmented ciliary epithelium and the increased fenestrations of the capillary walls might take place in order to compensate for this impairment, so that the entire system remains functionally intact until the end of life, although finally at lower levels.

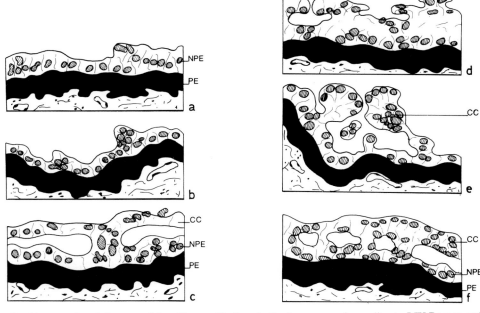

Fig. 14. Age-related changes of the ciliary epithelium in the human eye (according to J.W. ROHEN and A. ZIMMERMANN, Graefes Arch. Klin. exp. Ophthalm. *179:* 302 – 317, 1970), Note the development of covering cells (CC) at the basal surface of the nonpigmented epithelial layer (NPE). PE = Pigmented epithelium.

a) = 10 months old patient        d) = 33 years old patient
b) = 2 years old patient          e) = 65 years old patient
c) = 26 years old patient         f) = 71 years old patient

A characteristic phenomenon is the development of cell protrusions or additional "covering cells" at the ciliary epithelial layers in the posterior pars plicata and the pars plana. These irregularly arranged cells seem to develop from the nonpigmented layer and are often squeezed between the zonular fiber bundles. At places, in histological sections they appear as clusters of additional cells on top of the nonpigmented epithelium (ROHEN and ZIMMERMANN 1970, TIMM 1972) (Fig. 14). The development of such cell protrusions might result from mechanical stress occurring in this region by changes in zonular fiber tension during accommodation.

Between the nonpigmented epithelium and the vitreous membrane hyalocyts are found which immunhistochemically stain positively for the enzyme hyaluronan-synthase (see contribution of Lütjen-Drecoll in this volume) and for different macrophage markers (FLÜGEL et al., submitted). The number of these cells seem to increase with age.

## 4. Ciliary muscle and presbyopia

The adult ciliary muscle consists of smooth muscle fibers grouped in bundles which are surrounded by nearly complete sheaths of fibroblasts (ISHIKAWA 1962, ROHEN 1964, VAN DER ZYPEN 1967, 1970). The individual muscle cells exhibit ultrastructural characteristics which differ from other smooth muscle cells of the body. The intermuscular spaces contain groundsubstance and a relatively small amount of connective tissue which consists only of collagen and of microfibrils. The microfibrils which lie adjacent to the basement membran of the muscle cells, were recently identified as type VI-collagen (Fig. 15). The basement membranes themselves contain type IV collagen and laminin (RITTIG et al. 1990). Within the ciliary muscle there are hardly any elastic fibers. However, the ciliary muscle tendons consist of elastic or elastic-like material which form a network with the elastic fibers of the trabeculum ciliare. With increasing age, particularly in monkeys, the interstitial connective tissue contains an increasing number of macrophages and large pigmented cells; the latter are considered to be migrating pigmented epithelial cells which could have reached the ciliary body by uveoscleral flow (ROHEN and LÜTJEN-DRECOLL 1984, LÜTJEN-DRECOLL et al. 1988 b).

With age, an increasing number of muscle fibers become atrophic or degenerate, particularly the fibers of the reticular and circular portion. The cells of the longitudinal portion remain relatively unchanged, even at advanced age (Fig. 16). In rhesus monkeys, age-related structural changes of the ciliary muscle become apparent beyond the age of 6 (LÜTJEN-DRECOLL et al. 1988 b, TAMM et al. 1990). Within the muscle cells lysosomes and lipid granules of various size are found (Fig. 17). The number of mitochondria and myofilaments decreases. A characteristic phenome-

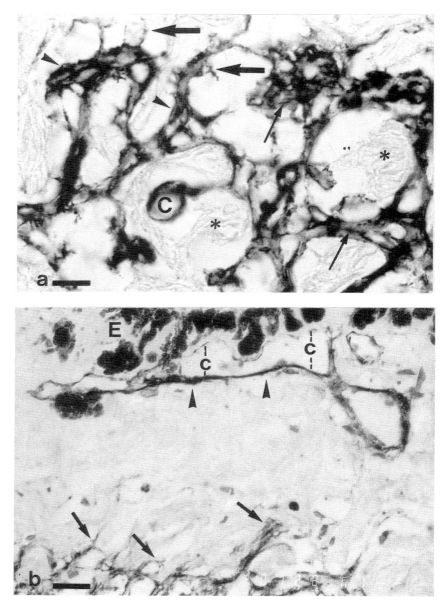

Fig. 15. Sagittal sections through the ciliary body of human eyes stained with antibodies against type-VI collagen. Fig. a – c = light micrographs, Fig. d = electron micrograph (according to M. RITTIG, E. LÜTJEN-DRECOLL et al., Cell and Tissue Res. *259:* 305 – 312, 1990)

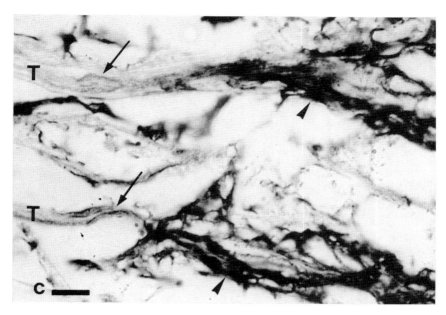

Fig. a). Reticular portion of the ciliary muscle (Bar: 10 μm). Staining is seen around single muscle cells (thin arrows) and is more intense around the muscle bundles (arrowheads). Note that groups of fine immunoreactive fibrils separate from the perimuscular fibers and extend into the intermuscular connective tissue (thick arrow). The hyalinized connective tissue among the muscle bundles remains unstained (asterisks). A positive reaction is also seen around the basement membrane of a capillary (C).
Fig. b). Inner portion of the ciliary body; (Bar: 20 μm). In this inner portion of the ciliary muscle, bundles of positive fibrils (arrows) separate from the muscle sheath and extend into the connective tissue between ciliary muscle and ciliary epithelium (E). The capillaries (C) beneath the epithelium show a stronger staining at the nonfenestrated aspect (arrowheads) facing the ciliary muscle than at the fenestrated aspect facing the ciliary epithelium. Note that the epithelial basement membrane is unstained.
Fig. c). Ciliary muscle tip with an anterior tendon; (Bar: 10 μm). The muscle tip shows intense staining (arrowheads). In the trabecular lamellae (T) immunopositive strands can be seen (arrows).                     ▶

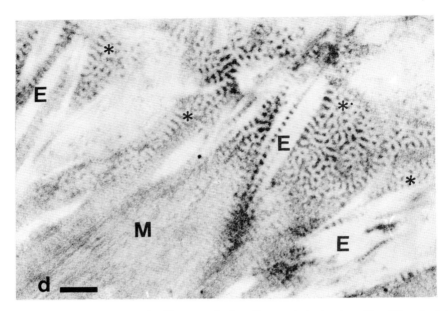

Fig. 15 d). Electron micrograph of a ciliary muscle tip with an anterior tendon; (Bar: 0.5 µm), stained with antibodies against type-VI collagen using the indirect peroxidase method. Fine fibrils are stained around the ciliary muscle cells (M). At the tip of the muscle the core of the elastic tendons (E) remains unstained. The longspacing collagen in the sheath of the elastic tendon is stained intensely (asterisks).

non of the ageing muscle cell is the appearance of "fingerprint"-like membranes regarded as myofibrils which have lost their connection to the dense bands (VAN DER ZYPEN 1970, LÜTJEN-DRECOLL et al. 1988 b, TAMM et al. 1990). They can also derive from endoplasmic reticulum membranes. In striated muscle cells, the "fingerprint"-membranes are found after experimental denervation or in certain muscular diseases.

Beside the degeneration of muscle fibers the intermuscular connective tissue is augmented and becomes gradually hyalinized (Fig. 18). The interstitial spaces become enlarged and filled with amorphous extracellular material and cellular

Fig. 16. Light micrographs of sagittal sections through the ciliary body of human eyes in different age groups. Note the form changes of the ciliary muscle, the hyalinization of the ciliary process stroma (arrows) and the increased amount of connective tissue in the circular portion of the ciliary muscle in the 80-year old patient (arrowhead) (according to E. TAMM et al., Mech. Aging Dev. *62:* 209–221, 1992).
a) = 34-year old patient
b) = 59-year old patient
c) = 80-year old patient
CM = Ciliary muscle; I = Iris; S = Sclera; SC = Schlemm's canal.                              ►

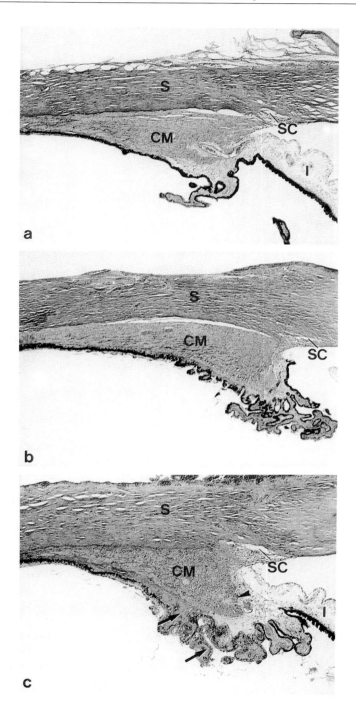

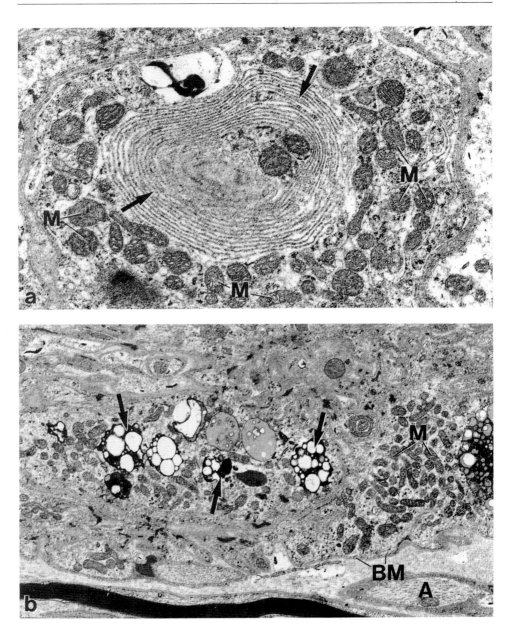

Fig. 17. Age-related changes in the ciliary muscle (electron micrographs of a 26-year old Rhesus monkey muscle; (a = x 57600; b = x 26000). Note the fingerprint-like, lamellated body (Fig. a) and the lipid granules (Fig. b) deposited within the cytoplasm of a ciliary muscle fiber (arrows). A = Nerve axon; BM = Basement membrane; M = Mitochondria.

debris, particularly within the circular muscle portion (STIEVE 1949, ROHEN 1964, ROHEN et al. 1984, 1985, LÜTJEN-DRECOLL et al. 1986 b, TAMM et al. 1992).

In the ciliary muscle of the Rhesus monkey, the connective tissue ground plate between muscle and ciliary processes thickens to some extent whereas – in contrast to man – there is only a slight increase in the intermuscular connective tissue. Up to age of ~ 25 the degenerative changes of the muscle fibers described above increase in frequency but little additional progression occurs in the last decade of life. In this species the progressive decline in functional accommodative amplitude is quite pronounced at the age of 20 but reaches a steady nadir at the age of 25 (BITO et al. 1982, KAUFMAN et al. 1983, LÜTJEN-DRECOLL et al. 1988 b). Recently it has been shown that the contractile responses of the Rhesus ciliary muscle as evidenced by morphometric measurements diminish with age at a rate similar to that of the accommodative decline (LÜTJEN-DRECOLL et al. 1988 b). In contrast to man the width and position of the aged ciliary muscle remains in a position similar to that seen in atropinized young eyes.

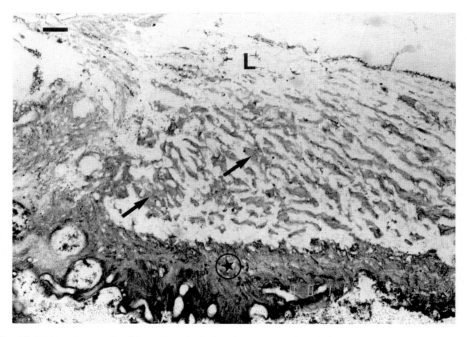

Fig. 18. Light micrograph of the ciliary body in a human eye (Bar: 100 μm). Staining with antibody against fibronectin. Intense staining is seen in the connective tissue between the ciliary epithelium and the ciliary muscle (ground plate) (asterisk), as well as in the intermuscular connective tissue (arrows). Only little staining is seen in the outer longitudinal part (L) of the muscle (according to M. RITTIG et al. Cell and Tissue Res. *259:* 305–312, 1990)

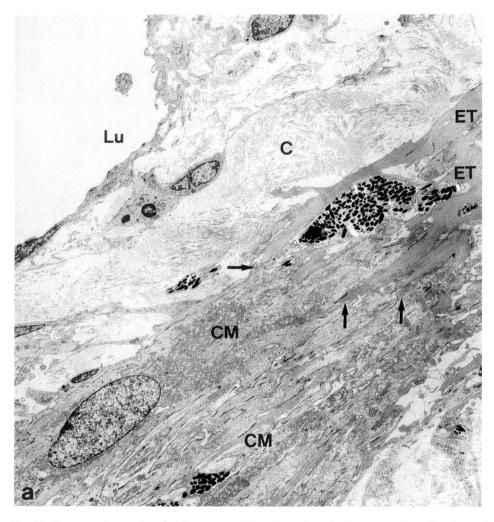

Fig. 19. Electron micrographs of oblique-tangential sections through the myotendinous junctions of the posterior attachment of the ciliary muscle to Bruch's membrane in a young (Fig. a) and old (Fig. b) Rhesus monkey (a = x 3300; b = x 7500) according to E. Tamm et al., Invest. Ophthalm. *32:* 1678 – 1692, 1991).

Fig. a). Ciliary muscle bundles (CM) of a young Rhesus monkey show tapered ends with long cyto-plasmic processes and invaginations (arrows) that are continuous with broad elastic tendons (ET). C = Collageneous fibers of the ciliary body stroma; Lu = Lumen of a blood vessel.

Fig. b). Myotendinous junction of an elastic tendon (ET) in the region of the posterior attachment of the meridional portion of the ciliary muscle in a 34-year-old monkey. Muscle cell (C) and tendon are surrounded by a great amount of electron-dense, amorphous, granular, extracellular material (aste-risks).                                                                                        ▶

Interestingly, in the Rhesus monkey the posterior attachment of the ciliary muscle tendons reveals characteristic age-related changes which could explain the immobility of the aged ciliary muscle. In contrast to the anterior muscle tendons the posterior ones represent exclusively elastic tendons which form an elastic network continuous with the elastic lamina of Bruch's membrane. In old Rhesus monkey eyes the posterior elastic tendons appear thickened and show increasing amounts of associated microfibrils (Fig. 19). The tendons become more and more surrounded by a dense layer of thick collagen fibrils which is always deposited in the space between the ciliary muscle and the pigmented epithelium, so that the anterior portion of Bruch's membrane is completely ensheathed by a thick layer of collagen fibers (TAMM et al. 1991). This age-related increase in nonelastic fibrillar material might cause a decreased compliance of the posterior insertion of the ciliary muscle and the system in a desaccommodated stage. Even if the muscle fibers themselves are still capable of contraction, an anterior-inward movement is hindered by the fixation of the posterior tendons. This finding might explain the marked decline of accommodative amplitude in rhesus monkeys older than 20 or 25 years (BITO et al. 1982, LÜTJEN-DRECOLL et al. 1988 b, TAMM et al. 1990, 1991).

Interestingly, the age-related changes in the ciliary muscle system of human eyes differ considerably if compared with those of monkey eyes. At advanced age the circular portion of the ciliary muscle becomes more prominent and located more

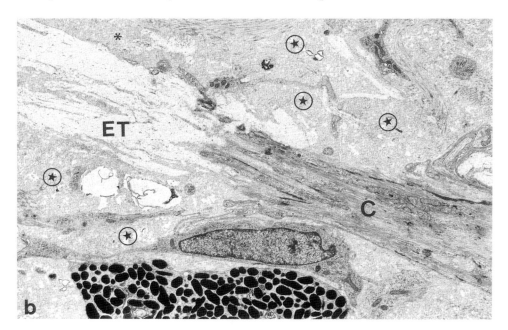

anteriorly (STIEVE 1949, ROHEN 1964). Recent morphometric studies have shown that the total area and length of the muscle decreases continuously with age (TAMM et al. 1992). The area of the longitudinal and reticular portion decreases continuously whereas the area of the circular portion increases with age, so that the distance of the inner aspect of the muscle to the scleral spur becomes shorter and the entire muscle system adopts an anterior-inward position, typical for contracted muscles in young eyes (Fig. 16). The reason for this marked difference in age-related changes between monkey and human eyes might be due to differences in age changes of the elastic fibers. In old human eyes morphologically the elastic fibers of Bruch's membrane and the posterior elastic tendons have a similar appearance as the elastic fibers in skin elastosis. If these elastic fibers loose their elasticity the muscle can contract, but the muscle cannot be pulled backwards again during desaccommodation.

In human eyes it has been shown that the attachment site of the zonules on the front surface of the lens changes as the lens ages and grows. With age the attachment site shifts from the equator onto the anterior lens surface. The zonules might become unable to relax if the front of the enlarged lens is so far from the ciliary muscle that the lens pulls the zonules taut. This might be prevented, at least for a time, by the anterior inward shift of the ciliary muscle position.

The surface of the lens does not flatten with age, but as shown by Brown in a careful work, the anterior and posterior lens curvatures become steeper with age. This finding was called the "lens paradox" as a steepening of the lens curvature implies rather an increase in refractive power which does not occur. It has been suggested based on computer simulation experiments that the overall sharpening of lens curvature happens to counteract the concomitant reduction in the indices of refraction of the lens mass. The age-related remodelling of the human ciliary muscle might also be a factor to maintain emmetropia, i. e. to keep the overall resting refraction relatively constant with age.

# References

ALVARADO, J., C. MURPHY, J. POLANSKY, R. JUSTER (1981): Age-related changes in trabecular meshwork cellularity. Invest. Ophthalmol. Vis. Sci. *21:* 714–727.

ALVARADO, J., C. MURPHY (1982): Histological determination of the normal human corneal dimensions as a function of age. Invest. Ophthalmol. Vis. Sci. *22:* 37.

BAILEY, A. J. (1987): Structure, Function and Ageing of the Collagens of the Eye. Eye *1:* 175–183.

BECKER, B. (1958): The decline in aqueous secretion and outflow facility with age. Am. J. Ophthalmol. *46:* 713–736.

BERAN, V. (1981): Age and the swelling of the cornea. In: TREVOR-ROPER, P. (Ed.) The cornea in health and disease. Academic, London, pp 445–448.

BILL, A., B. SVEDBERGH (1972): Scanning electron microscopic studies of the trabecular meshwork and the canal of Schlemm – an attempt to localize the main resistance to outflow of aqueous humor in man. Acta Ophthalmologica 50: 295 – 320.

BINNINGER, E. A., D. O. SCHACHTSCHABEL, J. W. ROHEN (1987): Exogenous glycosaminoglycans stimulate hyaluronic acid synthesis by cultured human trabecular meshwork cells. Exp. Eye Res. 45: 169 – 177.

BITO, L. Z., C. J. DEROUSSEAU, P. L. KAUFMAN, L. W. BITO (1982): Age-dependent loss of accommodative amplitude in rhesus monkeys: an animal model for presbyopia. Invest. Ophthalmol. Vis. Sci. 23: 23 – 31.

BRUBAKER, R. F., S. NAGATAKI, D. J. TOWNSEND, R. R. BURNS, R. G. HIGGINS, W. WENTWORTH (1981): The effect of age on aqueous humor formation in man. Ophthalmol. 88: 283 – 287.

CHAN-LING, T., J. CURMI (1988): Changes in corneal endothelial morphology in cats as a function of Age. Current Eye Res. 7: 387 – 392.

FLÜGEL, C., E. TAMM, E. LÜTJEN-DRECOLL, F. H. STEFANI (1992): Age-related loss of α-smooth muscle actin in human trabecular meshwork. J. of Glaucoma 1: 165 – 173.

FLÜGEL, C., R. W. KINNE, J. W. STREILEIN, E. LÜTJEN-DRECOLL (1992): Distinctive distribution of HLA class II presenting and bone marrow derived cells in the anterior segment of human eyes (Current Eye Res. 12: 1173 – 1183).

GAASTERLAND, D., C. KUPFER, R. MILTON, K. ROSS, MCCAIN, H. MCLELLAN (1978): Studies of aqueous humour dynamics in man. VI. Effect of age upon parameters of intraocular pressure in normal human eyes. Exp. Eye Res. 26: 651 – 656.

GÄRTNER, J. (1971): Aging changes of the ciliary epithelium border layers and their significance for intraocular pressure. Am. J. Ophthalmol. 72: 1079 – 1093.

GRIERSON, I., R. C. HOWES, Q. WANG (1984): Age-related changes in the canal of Schlemm. Exp. Eye Res. 39: 505 – 512.

GRIERSON, I., W. R. LEE, S. ABRAHAM (1977): Effects of pilocarpine on the morphology of the human outflow apparatus. Brit. J. Ophthalmol. 62: 302 – 313.

GRIERSON, I., W. R. LEE, H. MOSELEY, S. ABRAHAM (1979): The trabecular wall of Schlemms canal: a study of the effects of pilocarpine by scanning electron microscopy. Brit. J. Ophthalmol. 63: 9 – 16.

GRIERSON, I., W. R. LEE (1973): Erythrocyte phagocytosis in the human trabecular meshwork. Brit. J. Ophthalmol. 57: 400 – 415.

GRIERSON, I., W. R. LEE (1978): Further observations on the process of haemophagocytosis in the human outflow system. A. v. Graefes Arch. Klin. Exp. Ophthalmol. 208: 49 – 64.

HARA, K., E. LÜTJEN-DRECOLL, J. PRESTELE, J. W. ROHEN (1977): Structural differences between regions of the ciliary body in primates. Invest. Ophthalmol. Vis. Sci. 16: 912 – 924.

HÖPER, J., R. FUNK, S. ZAGORSKI, J. W. ROHEN (1989): Oxygen delivery to the anterior chamber of the eye – a novel function of the anterior iris surface. Curr. Eye Res. 7: 649 – 659.

HORSTMANN, H.-J., J. W. ROHEN, K. SAMES (1983): Age-related changes in the composition of proteins in the trabecular meshwork of the human eye. Mech. Ageing and Development 21: 121 – 136.

ISHIKAWA, T. (1962): Fine structure of the human ciliary muscle. Invest. Ophthalmol. Vis. Sci. 1: 587 – 608.

KAUFMAN, P. L., L. Z. BITO, C. J. DEROUSSEAU (1983) The development of presbyopia in primates. Trans. Ophthalmol. Soc. U. K. 102: 323 – 326.

KAUFMAN, P. L., J. W. ROHEN, E. H. BÁRÁNY (1979): Hyperopia and loss of accommodation following ciliary muscle disinsertion in the cynomolgus monkey: Physiologic and scanning electron microscopic studies. Invest. Ophthalmol. Vis. Sci. 18: 665 – 673.

KAUFMAN, P. L. (1986): Aging and aqueous humor dynamics. In: Proceed. Internat. Symposium on "the fundamental aging processes of the eye" (Capri), Atti della Fondazione Giorgio Ronchi (in press).

KENT, M. J. C., N. D. LIGHT, A. J. BAILEY (1985): Evidence for glucose-mediated covalent cross-linking of collagen after glycosylation in vivo. Biochem. J. 225: 745 – 752.

KUPFER, C. (1973): Clinical significance of pseudofacility. Am. J. Ophthalmol. 75: 193 – 204.

LÜTJEN-DRECOLL, E., T. DIETL, R. FUTA, J.W. ROHEN (1982): Age-changes of the trabecular mesh-work; a preliminary morphometric study. In: HOLLYFIELD, J. G. (Ed.), The Structure of the Eye, Elsevier Verlag Inc. Holland p. 341–348.

LÜTJEN-DRECOLL, E., R. FUTA, J.W. ROHEN (1981): Ultrahistochemical studies on tangential sections of the trabecular meshwork in normal and glaucomatous eyes. Invest. Ophthalmol. Vis. Sci. *21:* 563–573.

LÜTJEN-DRECOLL, E., M. RITTIG, J. RAUTERBERG, R. JANDER, J. MOLLENHAUER (1989): Immunomi-croscopical Study of Type VI Collagen in the Trabecular Meshwork of Normal and Glaucomatous Eyes. Exp. Eye Res. *48:* 139–147.

LÜTJEN-DRECOLL, E., T. SHIMIZU, M. ROHRBACH, J.W. ROHEN (1986 a): Quantitative analysis of pla-que-material in the inner and outer wall of Schlemms canal in normal and glaucomatous eyes. Exp. Eye Res. *42:* 443–455.

LÜTJEN-DRECOLL, E., T. SHIMIZU, M. ROHRBACH, J.W. ROHEN (1986 b): Quantitative analysis of pla-que-material between ciliary muscle tips in normal and glaucomatous eyes. Exp. Eye Res. *42:* 457–465.

LÜTJEN-DRECOLL, E., E. TAMM, P.L. KAUFMAN (1988 b): Age changes in Rhesus monkey ciliary muscle. Exp. Eye Res. *47:* 885–899.

LÜTJEN-DRECOLL, E., E. TAMM, P.L. KAUFMAN (1988 a): Age-related loss of morphologic responses to pilocarpine in rhesus monkey ciliary muscle. Arch. Ophthalmol. *106:* 1591–1598.

LÜTJEN-DRECOLL, E. (1973): Structural factors influencing outflow facilities and its changeability and drugs; A study in Macaca arctoides. Invest. Ophthalmol. Vis. Sci. *12:* 280–294.

MÄEPEA, O., A. BILL (1989): The pressure in the episcleral veins, Schlemm's canal and the trabecular meshwork in monkeys. Effects of changes in IOP. Exp. Eye Res. *49:* 645–654.

O'NEAL, M.R., K.A. POLSE (1986): Decreased Endothelial Pump Function With Aging. Invest. Oph-thalmol. Vis. Sci. *27:* 457–463.

OKAMURA, R., E. LÜTJEN-DRECOLL (1973): Elektronenmikroskopische Untersuchungen über die strukturellen Veränderungen der menschlichen Iris beim Glaukom. A.v. Graefes Arch. Klin. Exp. Ophthalmol. *186:* 271–281.

POLSE, K.A., R. BRAND, R. MANDELL, D. VASTINE, D. DEMARTINI, R. FLOM (1982): Age Diffe-rences in Corneal Hydration Control. Invest. Ophthalmol. Vis. Sci. *30:* 392–399.

REIM, M. (1984): The Eye in the Aging Patient: Cornea. In: Geriatrics 3, D. PLATT (Ed.), Springer Verl. Berlin, 310–325.

RITTIG, M., E. LÜTJEN-DRECOLL, J. RAUTERBERG, R. JANDER, J. MOLLENHAUER (1990): Type-VI col-lagen in the human iris and ciliary body. Cell Tissue Res. *259:* 305–321.

ROBINS, S.P., A.J. BAILEY (1972): Age-related changes in collagen. Biochem. Biophys. Res. Com-mun. *48:* 76–84.

ROHEN, J.W. (1964): Das Auge und seine Hilfsorgane. In: MÖLLENDORF, W. v., W. BARGMANN (Eds.): Handbuch der mikroskopischen Anatomie des Menschen. Springer Verlag, Heidelberg, Vol. III/4, p. 348–354.

ROHEN, J.W. (1951): Der Bau der Regenbogenhaut beim Menschen und einigen Säugern. Gegenbaurs Morph. Jb. *91:* 140–181.

ROHEN, J.W. (1982): The evolution of the primate eye in relation to the problem of glaucoma. In: LÜTJEN-DRECOLL, E. (Ed.), Basic Aspects of Glaucoma Research. Schattauer Verlag Stuttgart – New York, p. 1–33.

ROHEN, J.W., R. FUTA, E. LÜTJEN-DRECOLL (1981 a): The fine structure of the cribriform meshwork in normal and glaucomatous eyes as seen in tangential sections. Invest. Ophthalmol. Vis. Sci. *21:* 574–585.

ROHEN, J.W., E. LÜTJEN, E.H. BÁRÁNY (1967): The reaction between the ciliary muscle and the tra-becular meshwork and its importance for the effect of miotics on aqueous outflow resistance. A.v. Graefes Arch. Klin. Exp. Ophthalmol. *172:* 23–47.

ROHEN, J.W., E. LÜTJEN-DRECOLL (1985): Age changes in the morphology of the anterior segment of the eye. In: Proceed. Internat. Symposium on „The fundamental aging processes of the eye" (Capri), Atti della Fondazione Giorgio Ronchi 40, N. 5–6, p. 635–645.

ROHEN, J.W., E. LÜTJEN-DRECOLL (1971): Age changes of the trabecular meshwork in human and monkey eyes. A light and electronmicroscopic study. Altern. Entwickl. *1:* 1–36.

ROHEN, J.W., E. LÜTJEN-DRECOLL (1981 b): Ageing and non-ageing processes within the connective tissues of the anterior segment of the eye. In: MÜLLER, W. E. G., ROHEN J.W (Eds.): Biochemical and morphological aspects of ageing. Abhandlung Akademie der Wissenschaften und Literatur, Mainz. Steiner, Wiesbaden, pp. 157–174.

ROHEN, J.W., E. LÜTJEN-DRECOLL (1982): Biology of the trabecular meshwork. In: E. LÜTJEN-DRECOLL (Ed.), Basic Aspects of Glaucoma Research. Schattauer Verlag Stuttgart – New York, p. 141–166.

ROHEN, J.W., E. LÜTJEN-DRECOLL (1984): Age-Related Changes in the Anterior Segment of the Eye. In: Geriatrics 3, D. PLATT (ed.), Springer Verl. Berlin, 326–351.

ROHEN, J.W., D. O. SCHACHTSCHABEL, R. WEHRMANN (1982): Structural changes of human and monkey trabecular meshwork following in vitro cultivation. A. v. Graefes Arch. Klin. Exp. Ophthalmol. *218:* 225–232.

ROHEN, J.W., H. H. UNGER (1959): Zur Morphologie und Pathologie der Kammerwasserbucht des Auges. Abhandlung Akademie der Wissenschaften und Literatur, Mainz. Nr. 3, Steiner, Wiesbaden.

ROHEN, J.W., A. ZIMMERMANN (1970): Altersveränderungen des Ziliarepithels beim Menschen. A. v. Graefes Arch. Klin. Exp. Ophthalmol. *179:* 302–317.

ROHEN, J.W., E. VAN DER ZYPEN (1968): The phagocytic activity of the trabecular meshwork endothelium. An electron microscopy study of the vervet (cercopithecus aethiops). A. v. Graefes Arch. Klin. Exp. Ophthalmol. *175:* 143–160.

SAMES, K., J.W. ROHEN (1978): Histochemical studies on the glycosaminoglycans in the normal and glaucomatous iris of human eyes. A. v. Graefes Arch. Klin. Exp. Ophthalmol. *207:* 157–167.

SAMES, K. (1979): Histochemical demonstration of acid glycosaminoglycans in the cell nuclei of the iris and other tissues. Acta Anat. *103:* 74–82.

SCHACHTSCHABEL, D. O., E. A. BINNINGER, J.W. ROHEN (1989): In vitro cultures of trabecular meshwork cells of human eyes as a model system for the study of cellulary ageing. Arch. Gerontol. Geriatr. *9:* 251–262.

SCHACHTSCHABEL, D. O., J.W. ROHEN, J. WEVER, K. SAMES (1982): Synthesis and composition of glycosaminoglycans by cultured human trabecular meshwork cells. A. v. Graefes Arch. Klin. Exp. Ophthalmol. *218:* 113–117.

SCHACHTSCHABEL, D. O., J. WEVER, J.W. ROHEN, B. BIGALKE (1981): Changes in glycosaminoglycans synthesis during the vitro ageing of cultured WI-38 cells and trabecular meshwork cells of the primate eye. In: MÜLLER, W. E. G., ROHEN, J.W. (Eds.): Biochemical and morphological aspects of ageing. Abhandlung Akademie der Wissenschaften und Literatur, Mainz. Steiner, Wiesbaden, pp. 175–185.

SHABO, A. L., D. S. MAXWELL (1972): Observations on the fate of blood in the anterior chamber. A light and electron microscopic study of the monkey trabecular meshwork. Am. J. Ophthalmol. *73:* 25–36.

SHERRARD, E. S., P. NOVAKOVIC, L. SPEEDWELL (1987): Age-Related Changes of the Corneal Endothelium and Stroma as Seen *in vivo* by Specular Microscopy. Eye *1:* 197–203.

SHERWOOD, N., TH. M. RICHARDSON (1981): Kinetics of the phagocytic process in the trabecular meshwork of cats and monkeys. Invest. Opthalmol. Vis. Sci. *20* (ARVO Suppl.): 65.

STIEVE, R. (1949): Über den Bau des menschlichen Ziliarmuskels, seine physiologischen Veränderungen während des Lebens und seine Bedeutung für die Akkommodation, Z. f. mikroskopisch-anatomische Forsch. *55:* 3–88.

TAMM, E., C. FLÜGEL, F. H. STEFANI, J.W. ROHEN (1992): Contractile cells in human scleral spur. Exp. Eye Res. *54:* 531–543.

TAMM, E., E. LÜTJEN-DRECOLL, W. JUNGKUNZ, J.W. ROHEN (1991): Posterior Attachment of Ciliary Muscle in Young, Accommodating and Old Presbyopic Monkeys. Invest. Ophthal. Vis. Sci. *32:* 1678–1692.

TAMM, E., E. LÜTJEN-DRECOLL, J.W. ROHEN (1990): Age-related Changes of the Ciliary Muscle in comparison with changes induced by treatment with prostaglandin F2a. Mech. Ageing and Development *51:* 101–120.

TAMM, S., E. TAMM, J.W. ROHEN (1992): Age-related changes of the human ciliary muscle. A quantitative morphometric study. Mech. Ageing and Development *62:* 209 – 211.

TIMM, G. (1972): Zur Frage der senilen Hyperplasie des Ziliarepithels. Zentralbl. Allg. Pathol.
*115:* 570 – 578.

WIGHAM, C. G., S. A. HODSON (1987): Physiological Changes in the Cornea of the Ageing Eye. Eye
*1:* 190 – 196.

WORMER, W., K. SAMES, J.W. ROHEN (1979): Histochemische Untersuchungen über Struktur und
Altersveränderungen des Descmet'schen Membran beim Rind. A. v. Graefes Arch. Klin. Exp. Ophthalmol. *211:* 217 – 278.

ZYPEN, VAN DER E., F. J. RENTSCH (1971): Altersbedingte Veränderungen am Ziliarepithel des menschlichen Auges. In: BREDT, H., J. W. ROHEN (Eds.) Altern. Entwickl., Schattauer Verlag Stuttgart –
New York, *1:* 37 – 69.

ZYPEN, VAN DER E. (1967): Licht- und elektronenmikroskopische Untersuchungen über den Bau und
die Innervation des Ziliarmuskels bei Mensch und Affe (Cercopithecus aethiops). A. v. Graefes
Arch. Klin. Exp. Ophthalmol. *174:* 143 – 168.

ZYPEN, VAN DER E. (1970): Licht- und elektronenmikroskopische Untersuchungen über die Altersveränderungen am M. ciliaris im menschlichen Auge. A. v. Graefes Arch. Klin. Exp. Ophthalmol.
*179:* 332 – 357.

*Institut für Klinische Physiologie, Klinikum Steglitz, Freie Universität Berlin*

# Regulation of electrolyte transport mechanisms in ciliary epithelium

M. WIEDERHOLT, H. HELBIG and C. KORBMACHER

Active ion transport and passive components (diffusion, ultrafiltration) are responsible for aqueous humor formation across the ciliary epithelium. It has been well established (BILL 1975; COLE 1977) that active electrolyte secretion is the main driving force in aqueous humor formation. Though passive forces alone cannot account for net secretion, modifications of blood circulation and permeability changes may be additional regulatory factors.

Investigation of transport properties in the ciliary body has been complicated by the unique anatomic situation of the ciliary epithelium, which consists of two different epithelial layers: the pigmented epithelium (PE) on the stromal side and the nonpigmented epithelium (NPE) facing the aqueous humor. PE and NPE cells are connected by gap junctions. The tight junctions, forming the effective barrier for paracellular diffusion, are located only between the NPE (RAVIOLA and RAVIOLA 1978). Though the NPE has been viewed as the functionally most important layer for transepithelial transport, recent research has also dealt with the PE.

This article will not attempt to review all available information on active secretion but will touch upon the significant recent developments and techniques in studying ciliary epithelial transport. This overview will mainly report data on cultured PE and NPE cells and present a model for transepithelial transport which assumes a functional syncytium between PE and NPE cells (WIEDERHOLT et al. 1991).

## 1.0 Approaches for studying ion transport across the ciliary epithelium

The flux of different radioactively labelled ions from blood to aqueous humor has been tested in living animals (FRIEDLAND and MAREN 1984; GARG and OPPELT 1970; MAREN 1988). These data indicate that the ciliary epithelium transports $Na^+$, $Cl^-$, and $HCO_3^-$ by mechanisms which are dependent on $Na^+/K^+$-ATPase and carbonic anhydrase.

To further analyse the transport mechanisms, several groups have mounted the isolated ciliary body (mostly including parts of the iris) for transepithelial electrical studies (CHU et al. 1986, 1987; CHU and CANDIA 1987, 1988; COLE 1977; KISHIDA et al.

1981, 1982, 1986; KRUPIN et al. 1984; PESIN and CANDIA 1982/1983; SAITO et al. 1980; WIEDERHOLT and ZADUNAISKY 1987). However, it has not been possible to localize the various transporters to the PE or NPE cells. An important finding of these studies was that not only electrogenic but also electroneutral transport mechanisms contribute to aqueous humor formation. Having recently succeeded in separating the PE and NPE layer for transepithelial studies, we were able to localize the effects of forskolin and bumetanide in PE cells (WIEDERHOLT et al. 1989). Electrical properties of the intact ciliary epithelium have been determined by using intracellular electrodes, and cell volume regulation of NPE has been measured (BERGGREN 1960, 1964; FAIN and FARAHBAKHSH 1989; FARAHBAKHSH and FAIN 1987; GREEN et al. 1985; MILLER and CONSTANT 1960; WIEDERHOLT and ZADUNAISKY 1986; YANTORNO et al. 1987, 1989). It has not been possible to establish a clear picture of ion transport across the ciliary body due to its complex anatomy with the double layer of epithelial cells.

Tissue culture techniques are useful for studying isolated PE and NPE cells under defined conditions. We as well as others have tried to investigate membrane properties of PE and NPE cells in tissue culture (FAIN and FARAHBAKHSH 1989; HELBIG et al. 1987, 1988 a, 1988 b, 1988 c, 1989 a, 1989 b, 1989 c, 1989 d, 1989 e, 1989 f, 1989 g, STRAUSS and WIEDERHOLT 1991; STRAUSS et al. 1991; YANTORNO et al. 1989). Although cells may change some of their properties during long-term culture, data from the intact ciliary epithelium support the results obtained under cell culture conditions. We used primary cultures and virus-transformed PE and NPE cells of the bovine and human eye. Membrane voltages were measured, and ion uptake was studied using radioactive isotopes (for methods, see WIEDERHOLT and JENTSCH 1990). Intracellular pH and calcium were determined using pH- and calcium-sensitive dyes (Fig. 1). From the data obtained under cell culture conditions, a model will be described for transport of $Na^+$, $Cl^-$, $HCO_3^-$, and ascorbate across the ciliary epithelium (Fig. 2). Most individual transporters have thus far been characterized only in cultured ciliary epithelial cells. We assume a functional syncytium between PE and NPE cells. The two layers are connected by an extraordinarily large number of gap junctions (RAVIOLA AND RAVIOLA 1978) which allow exchange of particles as large as m-RNA and provide for electrical coupling between cells. Electrical coupling has indeed been observed between PE and NPE cells (GREEN et al. 1985; WIEDERHOLT and ZADUNAISKY 1986). The thight junctions between the two layers (RAVIOLA and RAVIOLA 1978) are the morphological substrate for the asymmetry of this syncytial epithelium.

# CULTURED EPITHELIAL CELLS

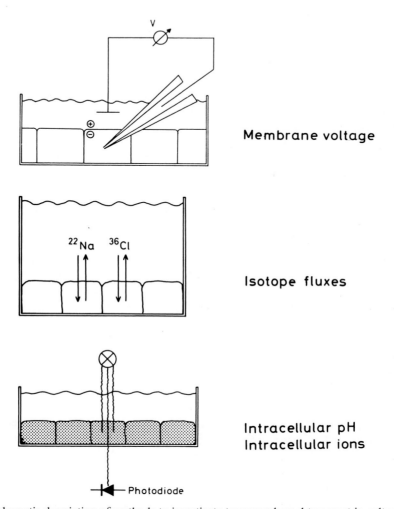

Membrane voltage

Isotope fluxes

Intracellular pH
Intracellular ions

Fig. 1. Schematic description of methods to investigate transmembranal transport in cultured cells.

## 2.0 Electrolyte transport mechanisms in cultured pigmented epithelial (PE) cells

### 2.1 $Na^+/K^+$ transport and $K^+$ conductance

As most other tissues, the ciliary epithelium has a lower sodium concentration intra- than extracellularly due to the activity of the $Na^+/K^+$-ATPase (see No. 1 in Fig. 2 and Table 1). The membrane voltage of pigmented epithelial cells was depolarized by ouabain, indicating an electrogenic component of the $Na^+/K^+$ transporter. Furthermore, electrical evidence has been presented for the dependence of ATPase on $Na^+$ and $K^+$ (HELBIG et al. 1987). Under physiological conditions, $Na^+/K^+$-ATPase is responsible for maintenance of the transmembrane $Na^+$ and $K^+$ gradients („housekeeping" ATPase). The concentration gradient and the intracellularly negative membrane potential constitute a powerful driving force for $Na^+$ entry into the cell. This $Na^+$ gradient can serve as a secondary "energy source" to transport other ions uphill against their electrochemical gradient (secondary active pumps). As will be shown later, the $Na^+$ gradient in the ciliary epithelium provides energy for $Cl^-$, $HCO_3^-$, and ascorbate to accumulate intracellularly in excess of their electrochemical equilibrium. By coupling PE and NPE cells via gap junctions, the $Na^+/K^+$ transport could also maintain the electrolyte gradients across the membrane of NPE cells. The $Na^+/K^+$-ATPase of pigmented cells probably differs functionally from that of NPE cells and does not contribute directly to transepithelial transport. The assumption of functional differences between the $Na^+/K^+$-ATPase in PE and NPE is supported by the observation that PE and NPE express different catalytic subunits of $Na^+/K^+$-ATPase (COCA-PRADOS and LOPEZ-BRIONES 1987).

Changing the extracellular potassium enabled us to characterize a $K^+$ conductance which contributes considerably to the membrane voltage of pigmented cells (HELBIG et al. 1987). The characteristics of $K^+$ conductance are summarized in Table 1. It is of special interest that changes in intracellular calcium and intra- as well as extracellular pH are able to modify the $K^+$ conductance. Furthermore, we assumed that high extracellular $K^+$ (or low voltage) opened $K^+$ channels which are less pH-sensitive at high $K^+$. The functional coupling of $K^+$ conductance to $Na^+/K^+$-ATPase (via $K^+$ recycling) is a physiological link between intra- and extracellular electrolyte concentrations and electrogenic $Na^+/K^+$ transport. In addition $K^+$-induced changes in membrane voltage are regulatory components of all electrogenic activities across the cell membranes. A similar voltage-dependent $K^+$ conductance has recently been demonstrated by applying the patch-clamp technique in cultured PE cells from the rabbit ciliary body (FAIN and FARAHBAKHSH 1989). A $Na^+$-dependent conductance was detected in the same preparation. The function of this conductance is unclear (FAIN and FARAHBARKHSH 1989).

## 2.2 $Na^+/H^+$ antiport and $HCO_3^-/Cl^-$ exchange

$Na^+/H^+$ exchange has been described as a significant mechanism in many different mammalian epithelial and non-epithelial cells. This transporter has been shown to control different physiological functions such as intracellular pH and volume regulation and mediation of responses to hormones and growth factors and is responsible for $Na^+$ uptake in several sodium-transporting epithelial Cole (COLE 1977) was probably the first to postulate, from theoretical considerations, the involvement of $Na^+/H^+$ exchange in ion transport across the ciliary epithelium. The measurement of membrane voltage, intracellular pH, and electrolyte fluxes has enabled us to characterize this transporter in cultured PE cells (HELBIG et al. 1988 a, 1988 c). It was concluded that $Na^+/H^+$ exchange regulates intracellular pH ($pH_i$) during steady state and after acid load (see chapter 2.3). In our model (No. 2 of Fig. 2), this transporter is involved in transepithelial sodium transport. A study of the kinetic properties revealed that $Na^+/H^+$ exchange was competitively inhibited by extracellular protons and amiloride, suggesting a kinetic model with only one common extracellular binding site for $Na^+$, $H^+$ and amiloride. The $IC_{50}$ for amiloride was 6 μmol/l at 5 mmol/l $Na^+$ and 36 μmol/l in the presence of 150 mmol/l $Na^+$. Thus, amiloride acted as a competitive inhibitor with a $K_i$ as described for several transporting epithelia. ($IC_{50}$ = concentration of an inhibitor which gives 50 % inhibition in the presence of the substrate concentration. $K_i$ = affinity constant for the inhibitor).

Radiolabelled chloride was used to investigate the pathways of $Cl^-$ transport in pigmented ciliary epithelial cells (HELBIG et al. 1989 b, 1989 d, 1989 g). $Cl^-$ uptake was typical for an anion exchanger and could be inhibited by the stilbene derivatives DIDS and SITS and stimulated by an outwardly directed $HCO_3^-$ gradient. This $HCO_3^-$-stimulated $Cl^-$ transport could be partly inhibited by furosemide and, to a lesser extent, by bumetanide, indicating an action of loop diuretics on the anion exchanger (HELBIG et al. 1988 b). Loop diuretics have a marked effect on short-circuit current (KISHIDA et al. 1981; SAITO et al. 1980; WIEDERHOLT and ZADUNAISKY 1987) and intracellular $Cl^-$ activity (WIEDERHOLT and ZADUNAISKY 1986, 1990) in the ciliary epithelium. Thus, cultured PE cells express a $Cl^-/HCO_3^-$ exchanger (No. 2 in Fig. 2) which may be involved in aqueous humor formation.

Although the $Na^+/H^+$ antiporter and the $Cl^-/HCO_3^-$ exchanger are largely independent, the evidence presented shows that they are functionally coupled via intracellular pH and carbonic anhydrases (HELBIG et al. 1989 g). In cultured PE cells, we found carbonic anhydrase activity in both the membrane-bound (CA IV) and soluble (cytoplasmic) form. Studies with inhibitors indicate that the soluble form is CA II (WISTRAND et al. 1986). CA activity was also detected in human NPE cells (WIEDERHOLT et al. 1991) as well as in the intact human and rabbit ciliary epithelium (LÜTJEN-DRECOLL and LÖNNERHOLM 1981; WISTRAND et al. 1986). Fig. 3 sum-

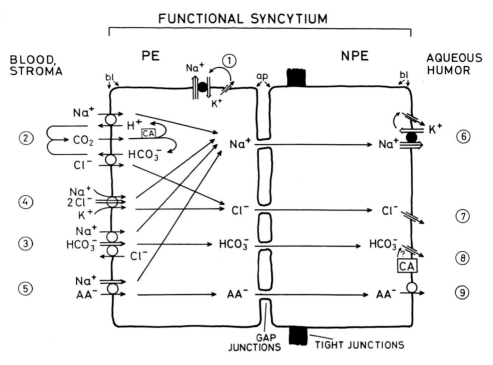

Fig. 2. Model of a functional syncytium between pigmented (PE) and non-pigmented (NPE) cells of the ciliary epithelium. bl = basolateral membranes, ap = apical membranes, $AA^-$ = ascorbic acid

Table 1: Characterization of $Na^+/K^+$ transport ($Na^+/K^+$-ATPase) and $K^+$ conductance in cultured PE cells

**$Na^+/K^+$-transport**
- electrogenic

- inhibited by ouabain, $Na^+$ or $K^+$ removal

- stimulated by recovery from $Na^+$ or $K^+$ depletion

**$K^+$ conductance**
- depends on $Ba^{2+}$, quinidine, $Ca^{2+}$, $pH_i$, $pH_o$, $K^+$, and voltage

- functionally coupled to $Na^+/K^+$ transport

Data from (HELBIG et al. 1987)

marizes in greater detail the coupling of the two transporters in PE cells including both forms of CA. Membrane-associated CA dehydrates extracellular carbonic acid, and $CO_2$ then can easily cross the cellular membrane. Cellular metabolism probably provides another source for intracellular $CO_2$ accumulation. The cytosolic

CA (CA II) hydrates $CO_2$ and thus provides $HCO_3^-$ and $H^+$ as substrates for $Na^+/H^+$ antiport (No. 2A) and $Cl^-/HCO_3^-$ exchange (No. 2B). As a net result of these mechanisms, NaCl is transported from the blood into the cell and $CO_2$ and/or $HCO_3^-/H^+$ are recycled across the membrane of PE cells. The transporters are coupled to each other by carbonic anhydrases and intracellular pH. These double exchange mechanisms could explain the fact that, in both the living animal and isolated ciliary-body preparations, carbonic anhydrase inhibitors reduce $Na^+$ and $Cl^-$ transport and thus aqueous humor secretion (BECKER 1955; FRIEDLAND and MAREN 1984; GARG and OPPELT 1970; KISHIDA et al. 1982, 1986; MAREN 1988). Despite the central role of $HCO_3^-$, a net transepithelial $HCO_3^-$ transport cannot be deduced from this model.

## 2.3 Na⁺-dependent HCO₃⁻/Cl⁻ exchange and intracellular pH regulation

*2.3 $Na^+$-dependent $HCO_3^-/Cl^-$ exchange and intracellular pH regulation*

By measuring intracellular pH ($pH_i$) in cultured PE cells, we described a $Cl^-$-dependent $Na^+/HCO_3^-$ transporter (No. 3 in Fig. 2) in addition to the $Na^+$-independent $Cl^-/HCO_3^-$ exchanger (No. 2 B in Fig. 3). The use of $Cl^-$-depleted PE cells permitted differentiation between $Cl^-$ dependent and $Cl^-$-independent cotransporters (HELBIG et al. 1988 b, 1989 d, 1989 f, 1989 g). The $Na^+$-dependent $HCO_3^-/Cl^-$ exchange could be inhibited by stilbene derivatives such as DIDS and SITS. A similar $Na^+/HCO_3^-$ symport was recently described in the corneal endothelium (for review, see WIEDERHOLT and JENTSCH 1990). Though clearly electrogenic in the corneal endothelium (carrying a net negative charge across the membrane), the symport seems to be electrically neutral in cultured PE cells. The coupled transport of $Na^+$ and $HCO_3^-$ contributes to the uptake mechanisms of $Na^+$ (see Fig. 2) and might explain the net uptake of $HCO_3^-$. This transporter could thus be an important mechanism in aqueous humor formation.

Finally, we described the mechanisms of $pH_i$ regulation under steady-state conditions and in acid- or alkaline-loaded PE cells (HELBIG et al. 1989 d). Fig. 4 presents a schematic summary of the transporters involved in $pH_i$ regulation (transporters No. 2A, 2B, and 3 in Fig. 2 and Fig. 3). In addition to $Na^+/H^+$ exchange, two $HCO_3^-$ transporters contribute towards $pH_i$ regulation in cultered PE cells. $Cl^-$-dependent $Na^+/HCO_3^-$ symport mainly regulates $pH_i$ during steady state and after an acid load, and $Na^+$-independent $Cl^-/HCO_3^-$ exchange is mainly involved in $pH_i$ recovery after an alkali load. The amiloride-sensitive $Na^+/H^+$ transporter (acid extruder) was strongly activated when PE cells were acid-loaded. In bicarbonate-free media (which inhibited $HCO_3^-$-dependent transporters), this acid extruder was also involved in regulating $pH_i$ under steady-state conditions. There is an internal modifier site that switches $Na^+/H^+$ exchange on or off depending on the $pH_i$. In $HCO_3^-$ Ringer's solution, $Na^+/H^+$ exchange was only activated when the

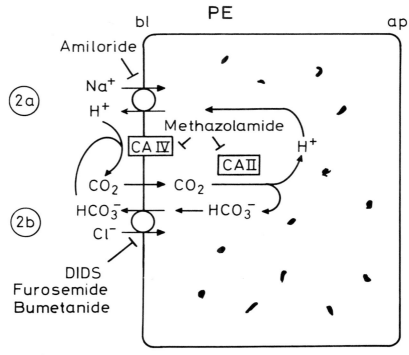

Fig. 3. Role of cytoplasmic and membrane bound carbonic anhydrases and intracellular pH on electrolyte transport in pigmented epithelial cells.

$pH_i$ fell to ~ 0.15 units below the steady-state level. Under stady state conditions, $Cl^-$-dependent $Na^+/HCO_3^-$ symport is the main driving force for $HCO_3^-$-uptake and thus keeps the cell more alkaline than would be expected if protons were passively distributed across the cell membrane at a membrane potential of $-40$ to $-60$ mV in PE cells (HELBIG et al. 1987). This "smart" transporter can be regarded as an alkali extruder in alkali-loaded cells and as an acid extruder in acid-loaded cells as well as under steady-state conditions. The $HCO_3^-/Cl^-$ exchanger (alkali extruder) was most active in alkali-loaded cells and showed only a low degree of activity under stady state conditions. $Na^+$- and $Cl^-$-dependent $HCO_3^-$ uptake mechanisms and their regulation of $pH_i$ have also been described in PE cells of the rabbit ciliary body (WOLOSIN et al. 1989).

### 2.4 $Na^+/2Cl^-/K^+$ symport

The interdependence of $Na^+$ and $Cl^-$ transport was examined in uptake studies with $^{22}Na$ and $^{36}Cl$ (HELBIG et al. 1989 g). The sodium- and chloride-dependence of both, $Na^+$ and $Cl^-$ uptake could be demonstrated. Further experiments using different blockers known as relatively specific ion transport inhibitors revealed two independent mechanisms for $Cl^-$-stimulated $Na^+$ uptake: a loop diuretic-sensitive $Na^+/2Cl^-/K^+$ symport (No. 4 in Fig. 2) and the exchange of $Cl^-$ (No. 2 in Fig. 2) coupled to the $Na^+/H^+$ antiporter. Only the latter component of $Cl^-$-stimulated $Na^+$ uptake was $HCO_3^-$-dependent. The $Na^+/2Cl^-/K^+$ symport could be inhibited by bumetanide. This transporter has been well characterized in a variety of epithelia and seems to be a key mechanism for transepithelial $Na^+$ and $Cl^-$ transport. A similar mechanism (sensitive to diuretics such as bumetanide and furosemide) has been documented in the intact ciliary epithelium of several species (CHU et al. 1987; CHU and CANDIA 1987; KISHIDA et al. 1982; KRUPIN et al. 1984; PESIN and CANDIA 1982/1983; SAITO et al. 1980; WIEDERHOLT and ZADUNAISKY 1987; WIEDERHOLT et al. 1989). Direct measurements of intracellular $Cl^-$ activity (WIEDERHOLT and ZADUNAISKY 1986) have shown that this transporter causes intracellular $Cl^-$ ions to exceed their equilibrium potential in pigmented (and non-pigmented) cells. Thus, $Cl^-$ ions are actively transported into the intracellular compartment of the ciliary epithelium.

## 2.5 Transport of absorbic acid

It is well known that the concentration of ascorbic acid in the aqueous humor is higher than in plasma in many species including humans and oxen (BARANY and LANGHAM 1955; BECKER 1967; KINSEY 1947). In cultured cells, we could characterize the basic transport mechanism for ascorbic acid secretion in the ciliary epithelium (HELBIG et al. 1989 a). The intracellular was about 40 times higher than the extracellular concentration of labeled ascorbate. This uptake mechanism exhibited first-order saturation kinetics with increasing ascorbate concentrations and second-order saturation kinetics with increasing sodium concentrations. These kinetics studies suggest a cotransport of 2 (or more) $Na^+$ and 1 ascorbate ion (see No. 5 in Fig. 2). The electrogenicity of the ascorbate transport was verified by cell membrane voltage measurements showing a depolarization on application of ascorbate (and $Na^+$) (HELBIG et al. 1989 a). This secondary active transport causes ascorbic acid (and $Na^+$) to accumulate in the cellular compartment of the ciliary epithelium. An exit step (No. 9 in Fig. 2) across the basolateral membrane of non-pigmented cells has to be postulated. This exit step has not yet been described in detail. Our model is supported by the finding that ascorbate uptake is $Na^+$- dependent in intact ciliary-body preparations (CHU and CANDIA 1988; SOCCI and DELAMERE 1988). In addition to the described mechanism, we found a $Na^+$-independent uptake mechanism for the oxidized form of the vitamin, dehydroascorbic acid (DHA), that is mediated by DHA reductase in the ciliary epithelium (HELBIG et al. 1989 a).

## 3.0 Electrolyte transport mechanisms in cultured non-pigmented epithelial (NPE) cells

### 3.1 Na⁺/K⁺ transport and K⁺ conductance

Intracellular membrane voltages were measured in a virus-transformed cell clone derived from human non-pigmented ciliary epithelial cells (HELBIG et al. 1989 b, 1989 e). Addition of ouabain immediately reduced the intracellular potential. The membrane voltage was depolarized by removal of extracellular $K^+$ and transiently hyperpolarized by its readdition after $K^+$ depletion. Both intracellular voltage changes were inhibited in the presence of ouabain. We concluded that cultured human and bovine NPE cells possess an electrogenic $Na^+/K^+$ transporter ($Na^+/K^+$-ATPase) that causes $Na^+$ to move from the cytoplasm of NPE across the basolateral membrane into the aqueous humor (No. 6 in Fig. 2).

Various methods have been used to identify this enzyme in the ciliary epithelium with high activity in the basolateral membrane of NPE cells facing the aqueous humor (COCA-PRADOS and LOPEZ-BRIONES 1987; COLE 1964; FLÜGEL and LÜTJEN-DRECOLL 1988; FLÜGEL et al. 1989; RILEY and KISHIDA 1986; SHIOSE and SEARS 1965). It should be mentioned again (see chapter 2.1) that the α-subunit of $Na^+/K^+$-ATPase differs in NPE and PE cells, suggesting functionally different enzymes (COCA-PRADOS and LOPEZ-BRIONES 1987). A $H^+/K^+$-ATPase has also been found in rabbit NPE cells (FAIN et al. 1988). Our studies as well as microelectrode studies in the intact ciliary epithelium (GREEN et al. 1985; WIEDERHOLT and ZADUNAISKY 1986, 1990) suggest that, driven by ATP hydrolysis the $Na^+/K^+$ transporter actively pumps $Na^+$ into the aqueous humor in exchange for $K^+$. This assumption is supported by earlier observations that injection of ouabain into the anterior chamber reduced aqueous humor formation and $Na^+$ transport (GARG and OPPELT 1970) and that ouabain inhibited transepithelial current in isolated ciliary epithelia (KRUPIN et al. 1984; PESIN and CANDIA 1982/1983; WIEDERHOLT and ZADUNAISKY 1987). We assume transepithelial $Na^+$ secretion into the aqueous humor to be effected through a functional syncytium of the PE and NPE cell: (1) The $Na^+/K^+$-ATPase (No. 1 in Fig. 2) establishes the concentration gradients of electrolytes across the membrane, (2) the $Na^+$ gradient is the driving force of the secondary active $Na^+$ transporters (No. 2 – 5 in Fig. 2) responsible for the uptake of $Na^+$, $Cl^-$, $HCO_3^-$ and other ions into the cell, (3) $Na^+$ ions (coupled with $Cl^-$, $HCO_3^-$, ascorbic acid, etc.) are distributed equally between PE and NPE cells via gap junctions, and (4) $Na^+$ is actively secreted (No. 6 in Fig. 2) into the aqueous humor. This simplified model is based on the assumption that PE and NPE cells are morphologically (RAVIOLA and RAVIOLA 1978) and electrically (GREEN et al. 1985; WIEDERHOLT and ZADUNAISKY 1986) coupled to a functional syncytium. It has indeed been shown that electrolyte activities are identical in both compartments (WIEDERHOLT and ZADUNAISKY 1986).

Finally, it should be mentioned that all these transporters and conductivities can be significantly modified by second messengers hormones, and various drugs (BIANCHI et al. 1986; CHU et al. 1986, 1987; CHU and CANDIA 1987, 1988; HELBIG et al. 1987, 1988 a, 1988 b, 1988 c, 1989 a, 1989 b, 1989 c, 1989 d, 1989 e, 1989 f, 1989 g; KISHIDA et al. 1981, 1982, 1986; KRUPIN et al. 1984; PESIN and CANDIA 1982/1983; SAITO et al. 1980; STRAUSS and WIEDERHOLT 1991; STRAUSS et al. 1991; WIEDER-HOLT and ZADUNAISKY 1986, 1987, 1990, WIEDERHOLT et al. 1989, 1991, WIEDER-HOLT and JENTSCH 1990).

The potassium ion is believed to recycle across the membrane through $K^+$ channels (No. 6 in Fig. 2). $K^+$ conductance is a common property of most cell membranes and contributes to the steady-state membrane-voltage. The marked depolarisation by increasing extracellular $K^+$ which we observed in cultured human and bovine NPE cells (HELBIG et al. 1989 b, 1989 e) is typical for $K^+$ conductance. This conductance could be partly blocked by $Ba^{2+}$ and quinidine, both common $K^+$ channel blockers. $K^+$ conductance in NPE cells has also been found in situ using microelectrodes and recently with patch clamp techniques, and $Ba^{2+}$ added to the aqueous side had a marked effect on transepithelial current and cell volume regulation in NPE cells (FAIN and FARAHBAKHSH 1989; FARAHBAKHSH and FAIN 1987; GREEN et al. 1985; YANTORNO et al. 1987, 1989). As in most cells, we also found the relative $K^+$ conductance to be dependent on pH and calcium in NPE cells, indicating that $K^+$ channels are modified in their open probability by $Ca^{2+}$ and $H^+$ ions. Since the reduction of $K^+$ conductance only occured at very low extracellular $Ca^+$ concentrations, we speculated that intracellular rather than extracellular $Ca^{2+}$ was the modulator of $K^+$ conductance (HELBIG et al. 1989 b, 1989 e).

In accordance with this hypothesis, we could demonstrate that $K^+$ conductance is regulated by hormones such as acetylcholine, for which intracellular $Ca^{2+}$ serves as second messenger (HELBIG et al. 1989 c). Such a hormonal regulation is exemplified in Fig. 5. Application of acetylcholine to human cultured NPE cells induced a biphasic membrane voltage response. An immediate transient hyperpolarization was followed by a sustained depolarization. These responses were irreversibly blocked by atropine. The acetylcholine-induced response of the membrane potential was not changed by either $Ca^{2+}$-free media or $Ca^{2+}$ channel blockers (verapamil, cobalt). However, the initial hyperpolarization was reduced in the presence of barium or quinidine. Both substances are typical $K^+$ channels blockers. From these results, it was postulated thast acetylcholine transiently hyperpolarizes membrane voltage in cultured human NPE cells by $K^+$ channel activation mediated by mobilization of $Ca^{2+}$ from intracellular stores. This hypothesis was confirmed by using the fluorescence of an intracellularly trapped dye (Fura-2) to measure cytoplasmic $Ca^{2+}$ activity. Addition of acetylcholine led to an immediate transient increase of cytoplasmic $Ca^{2+}$ activity (HELBIG et al. 1989 c). The sustained depolarization after application of acetylcholine is probably due to the opening of an unspecific cation channel. The model described in Fig. 5 seems to be applicable in a more general way. The effects of histamine and endothelin on cultured cells were similar to those of acetylcholine. $H_1$ and endothelin receptors mediate membrane voltage changes by increasing $K^+$ conductance via transient intracellular calcium elevation (STAHL et al. 1992). Modifications of $K^+$ channel activity could affect $K^+$ recycling and indirectly influence the $Na^+$ transport rate. Thus, the action of substances such as acetylcholine on $K^+$ channels could explain a modulation of ion transport and aqueous humor secretion across the ciliary epithelium.

## RELATIVE ACTIVITY OF IONIC TRANSPORTERS INVOLVED IN pH_i REGULATION IN CILIARY PIGMENTED EPITHELIAL CELLS

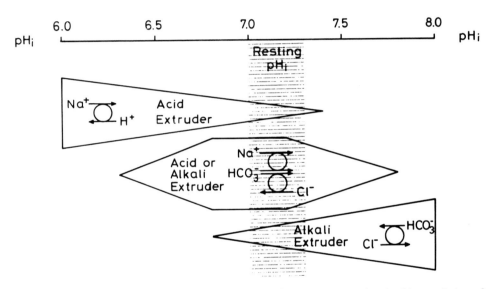

Fig. 4. Schematic representation of the relative activity of the transporters involved in regulation of intracellular pH (pH_i).

### 3.2 Cl⁻ conductance

Extracellular $Cl^-$ replacement led to a transient depolarization (HELBIG et al. 1989b, 1989e) which is compatible with a $Cl^-$ conductance (No. 7 in Fig. 2). At present we have no specific inhibitors available to block $Cl^-$ channels. Most of the blockers which are used in other epithelia had only a small effect on cultured NPE cells. However, the effect was most marked with stilbene disulfonate derivatives (DIDS, SITS). These substances inhibit not only anion exchangers and $Na^+$/

$HCO_3^-$ cotransporters but also $Cl^-$ conductance pathways. Thus, NPE cells express a $Cl^-$ conductance sensitive to stilbene derivatives. The downregulation of $Cl^-$ channel activity during $Cl^-$ depletion could be a feedback mechanism which protects the cell from massive changes in membrane voltage and intracellular $Cl^-$. A recent patch clamp study also described $Cl^-$ channels in cultured NPE cells (YANTORNO et al. 1987), and application of DIDS to the aqueous humor reduced transepithelial electrical current (CHU et al. 1987; PESIN and CANDIA 1982/1983). Furthermore, the use of plasma membrane vesicles led to the postulation of a chloride channel in human and bovine NPE cells but not in pigmented epithelial cells. The putative chloride channel was activated by epinephrine and partially blocked by β-blockers (CHERKSEY et al. 1991).

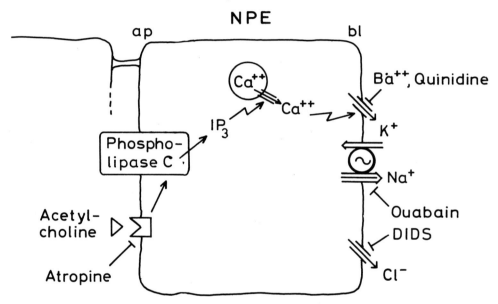

Fig. 5. Modulation of $K^+$ conductance in non-pigmented epithelial cells by acetylcholine.

### 3.3 $HCO_3^-$ exit step

The transport of bicarbonate is basically rather difficult to investigate, since $HCO_3^-$ is in a pH-dependent equilibrium with $CO_2$. Our results from cultured NPE cells suggest a $HCO_3^-$ conductance (HELBIG et al. 1989 b, 1989 e); however, other transfer mechanisms such as cotransporters could not be excluded (see No. 8 in Fig. 2). A $Na^+/HCO_3^-$ cotransport has recently been postulated as an exit step from NPE cells into the aqueous humor (WOLOSIN et al. 1989; YANTORNO et al. 1987). The basolateral membrane of NPE cells stained histochemically for carbonic anhydrase (LÜTJEN- DRECOLL and LÖNNERHOLM 1981). This membrane-bound carbonic anhydrase enzyme could be involved in ion transport across the NPE cell and thus secretion of aqueous humor. Wistrand (WISTRAND 1984) postulated an interesting model: membrane-bound CA (CA IV) hydrates $CO_2$ to $H_2CO_3$, and carbonic acid cleaves into $H^+$ and $HCO_3^-$. If this happens within the membrane the negative membrane voltage inside the cell would cause $H^+$ and $HCO_3^-$ to move in opposite directions. $H^+$ would pass into the cytoplasm and $HCO_3^-$ into the aqueous humor. Thus, carbonic anhydrase in the basolateral membrane of NPE cells is probably important for the exit step of $HCO_3^-$.

Concerning mechanisms of transport across the membranes of NPE (and PE) cells, it should be mentioned that we compared the membrane properties of virus-transformed human NPE cells with bovine NPE cells in primary culture (HELBIG et al. 1989 b, 1989 c, 1989 e). Results in cultured bovine and human NPE cells were identical for $Na^+/K^+$ transport, pH- and $Ca^{2+}$-modulated $K^+$ conductance, stilbene-sensitive $Cl^-$ conductance, and voltage responses to removal of $Na^+$ and $HCO_3^-$ or addition of acetylcholine.

In summary, the functional syncytium of PE and NPE cells with the various transporters and conductances could be used as a model to explain transepithelial transport of sodium, chloride, bicarbonate, and ascorbic acid across the ciliary epithelium, and to describe the involvement of the carbonic anhydrase and various hormones and drugs in aqueous humor formation.

## Acknowledgement

Supported by Deutsche Forschungsgemeinschaft (Grant Wi 328/11).

## References

BÁRÁNY, E., M. E. LANGHAM (1955): On the origin of the ascorbic acid in the aqueous humor of guinea pigs and rabbits. Acta Physiol. Scand. *34:* 99 – 115.

BECKER, B. (1955): The mechanism of the fall in intraocular pressure induced by the carbonic anhydrase inhibitor Diamox. Am. J. Ophthalmol. *39;* 177 – 184.

BECKER, B. (1967): Ascorbate transport in guinea pig eyes. Invest. Ophthalmol. *6:* 410 – 415.

BERGGREN, L. (1960): Intracellular potential measurements from the ciliary processes of the rabbit eye in vivo and in vitro. Acta, Physiol. Scand. *48:* 461 – 470.

BERGGREN, L. (1964): Direct observation of secretory pumping in vitro of the rabbit eye ciliary processes. Invest. Ophthalmol. *3:* 266 – 272.

BIANCHI, C., M. B. ANAND-SRIVASTAVA, A. DE LEÁN, L. GUTKOWSKA, D. FORTHOMME, J. GENEST, M. CANTIN (1986): Localization and characterization of specific receptors for atrial natriurectic factor in the ciliary processes of the eye. Curr. Eye Res. *4:* 283 – 293.

BILL, A. (1975): Blood circulation and fluid dynamics in the eye. Physiol. Rev. *55:* 383 – 417.

CHERKSEY, B. D., D. J. FAUSS, J. A. ALVARADO, J. R. POLANSKY (1991): Dose-response effectiveness for opthalmic beta blockade of ciliary epithelial anion channel: activities of metipranolol and 1-bunolol metabolite compared to timolol. Invest. Ophthalmol. Vis. Sci. *32:* 868.

CHU, T. C., O. A., CANDIA, S. IIZUKA (1986): Effects of forskolin, prostaglandin $F_{2}\alpha$ and $Ba^{2+}$ on the short-circuit current of the isolated rabbit iris-ciliary body. Curr. Eye Res. *7:* 511 – 516.

CHU, T. C., O. A. CANDIA, S. M. PODOS (1987): Electrical parameters of the isolated monkey ciliary epithelium and effects of pharmacological agents. Invest. Ophthalmol. Vis. Sci. *28:* 1644 – 1648.

CHU, T. C., O. A. CANDIA (1987): Electrically silent $Na^+$ and $Cl^-$ fluxes across the rabbit ciliary epithelium. Invest. Ophthalmol. Vis. Sci. *28:* 445 – 450.

CHU, T. C., O. A. CANDIA (1988): Active transport of ascorbate across the isolated rabbit ciliary epithelium. Invest. Ophthalmol. Vis. Sci. *29:* 594 – 599.

COCA-PRADOS, L. M., G. LOPEZ-BRIONES (1987): Evidence that the α and α (+) isoforms of the catalytic subunit of $(Na^+, K^+)$ ATPase reside in distinct ciliary epithelial cells of the mammalian eye. Biochem. Biophys. Res. Comm. *145:* 460 – 466.

COLE, D. F. (1964): Location of ouabain-sensitive adenosine triphosphatase in ciliary epithelium. Exp. Eye Res. *3:* 72 – 75.

COLE, D. F. (1977): Secretion of aqueous humor. Exp. Eye Res. 25 (Suppl.): 161 – 176.

FAIN, G. L., A. SMOLKA, M. C. CILLUFFO, M. J. FAIN, D. A. LEE, N. C. BRECHA, G. SACHS (1988): Monoclonal antibodies to the $H^+$-$K^+$ ATPase of gastric mucosa selectively stain the non-pigmented cells of the rabbit ciliary body epithelium, Invest. Ophthalmol. Vis. Sci. *29:* 785 – 794.

FAIN, G. L., N. A. FARAHBAKHSH (1989): Voltage-activated currents recorded from rabbit pigmented cilliary body epithelial cells in culture. J. Physiol. *417:* 83 – 103.

FARAHBAKHSH, N. A., G. L. FAIN (1987): Volume regulation of non-pigmented cells from ciliary epithelium. Invest. Ophthalmol. Vis. Sci. *28:* 934 – 944.

FLÜGEL, C., E. LÜTJEN-DRECOLL (1988): Presence and distribution of $Na^+/K^+$-ATPase in the ciliary epithelium of the rabbit. Histochemistry *88:* 613 – 621.

FLÜGEL, C., E. LÜTJEN-DRECOLL, J. A. ZADUNAISKY, M. WIEDERHOLT (1989): Regional differences in the morphology and enzyme distribution of the spiny dogfish (*Squalus acanthias*) ciliary epithelium. Exp. Eye Res. *49:* 1097 – 1114.

FRIEDLAND, B. R., T. H. MAREN (1984): Carbonic anhydrase: Pharmacology of inhibitors and treatment of glaucoma. In: Pharamcology of the eye. SEARS, M. L. (Ed.), Springer Verlag, Berlin, Heidelberg, New York, pp. 279 – 309.

GARG, L. C., W. W. OPPELT (1970): The effect of ouabain and acetazolamide on transport of sodium and chloride from plasma to aqueous humor. J. Pharmacol. Exp. Ther. *175:* 237 – 247.

GREEN, K., C. BOUNTRA, P. GEORGIOU, C. R. HOUSE (1985): An electrophysiological study of rabbit ciliary epithelium. Invest. Ophthalmol. Vis. Sci. *26:* 371 – 381.

HELBIG, H., C. KORBMACHER, M. WIEDERHOLT (1987): $K^+$-conductance and electrogenic $Na^+/K^+$ transport of cultured bovine pigmented ciliary epithelium. J. Membrane Biol. *99:* 173 – 186.

HELBIG, H., C. KORBMACHER, S. BERWECK, D. KÜHNER, M. WIEDERHOLT (1988 a): Kinetic properties of $Na^+/H^+$ exchange in cultured bovine pigmented ciliary epithelial cells. Pflügers Arch. *412:* 80 – 85.

HELBIG, H., C. KORBMACHER, D. KÜHNER, S. BERWECK, M. WIEDERHOLT (1988 b): Characterization of $Cl^-/HCO_3^-$-exchange in cultured bovine pigmented ciliary epithelium. Exp. Eye Res. *47:* 515 – 523.

HELBIG, H., C. KORBMACHER, F. STUMPFF, M. COCA-PRADOS, M. WIEDERHOLT (1988 c): $Na^+/H^+$ exchange regulates intracellular pH in a cell clone derived from bovine pigmented ciliary epithelium. J. Cell Physiol. *137:* 384 – 389.

HELBIG, H., C. KORBMACHER, J. WOHLFARTH, S. BERWECK, D. KÜHNER, M. WIEDERHOLT (1989 a): Electronic $Na^+/ascorbate$ cotransport in cultured bovine pigmented ciliary epithelial cells. Amer. J. Physiol. *256:* C44 – C49.

HELBIG, H., C. KORBMACHER, J. WOHLFARTH, M. COCA-PRADOS, M. WIEDERHOLT (1989 b): Electrical membrane properties of a cell clone derived from human nonpigmented ciliary epithelium. Invest. Ophthalmol. Vis. Sci. *30:* 882 – 889.

HELBIG, H., C. KORBMACHER, J. WOHLFARTH, M. T. CORONEO, C. LINDSCHAU, P. QUASS, H. HALLER, M. COCA-PRADOS, M. WIEDERHOLT (1989 c): Effect of acetylcholine on membrane potential of cultured human nonpigmented ciliary epithelial cells. Invest. Ophthalmol. Vis. Sci. 30: 890 – 896.

HELBIG, H., C. KORBMACHER, F. STUMPFF, M. COCA-PRADOS, M. WIEDERHOLT (1989 d): Role of $HCO_3^-$ in the regulation of cytoplasmic pH in a cell clone derived from bovine pigmented ciliary epithelium. Am. J. Physiol. 257: C696 – C705.

HELBIG, H., C. KORBMACHER, J. WOHLFARTH, M. COCA-PRADOS, M. WIEDERHOLT (1989 e): Intracellular voltage recordings in bovine nonpigmented ciliary epithelial cells in primary culture. Current Eye Res. 8: 793 – 800.

HELBIG, H., C. KORBMACHER, M. NAWRATH, C. ERB, M. WIEDERHOLT (1989 f): Sodium bicarbonate cotransport in cultured pigmented ciliary epithelial cells. Current Eye Res. 8: 595 – 598.

HELBIG, H. C. KORBMACHER, C. ERB, M. NAWRATH, K. G. KNUUTTILA, P. WISTRAND, M. WIEDERHOLT (1989 g): Coupling of $^{22}$Na and $^{36}$Cl uptake in cultured pigmented ciliary epithelial cells: a proposed role for the isoenzymes of carbonic anhydrase. Current Eye Res. 8: 1111 – 1119.

KINSEY, V. E. (1947): Transfer of ascorbic acid and related compounds across the blood aqueous barrier. Am. J. Ophthalmol. 30: 1262 – 1266.

KISHIDA, K., T. SASABE, R. MANABE, T. OTORI (1981): Electric characteristics of the isolated rabbit ciliary body. Jpn. J. Ophthalmol. 25: 407 – 416.

KISHIDA, K., T. SASABE, S. IIZUKA, R. MANABE, T. OTORI (1982): Sodium and chloride transport across the isolated rabbit ciliary body. Curr. Eye. Res. 2: 149 – 152.

KISHIDA, K., Y. MIWA, C. IWATA (1986): 2-substituted 1, 3, 4-thiadiazole-5-sulfonamides as carbonic anhydrase inhibitors: their effects on the transepithelial potential difference of the isolated rabbit ciliary body and on the intraocular pressure of the living rabbit eye. Exp. Eye Res. 43: 981 – 995.

KRUPIN, T., P. S. REINACH, O. A. CANDIA, S. M. PODOS (1984): Transepithelial electrical measurements in the isolated rabbit iris-ciliary body. Exp. Eye Res. 38: 115 – 123.

LÜTJEN-DRECOLL, E., G. LÖNNERHOLM (1981): Carbonic anhydrase distribution in the rabbit eye by light and electron microscopy. Invest. Ophthalmol. Vis. Sci. 21: 782 – 797.

MAREN, T. H. (1988): The kinetics of $HCO_3^-$ synthesis related to fluid secretion, pH control, and $CO_2$ elimination. Ann. Rev. Physiol. 50: 695 – 717.

MILLER, J. E., M. A. CONSTANT (1960): The measurement of rabbit ciliary epithelium potentials in vitro. Am. J. Physiol. 50: 855 – 861.

PESIN, S. R., O. A. CANDIA (1982/1983): $Na^+$ and $Cl^-$ fluxes, and effects of pharmacological agents on the short-circuit current of the isolated rabbit iris-ciliary body. Curr. Eye. Res. 2: 815 – 827.

RAVIOLA, G., E. RAVIOLA (1978): Intercellular junctions in the ciliary epithelium. Invest. Ophthalmol. Vis. Sci. 17: 958 – 981.

RILEY, M. V., K. KISHIDA (1986): ATPases of ciliary epithelium: Cellular and subcellular distribution and probable role in secretion of aqueous humor. Exp. Eye Res. 42: 559 – 568.

SAITO, Y., K. ITOI, K. HORIUCHI, T. WATANABE (1980): Mode of action of furosemide on the chloride-dependent short-circuit current across the ciliary body epithelium of toad eyes. J. Membrane Biol. 53: 85 – 93.

SHIOSE, Y., M. SEARS (1965): Localization and other aspects of the histochemistry of the nucleoside phosphatases in the ciliary epithelium of albino rabbits. Invest. Ophthalmol. 4: 64 – 75.

SOCCI, R. R., N. A., DELAMERE (1988): Characteristics of ascorbate transport in the rabbit iris ciliary body. Exp. Eye res. 46: 853 – 861.

STAHL, F., H.-J. GARUS, A. LEPPLE-WIENHUES, M. WIEDERHOLT (1992): Effects of histamine on membrane potential of cultured human nonpigmented ciliary epithelial cells. German J. Ophthalmol. 1: 62 – 66.

STRAUSS, O., M. WIEDERHOLT (1991): Transepithelial resistance of ciliary epithelial cells in culture: Functional modification by protamine and extracellular calcium. Comp. Biochem. Physiol. 100 A: 987 – 993.

STRAUSS, O., F. STAHL, M. WIEDERHOLT (1991): Stimulation of the calcium messenger system by histamine in cultured human nonpigmented cells of the ciliary epithelium. Pflüglers Arch. 418 (Suppl. 1): R 76.

WIEDERHOLT, M., J. A. ZADUNAISKY (1986): Membrane potentials and intracellular chloride activity in the ciliary body of the shark. Pflüglers Arch. *407:* (Suppl. 2): S112 – S115.

WIEDERHOLT, M., J. A. ZADUNAISKY (1987): Effects of ouabain and furosemide on transepithelial electrical parameters of the isolated shark ciliary epithelium. Invest. Ophthalmol. Vis. Sci. *28:* 1353 – 1356.

WIEDERHOLT, M., C. FLÜGEL, E. LÜTJEN-DRECOLL, J. A. ZADUNAISKY (1989): Mechanically stripped pigmented and nonpigmented epithelium of the shark ciliary body: Morphology and transepithelial electrical properties. Exp. Eye Res. *49:* 1031 – 1043.

WIEDERHOLT, M., T. J. JENTSCH (1990): Cell culture of bovine corneal endothelial cells and its application to transport studies. In: Methods in enzymology. (Eds. S. FLEISCHER, B. FLEISCHER), Vol. *192:* Biomembranes Part W, Cellular and subcellular transport: Epithelial cells. Academic Press, San Diego, New York, Boston, London, Sydney, Tokyo, Toronto, pp. 571 – 582.

WIEDERHOLT, M., J. A. ZADUNAISKY (1990): Electrolyte transport across the ciliary epithelium of the shark. In "Animal Nutrition and Transport Processes. 2. Transport, Respiration and Excretion: Comparative and Environmental Aspects" (Eds. J.-P. TRUCHOT and B. LAHLOU), Comp. Physiol. Basel, Karger, Vol. 6, pp. 171 – 184.

WIEDERHOLT, M., H. HELBIG, C. KORBMACHER (1991): Ion transport across the ciliary epithelium: lessons from cultured cells and proposed role of carbonic anhydrase. In: Carbonic Anhydrase. (Eds. F. BOTRE, G. GROSS, B. T. STOREY) VCH, Weinheim, New York, Basel, Cambridge, pp. 232 – 244.

WISTRAND, P. J. (1984): Properties of membrane-bound carbonic anhydrase., Ann. N.Y. Acad. Sci. *429:* 195 – 206.

WISTRAND, P. J., N. SCHENHOLM, G. LÖNNERHOLM (1986): Carbonic anhydrase isoenzymes CA I and CA II in the human eye. Invest. Ophthalmol. Vis. Sci. *27:* 419 – 428.

WOLOSIN, M., J. A. BONANNO, T. E. MACHEN (1989): Na-dependent $HCO_3^-$ transport and $Cl^-/HCO_3^-$ exchange in ciliary epithelium. Ann. N.Y. Acad. Sci. *574:* 131 – 133.

YANTORNO, R. E., T. KRUPIN, M. CIVAN (1987): Selective and nonselective ion channels in intact rabbit ciliary epithelium. Invest. Ophthalmol. Vis. Sci. *28* (Suppl.): 347.

YANTORNO, R. E., M. COCA-PRADOS, T. KRUPIN, M. CIVIAN (1989): Volume regulation of cultured, transformed, nonpigmented epithelial cells from human ciliary body. Exp. Eye Res. *49:* 423 – 437.

*Cellular Pharmacology Laboratory,*
*Departement of Ophthalmology, University of California,*
*Medical Center, San Francisco, CA*

# Receptor characterization of cultured human non-pigmented and pigmented ciliary epithelial cells using cyclic nucleotide responses

J. R. POLANSKY, G. M. LUI, J. A. ALVARADO and D. J. FAUSS

## Introduction

There has been substantial interest in the individual properties of non-pigmented ciliary epithelium (NPE) and pigmented ciliary epithelium (CPE), as well as their functional interrelationships, with regard to the secretion of aqueous humor. The mechanisms underlying active secretion along with selective barrier characteristics of the double layered epithelium are being investigated by several groups to understand the regulatory controls over the flow rate and composition of aqueous humor. Many important classes of drugs (e.g. beta blockers, alpha adrenergic agents, and possibly carbonic anhydrase inhibitors) could potentially exert their therapeutic effects by an action on the NPE and/or CPE cells. The NPE and/or CPE also represent possible target sites for the action of a wide variety of hormones and other regulatory factors (including vasoactive intestinal peptide [VIP], atrial naturetic peptide [ANP], and dopaminergic agents) which may play a role in the physiological regulation of aqueous inflow. A number of laboratories are currently evaluating direct receptor-mediated effects of these and other regulatory agents on the ciliary epithelium *in vivo* and *in vitro* using a variety of methods; recent models summarizing potential interactions between the properties of the NPE and CPE cell types and their potential interrelationships in the ciliary body have recently been presented (see WIEDERHOLT, HELBIG and KORMACHER 1991; WOLOSIN et al. 1989).

Our first pharmacologic evaluations involving the ciliary epithelium involved beta adrenergic and muscarinic cholinergic radioligand binding in isolated bovine NPE cells (POLANSKY and ALVARADO 1985; POLANSKY et al. 1985). Methods were developed to obtain >95% pure NPE cells free from CPE and other tissues of fresh bovine ciliary processes by gentle agitation under appropriate conditions. The bovine NPE demonstrated a selectivity for beta adrenergic drugs compatible with $\beta_2$ receptors and showed specific muscarinic cholinergic binding sites as defined in competition studies with a variety of antagonists and agonists. These NPE preparations also provided useful tissue/cell culture correlations for ion channel studies conducted by our collaborators (CHERKSEY et al. 1988, 1991). The fractionated bovine NPE did not appear useful for cell culture, since they showed little capacity for cell division. The bovine NPE isolated in this manner also did not show drug-induced elevations of cyclic-AMP in whole cells assays, probably due to membrane damage which occurred during our separation procedures of the NPE from the CPE. Other laboratories were able to use mechanical separation of rabbit NPE and CPE cells for membrane adenylate cyclase measurements (MITTAG, TORMAY and PODOS 1987) and evaluations of specific ATP-ases (MARTIN-VASALLO, GHOSH and COCA-PRADOS 1989). Tissue fractionation also appeared to provide a sufficient number of viable cells for some cell culture approaches using viral transformation to expand the ciliary epithelial cell cultures as described by COCA-PRADOS and WAX (1986). Pharmacologic responses, especially for effects involving inositol phosphate metabolism and $Ca^{++}$, have been presented by those investigators using the SV40 transformed ciliary epithelial cells (WAX and COCA-PRADOS 1989; LEE, REISINE and WAX 1989).

Concurrent with the studies being conducted on the transformed ciliary body cells, we began to conduct evaluations of pharmacologic receptors/responses, using nontransformed human NPE and CPE cells. This appeared particularly important for our interests in drugs which influence cyclic nucleotide pathways, since SV40 transformation could produce alterations influencing these pathways. It was also likely that viral transformation would alter cell growth properties, so that certain differentiated cell responses would not be recovered readily. We were interested in human rather than animal cells because of potential species-related pharmacologic differences.

Over the past six years we have developed effective methods for the propagation of fetal human NPE and CPE cells which overcome the obstacles observed using standard culture conditions. The advances made include (i) the ability to dissect the separate cell layers using ciliary processes of five month old fetal and young postnatal eyes, (ii) the definition of appropriate growth conditions for fetal human NPE and CPE cells permitting serial cell division and preservation of the morphology of the original cultures (LUI et al. 1986; ALVARADO et al. 1987), and (iii) the demonstration of expected pharmacologic specificity for the fetal human NPE and CPE cell types (POLANSKY et al. 1986; 1988). In spite of this progress, substantial work remains to properly define these systems and to obtain useful NPE and CPE cultures for evaluating drug effects (especially for postnatal cultures).

This paper summarizes the current state of our knowledge concerning drug effects on cyclic-nucleotide levels using fetal human NPE and CPE cells, with an emphasis on those drugs which may be useful in understanding NPE and CPE cell differentiated properties. In this regard, NPE cell responses to VIP, dopamine ($D_1$), and $\alpha_2$-adrenergic agents appear relevant.

## Methods

### Cell culture

Human tissues were obtained within 24 hours post-mortem in accordance with the guidelines of the UCSF Human Experimentation Committee, and were refrigerated in a McCarey-Kaufman tissue storage medium until dissected (usually within 24 hours after specimen collection). Dissection of the specimens was carried out in a sterile environment using a Zeiss operating microscope. The specimens were rinsed with Neosporin solution and placed in Earl's Balanced Salt Solution (EBSS) (Grand Island Biologicals, Grand Island, NY). Standard ophthalmic surgical tools were employed to open the eye along the equator. The non-pigmented epithelial layer was dissected free from the pigmented ciliary epithelium of the pars plicata, and the pigmented ciliary epithelium separated from the underlying ciliary stroma using a jeweler's forceps. The dissections were accomplished efficiently in tissue from five month old fetal eyes, and with greater difficulty in the postnatal eyes.

The tissues were observed under phase contrast microscopy to assure that dissected NPE and CPE cell layers were cleanly separated before a given tissue piece was used for explant migration. Preparation of 35 mm dishes coated with extracellular matrix (ECM) was conducted by minor modifications of the methods described by GOSPODAROWICZ et al. (1986). Use of ECM facilitated adherence of the explants and encouraged the outgrowth of cells from the small explants (50 to 500 cells). The dissected tissues were placed in the tissue culture dishes with 0.8 ml of media (M 199-EBSS [M199] supplemented with 15% fetal calf serum [FCS] and basic fibroblast growth factor [FGF, 500 ng/ml] partially purified extract using a G-75 column) for approximately twelve hours. After this time most of the explants had attached to the ECM substrate and the media volume could be increased to 2 ml/dish. Media was changed every other day until the primary outgrowth of cells was observed. In most cultures, approximately one week was required before a discernable colony (approximately $3\text{-}5 \times 10^3$ cells) had migrated and divided free from the explants. The cells of the colony were dispersed and passaged using STV (0.05% trypsin, 0.02% EDTA in 0.9% NaCl, pH 7.4) onto new 35 mm ECM-coated dishes and grown in 15% FCS with FGF as described above. As soon as these cultures became confluent, they were again passaged, using a ratio of 1:10 to 1:20. The NPE and CPE cultures were frozen down at various passages (2nd through 5th) and stored in liquid nitrogen at $10^6$ cells/ml (in culture media with 10% DMSO). Recent studies have shown that 1 to 5 ng/ml purified recombinant human bFGF (Intergen, Purchase, NY) produced maximal NPE and CPE stimulation of cell division and reasonable culture morphology. We are currently growing NPE and CPE cells with this recombinant bFGF, but the cultures have not yet been properly characterized.

For the current experiments NPE and CPE were propagated from second through fourth passage cells. The frozen stocks of cells were thawed and placed in 24-well multiwells (Falcon Plastics, Oxnard, CA) coated with ECM at 1 to $5 \times 10^4$ cells/well in culture medium at 37 °C. At confluency, which requires approximately 5 to 8 days of growth, the cells were shifted to maintenance media (M199 culture medium with 10% FCS and no FGF). Cells were changed every second day using maintenance media for a minimum of 4 days prior to experiments.

Human trabecular meshwork cells and human scleral fibroblasts, obtained and cultured as previously described (POLANSKY et al. 1979), were used as controls for some experiments.

### Pharmacologic testing and cyclic nucleotide assays

Twenty-four hours prior to testing, confluent cultures of the NPE and CPE cells were changed to 1 ml of maintenance medium containing 1 µM indomethacin. One-half hour prior to testing, the cells were changed to serum-free M-199, with 1 µM indomethacin and 1 mM isobutylmethylxanthine (IBMX), a phosphodiesterase inhibitor. Drugs to be tested were prepared immediately before the experiment in the above serum free medium and then added to the cells in a timed, sequential fashion. The cells were incubated at 37 °C in a 5% $CO_2$ incubator for the indicated lengths of time, after which the media was rapidly removed by aspiration, and 0.5 ml 6% cold trichloroacetic acid (TCA) was added. The samples were extracted four times with two volumes of water saturated diethylether and stored at −20 °C prior to assay.

Cellular cyclic-AMP and cyclic-GMP were measured by radioimmunoassay according to standard methods. Antibody was obtained from Sigma Chemical Co., St. Louis, MO. Labeled cAMP and cGMP were obtained from New England Nuclear Corp., Boston, MA.

### Results

Human fetal NPE and CPE cells were propagated using third- and fourth-passage cells, as described in Methods. As shown in Fig. 1, passaged human fetal NPE and CPE retain their original plating morphology through serial passage at high split ratios (1 : 10 to 1 : 20). The fetal NPE pack in to form relatively uniform monolayers of cells which are larger than the CPE. The fetal CPE lose their pigmentation during active cell division and can then be observed to regain dark pigmentation on the culture dish. An increase in pigmentation and a more uniform epithelial morphology are observed if the CPE are maintained for several weeks after

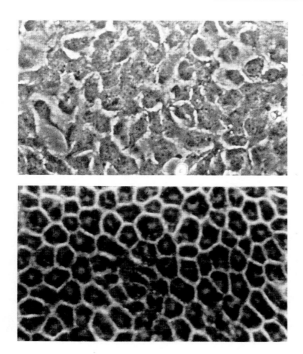

Fig. 1. Phase contrast microscopy of fourth passage human fetal NPE and CPE cells grown in culture according to Methods A. NPE cells were maintained in monolayer culture for 6 days after confluency (magnification approximately 450 x). B. CPE maintained in monolayer culture for 4 weeks showing dark pigmentation (magnification approximately 750x). Note that the CPE pack in tightly and are about half the size of the NPE. The CPE during active cell division and at initial confluency show no visible pigmentation.

confluency (the culture shown was maintained approximately one month post confluency). The fetal NPE cells can be maintained for several weeks after confluency, but these cultures show patches of cell loss and disruption of the mono-layer, approximately one to two weeks after confluency. It is clear that improved conditions are required for long-term maintenance of the NPE cell type (perhaps involving factors produced by the CPE). The NPE and CPE cells used for pharma-cologic evaluations presented in this section were routinely maintained for four to ten days post confluency, a time when both monolayers appear uniform but only minor CPE pigmentation is observed.

The first potentially specific agent tested was vasoactive intestinal peptide (VIP). This neurogastrointestinal peptide was of interest because Mittag's data (MITTAG, TORMAY and PODOS 1987) had suggested a VIP response in NPE but not CPE in rabbit ciliary processes and Bill's laboratory (NILSSON, SPERBER and BILL 1986) had shown a VIP effect on aqueous humor inflow in primates. Human trabecular meshwork (HTM) cells and human scleral fibroblasts (HSF) were employed as additional controls for the human NPE and CPE cells. Fig. 2, shows that VIP (1 µM) produced a 5-10 fold stimulation of cyclic-AMP, with no significant responses observed in the CPE, HTM, or HSF cell lines.

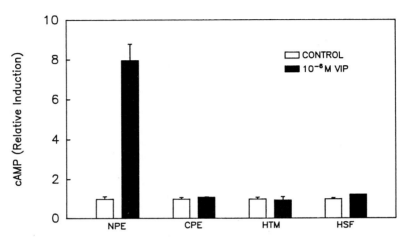

Fig. 2. VIP responses in human non-pigmented ciliary epithelium (NPE), pigmented ciliary epithelium (CPE), human trabecular meshwork (HTM) cells and human scleral fibroblasts (HSF). The NPE and CPE cells were from a five month-old fetal donor; the HTM cells and HSF cells were from an adult 30 year-old donor. Cultured cells were treated as described in Methods with 1 µM VIP for 10 minutes and cAMP was then assayed. Values are expressed as fold stimulation relative to control.

We had previously characterized an isoproterenol (ISO)-induced cyclic-AMP response in NPE and CPE, and antagonist effects compatible with $\beta_2$-adrenergic receptors. ISO-induced cyclic-AMP increases were used to help validate the differences between NPE and CPE following VIP stimulation. When NPE and CPE cells were grown and tested in parallel for ISO and VIP effects, the NPE showed a substantial stimulation by both agents (a 9-fold stimulation with 10 µM ISO and a 7-fold stimulation with 10 µM VIP), while the CPE showed a large ISO, but no VIP effect (13-fold stimulation with 10 µM ISO; no stimulation above baseline with 10 µM VIP). A positive VIP response in NPE cells and the lack of response in CPE cells was reported in two additional cell lines of each in which positive ISO responses were observed. Other agents which could influence aqueous flow were tested for cyclic-nucleotide effects. For example, $PGE_2$ and calcitonin gene related peptide (CGRP) showed expected increases in cyclic-AMP, and atrial naturetic peptide (ANP) showed increases in cyclic-GMP in both NPE and CPE cell types.

Since the doses of VIP used in these screening studies were chosen to be quite high to take into account the possibility of a low affinity receptor (which could be responding with the pharmacologic IOP changes noted), we next conducted studies to define the affinity and specificity of the putative VIP receptor. As presented in

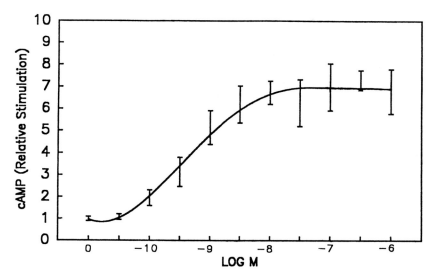

Fig. 3. Dose response effects of VIP on human fetal NPE grown and evaluated as described in Methods. The incubations were for 10 minutes and then terminated and assayed also as described in Methods.

Fig. 3, dose-response studies for VIP effects on the NPE showed an $EC_{50}$ of approximately 0.6 nM with a saturation of the response observed between 10-30 nM, comparable to the high affinity VIP receptor described in other systems. The specificity of the NPE response was evaluated using other neuro-gastrointestinal peptides which have homology with VIP, including glucagon, secretin and certain related hormones (Peptide Histidine Methionine [PHM] and Peptide Histidine Isoleucine [PHI]). VIP was the only peptide to elevate cAMP when added in the 0.1-10 nM range. PHM and PHI showed nearly maximal inductions at 1 μM concentrations with $EC_{50}$s of approximately 50 nM and 300 nM. Secretin was a submaximal inducer and showed only a minimal stimulation of cAMP at 1 μM concentrations. Glucagon and VIP fragment 10-28 showed no response at any concentration tested. The affinity and selectivity observed supports the view that VIP, and perhaps related bioactive peptides, can act at low concentrations to exert specific target cell effects on the NPE.

The finding of specific VIP responses in the cultured human fetal NPE and not CPE cells encouraged us to conduct experiments on alpha adrenergic and dopaminergic compounds, since these agents were also expected to influence IOP through effects on aqueous humor production. Pharmacologic responses to drugs in these classifications could also provide markers for the NPE compared to the CPE. It has been shown that $\alpha_2$-adrenergic agents antagonize the increase of cyclic-AMP seen with VIP treatment of rabbit ciliary processes, suggesting that both $\alpha_2$-adrenergic and VIP receptors are present in NPE cells (BAUSHER et al. 1987). Also, dopamine is believed to stimulate phosphorylation of the DARPP-32 protein in the non-pigmented rather than in the pigmented ciliary epithelium (STONE et al. 1986). Our studies on the cultured fetal human ciliary epithelium cells support the view that $\alpha_2$-adrenergic and dopaminergic ($D_1$) cyclic-AMP responses are found in the NPE cell type but not the CPE cell type (POLANSKY et al. 1986; 1988).

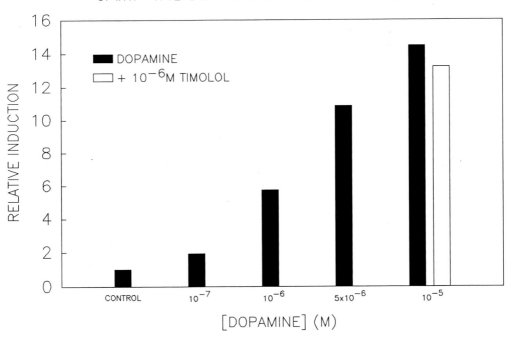

Fig. 4. Dose response induction of cyclic-AMP by dopamine in cultured human fetal NPE cells, conducted according to Methods. Timolol was added 5 minutes prior to the stimulation by dopamine at a dose which fully blocked $10^{-5}$ M isoproterenol effects on cyclic-AMP in the cells (from Fauss and Polansky, submitted).

As shown in Fig. 4, the addition of dopamine to the NPE cells produced a dose-dependent rise in cellular cyclic-AMP with a half maximal effect at approximately

$3 \times 10^{-6}$ M. The $10^{-5}$ M dose was shown not to be exerting its primary effect by a crossover to beta adrenergic receptors, since $10^{-6}$ M timolol produced only a minor decrease in the dopamine response (at this dose it completely abolishes $10^{-5}$ M ISO stimulation of cyclic-AMP). The dopamine stimulation could be effectively blocked with the $D_1$ antagonist SCH23390, but not with the relatively selective $D_2$ antagonist sulpiride, as shown in Fig. 5. No dopamine effect was observed in CPE, HTM, or HSF cell types.

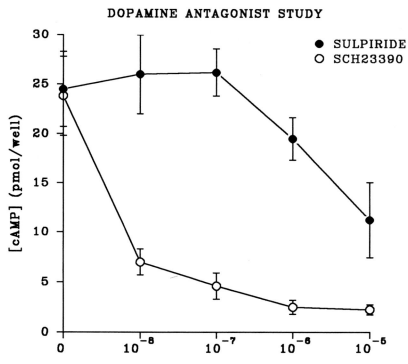

Fig. 5. Inhibition of dopamine stimulation of cyclic-AMP by SCH23390 and sulpiride in cultured human NPE cells, according to Methods. The antagonists were added 5 minutes prior to the addition of $10^{-5}$ M dopamine, with cyclic-AMP measured 10 minutes after addition of the agonist (from Fauss and Polansky, submitted).

Fig. 6 presents representative data obtained supporting an $\alpha_2$-adrenergic inhibition of cyclic-AMP levels in NPE cells. In the experiment shown, ISO-induced cyclic-AMP elevation was inhibited approximately 60% using the $\alpha_2$-adrenergic agonist clonidine. The inhibitory effect was overcome to a large degree with 1 μM rauwolscine, an $\alpha_2$-antagonist. In other experiments, BHT-920 also produced an effective inhibition of ISO and $PGE_2$-stimulated cyclic-AMP levels in NPE cells

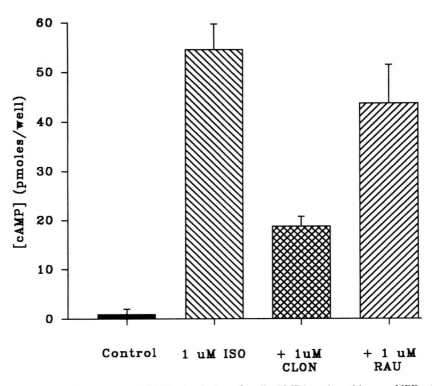

Fig. 6. Inhibition of isoproterenol (ISO) stimulation of cyclic-AMP in cultured human NPE cells by clonidine (CLON). Clonidine was added, with or without the prior addition of the $\alpha_2$-adrenergic antagonist rauwolscine (RAU), 5 minutes prior to addition of ISO. Cellular cyclic-AMP levels determined 10 minutes after addition of the beta agonist.

but not CPE cells, and this inhibition was reversed by phentolamine. No $\alpha_2$-adrenergic effect was seen in HTM or HSF cell types. In preliminary studies conducted by Mittag (unpublished data) on our cultured cells, $\alpha_2$-adrenergic receptor binding was detected in NPE but not CPE cells. These findings require further investigation, especially because the ability of NPE cultures to show their expected $\alpha_2$-adrenergic responses appears dependent upon appropriate culture conditions.

If NPE cells are grown on plastic rather than ECM, or without appropriate media, sera or growth factors, loss of both dopamine and $\alpha_2$-adrenergic responses is observed along with loss of normal epithelial morphology. Suboptimal growth may in part explain the diminished dopamine response and no $\alpha_2$-adrenergic response observed in our initial evaluations of postnatal NPE cultures, which are harder to propagate than the fetal cultures. Interestingly, postnatal NPE cells and fetal NPE grown on plastic preserve their appropriate VIP responses.

Further evaluations of specific receptors and transduction mechanisms in NPE and CPE cells may help in obtaining defined sources of these cells for more detailed physiological and pharmacological studies.

## Discussion

In this paper, we have shown the fetal human NPE and CPE cells grown in culture are morphologically distinct from each other and express differentiated receptor characteristics as defined by their cyclic nucleotide responses.

The specific responses of the NPE to VIP, dopamine, and $\alpha_2$-adrenergic agents are in general agreement with the concept that the NPE cell type is an important regulatory site for the active secretion of aqueous humor and pharmacologic regulation of IOP. CPE cells are quite responsive to other agonists in terms of their cyclic nucleotide responses (e.g. they show equal or greater effects on a cell basis for $PGE_2$, isoproterenol and CGRP stimulated cyclic-AMP, as well as for atrial naturetic peptide [ANP] stimulated cyclic-GMP [FAUSS and POLANSKY, unpublished observation]), although the CPE cells do not respond to the drugs which influence the NPE listed above.

The fact that all of the NPE (but none of the CPE) cultures tested have shown a positive VIP response, emphasizes that this receptor/response can provide a useful marker to distinguish two cell types. Studies by Crook et al. (CROOK et al. 1989; CROOK, BAZAN and POLANSKY 1991; CROOK and POLANSKY in press; CROOK, LUI and POLANSKY in press) demonstrated other specific drug and hormone effects on the NPE using assays of inositol phosphate/diacylglycerol (IP/DAG) metabolism. Some of these agents appear to distinguish NPE from CPE cells (unpublished data). Together, these studies suggest that the NPE and CPE cell types may play separate roles in their cooperative production of aqueous humor.

Studies of both cyclic-AMP responses and inositol phosphate metabolism (and $Ca^{++}$) have also emphasized the need for an optimization in the culture environment to achieve important receptor-mediated effects. Dopamine $D_1$ and $\alpha_2$-adrenergic responses, since they appear to be modulated by culture conditions, provide potentially useful differentiation markers for evaluating cultured human NPE cells. Time after confluency may be required to see the normal receptor/response. For example, the muscarinic cholinergic receptor described in NPE cells by Crook and POLANSKY (in press) is regained only after the cells have remained confluent for more than four days.

The use of molecular probes for the relevant mRNAs for these and other receptor types may help to characterize these systems and provide additional pharmacological markers for the NPE and CPE cell types. It is also possible that molecular biology approaches will help in the identification of unique receptor types, which might help to explain some of the anomalies observed in the evaluations of drug effects on IOP.

Improved methods for human NPE and CPE cultures are required to assure that appropriate receptor-mediated responses are preserved. Postnatal NPE and CPE cultures appear more difficult to propagate than fetal cultures, and all of the expected pharmacologic responses are not observed in these cells. As mentioned, our preliminary studies of postnatal NPE showed that the VIP response is maintained, but the dopamine response was diminished and no $\alpha_2$-adrenergic response was observed. Specific growth factor requirements, defined substrates for cell growth, as well as the potential role of NPE/CPE cell interactions and conditioned media, represent some of the variables which will be evaluated in an attempt to recover the missing or diminished responses.

## Summary and conclusion

The abililty to propagate human fetal nonpigmented ciliary epithelium (NPE) and pigmented ciliary epithelium (CPE) in culture provides an opportunity to examine the individual properties and pharmacologic responses of these two distinct cell types. In this report, drugs which may influence IOP by an effect on cyclic nucleotides were examined using methods developed for the effective propagation of these two important cell types. Both cell types show cyclic-AMP elevation with adrenergic agents (antagonist effects compatible with $\beta_2$ receptors), as well as with $PGE_2$ and CGRP; both cell types show cyclic-GMP elevation with ANP. However, NPE cells and not CPE cells show cyclic-AMP responses to vasoactive intestinal peptide (VIP), $\alpha_2$-adrenergic agents, and dopamine. Dose-response and selectivity studies for the cyclic-AMP changes indicated the presence of specific receptors for these drugs in the NPE cultures. The VIP stimulation of cyclic-AMP showed the expected high affinity response and specificity compared to other bioactive peptides known to influence the VIP receptor. It appears that VIP responses will provide a useful pharmacologic marker for the NPE cell type in culture. The dopamine stimulation of cyclic-AMP in NPE cells was not blocked by timolol and showed antagonist effects compatible with $D_1$ receptors. The NPE cells demonstrated an inhibition of isoproterenol stimulated cyclic-AMP levels with $\alpha_2$-adrenergic drugs, which was reversed by rauwolscine or phentolamine. The expression of dopaminergic and $\alpha_2$-adrenergic responses in NPE cells appeared to be dependent on culture conditions, and these responses were often lost if the passaged cultures did not form the orderly epithelial appearance of their original plating; the VIP responses in the NPE cells were much less dependent on the culture environment. Further studies of the expression of individual drug receptors/ responses will aid in evaluating the cells' differentiated features, and should help in conducting pharmacologic investigations. This will be important in attempting to investigate the multiple regulatory controls over aqueous humor production and to understand basic therapeutic mechanisms.

## Acknowledgements

Supported by NIH grant EY03980 and That Man May See Foundation.

## References

ALVARADO, J. A., J. R. POLANSKY, G. M. LUI (1987): Human pigmented ciliary epithelium: serial propagation of differentiated cells in culture. Invest. Ophthalmol. Vis. Sci. (ARVO Suppl.) 28: 283.

BAUSHER, L. P., D. S. GREGORY, M. L. SEARS (1987): Interaction between $\alpha_2$-adrenergic responses in rabbit ciliary processes. Curr. Eye Res. 6: 497–505.

CHERKSEY, B. D., J. A. ALVARADO, J. R. POLANSKY (1988): Ion channel activity of ciliary process epithelium vesicles reconstituted into planar bilayers. Invest. Ophthalmol. Vis. Sci. (Suppl) 29: 187.

CHERKSEY, B. D., D. J. FAUSS, J. A. ALVARADO, J. R. POLANSKY (1991): Dose-response effectiveness for ophthalmic beta blockade of ciliary epithelial anion channel: Activities of metapranolol and L-bunolol metabolite compared to timolol. Invest. Ophthalmol. Vis. Sci. (Suppl) 32: 868.

COCA-PRADOS, M., M. B. WAX (1986): Transformation of human ciliary epithelial cells by simian virus 40: Induction of cell proliferation and retention of $\beta_2$-adrenergic receptors. Proc. Natl. Acad. Sci. USA 83: 8754–8758.

CROOK, R. B., N. G. BAZAN, J. A. ALVARADO, J. R. POLANSKY (1989): Histamine stimulation of inositol phosphate metabolism in cultured human non-pigmented ciliary epithelial cells. Curr. Eye Res. 8: 415–421.

CROOK, R. B., N. G. BAZAN, J. R. POLANSKY (1991): Histamine $H_1$ receptor occupancy triggers inositol phosphates and intracellular calcium mobilization in human non-pigmented ciliary epithelial cells. Curr. Eye Res. 10: 593–600.

CROOK, R. B., J. R. POLANSKY: Neurotransmitters and neuropeptides stimulate inositol phosphates and intracellular calcium in cultured human nonpigmented ciliary epithelium. Invest. Ophthalmol. Vis. Sci. (in press).

CROOK, R. B., G. M. LUI, J. R. POLANSKY: Thrombin stimulates inositol phosphates formation, intracellular calcium levels and DNA synthesis in cultured human nonpigmented ciliary epithelial cells. Exp. Eye Res. (in press).

GOSPODAROWICZ, D. (1986): Preparation of extracellular matrices produced by cultured bovine corneal endothelial cells and PF HR-9 teratocarcinoma cells; their use in the study of cell proliferation and differentiation. In: Methods in Molecular and Cell Biology (BARNES, E. B., Ed.), LISS, A. R., New York, pp. 275–294.

LEE, C. H., T. D. REISINE, M. B. WAX (1989): Alterations of intracellular calcium in human nonpigmented ciliary epithelial cells of the eye. Exp. Eye Res. 48: 733–743.

LUI, G. M., J. A. ALVARADO, J. R. POLANSKY (1986): Isolation and serial propagation of human non-pigmented ciliary epithelium in tissue culture. Invest. Ophthalmol. Vis. Sci. (ARVO Suppl.) 27: 163.

MARTIN-VASELLO, P., S. GHOSH, M. COCA-PRADOS (1989): Expression of $Na^+ K^+$-ATPase $\alpha$-subunit isoforms in the human ciliary body and cultured ciliary epithelial cells. J. Cell. Physiol. 141: 243–52.

MITTAG, T. W., A. TORMAY, S. B. PODOS (1987): Vasoactive intestinal peptide and intraocular pressure: adenylate cyclase activation and binding sites for vasoactive intestinal peptide in membranes of ocular ciliary processes. J. Pharm. Exp. Therap. 241: 230–235.

NILSSON, S. F., G. SPERBER, A. BILL (1986): Effects of vasoactive intestinal peptide (VIP) in intraocular pressure, facility of outflow and formation of aqueous humor in the monkey. Exp. Eye Res. 43: 849–857.

POLANSKY, J. R., R. N. WEINREB, J. D. BAXTER, J. A. ALVARADO (1979): Human trabecular cells. I. Establishment in tissue culture and growth characteristics. Invest. Ophtalmol. Vis. Sci. *18:* 1043 – 1049.

POLANSKY, J. R., D. ZLOCK, A. BRASIER, E. BLOOM (1985): Adrenergic and cholinergic receptors in isolated non-pigmented ciliary epithelial cells. Curr. Eye Res. *4(4):* 517 – 522.

POLANSKY, J. R., G. M. LUI, J. A. ALVARADO (1986): Cultured human ciliary epithelium: serial propagation and pharmacologic responses. Proc. Int. Soc. Eye. Res. *7:* 136.

POLANSKY, J. R., D. J. FAUSS, G. M. LUI, T. W. MITTAG, J. A. ALVARADO (1988): Target cell effects of new glaucoma agents: α-adrenergic and dopamine effects on cultured human non-pigmented ciliary epithelium. Invest. Ophthalmol. Vis. Sci. (Suppl.) *29:* 16.

POLANSKY, J. R., J. A. ALVARADO (1985): Isolation and evaluation of target cells in glaucoma research: hormone receptors and drug responses. Curr. Eye Res. *4:* 267 – 279.

STONE, R. A., A. M. LATIES, A. C. Jr. HEMMINGS, C. C. OUIMET, P. GREENGARD (1986): DARPP-32, a dopamine-regulated phosphoprotein in the ciliary epithelium of the eye. J. Histochem. Cytochem. *34:* 1465 – 1468.

WAX, M. B., M. COCA-PRADOS (1989): Receptor-mediated phosphoinositide hydrolysis in human ocular ciliary epithelial cells. Invest. Ophthalmol. Vis. Sci. *30:* 1675.

WIEDERHOLT, M., H. HELBIG, C. KORBMACHER (1991): Ion transport across the ciliary epithelium: Lessons from cultured cells and proposed role of the carbonic anhydrase. In: Carbonic Anhydrase (BOTRE, F., G. GROSS, B. T. STOREY, VCH WEINHEIM [Eds.]: New York, Basel Cambridge) pp. 232 – 244.

WOLOSIN, M., J. A. BONANNO, T. E. MACHEN (1989): Na-dependent $HCO_3^-$ transport and $Cl^-/HCO_3^-$ exchange in ciliary epithelium. Ann. N.Y. Acad. Sci. *574:* 131 – 133.

*Department of Ophthalmology, University of Wisconsin Medical School,*
*Madison, Wisconsin, USA*

# Aging, accommodation and outflow facility

P. L. KAUFMAN, B. T. GABELT

Primary open-angle glaucoma (POAG) is a disease of aging. In the United States, the average age of the newly diagnosed POAG patient is 60 years, and two-thirds of all POAG patients are over the age of 65. The risk of POAG increases progressively throughout the adult years. While the prevalence of the disease is perhaps 0.5 to 1 % overall, it occurs in 3 – 5 % of the white and over 10 % of the black population over the age of 80 years (Fig. 1) (LESKE 1983; TIELSCH 1991; TIELSCH et al. 1991.)

While intraocular pressure is only one of perhaps many factors contributing to the disease, it is certainly a major one. Intraocular pressure also rises throughout life in many populations, although in some the age relationship is obscured when other factors, such as systemic blood pressure are taken into account (KAUFMAN 1987; SHIOSE and KAWASE 1986). Given this age-dependence, it is reasonable to examine the age-dependence of various factors which influence the intraocular pressure.

There is a statistically definite, but minimal and probably clinically unimportant age-related reduction in the rate of aqueous humor formation (KAUFMAN 1987). Episcleral venous pressure probably does not change with age (KAUFMAN 1987). The relationship of uveoscleral outflow to age has not been well studied. The percentage of total outflow constituted by uveoscleral outflow has been measured directly in only 12 human eyes, all of which were being enucleated for posterior segment tumors but presumably had no anterior segment abnormalities. Excluding those which were pretreated with pilocarpine, uveoscleral outflow comprised on average about 11 % of total outflow in these 9 patients averaging about 61 years of age (BILL and PHILLIPS 1971). Using a less direct non-invasive technique, TOWN- SEND and BRUBAKER (1980) were able to estimate pressure sensitive and pressure insensitive outflow in the control eyes of their unilaterally epinephrine treated patients, a group of young individuals averaging about 24 years of age. In these 10 patients, pressure insensitive outflow, presumably representing primarily uveoscleral outflow, comprised more than 30 % of total outflow, a figure closer to that seen in young normal monkeys (BILL 1971). Although these techniques are vastly different and the data were collected by different research groups, there are anatomic changes in the aging human ciliary muscle (hyalinization, increased pigment deposition in the intramuscular spaces, increased connective tissue content in the ciliary muscle, etc.) consistent with such an age-related decline of uveoscleral outflow (STIEVE 1949).

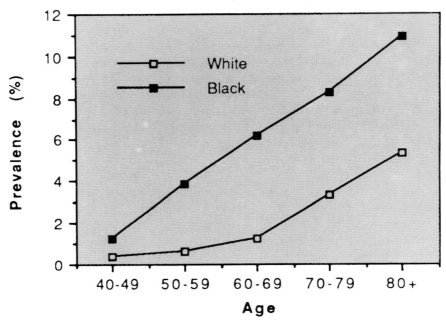

Fig. 1. Prevalence of primary open-angle glaucoma by age and race. (From TIELSCH 1991).

Total and trabecular outflow facility clearly decline with age in the human (KAUFMAN 1987). The magnitude of the decline from young adulthood to old age has been estimated to be 30% or more. It has been variously attributed to loss of trabecular cells presumably compromising trabecular function in some as yet unknown way (ALVARADO et al. 1984), increased deposition of "plaque" or other extracellular material within the meshwork, decreased phagocytic capability, some combination thereof, or other factors (LÜTJEN-DRECOLL et al. 1986).

We know from work done largely within Professor Rohen's institute that the ciliary muscle has an intimate anatomic relationship with the trabecular meshwork (ROHEN et al. 1967; LÜTJEN-DRECOLL et al. 1981; ROHEN et al. 1981; ROHEN 1982).

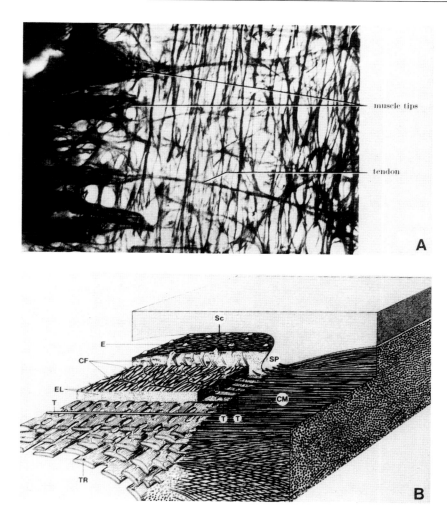

Fig. 2. A. Thick tangential sections through superficial layers of the meshwork and adjacent structures of the vervet monkey (Gomori's silver inpregnation, 115x). Torpedo-shaped muscle tips giving off slender straight tendons. (From ROHEN, LÜTJEN and BARANY 1967). B. Schematic drawing of the architecture of the cribriform region and ciliary muscle (CM) tendon attachments in humans and higher monkeys. One type of tendon connects the anterior muscle tips to the scleral spur (SP). A second type (T) traverses the entire meshwork to insert into the corneal stroma. A third tendon type fans out in brush-like endings within the mesh and, via an elastic network and connecting fibril (CF), attaches to the juxtacanalicular and inner wall region. E, endothelium of Schlemm's canal (SC); Tr, trabecular lamellae. (From ROHEN 1982).

The anterior tips of the muscle bundles taper down to true tendons. Some of these tendons pass through the trabecular meshwork and anchor the muscle to the peri-

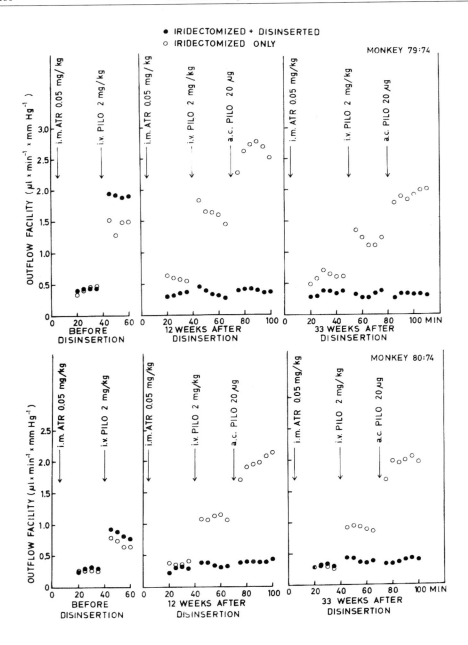

Fig. 3. Outflow facility and facility responses to intravenous and intracameral pilocarpine-HCl (i. v. PILO; a. c. PILO) before and after unilateral ciliary muscle disinsertion in two typical bilaterally iridectomized monkeys. Intramuscular atropine sulfate (i. m. ATR) was given before each perfusion to minimize systemic effects of intravenous pilocarpine. Note absence of facility increase following in- ▶

pheral cornea. Others splay out within the meshwork where they intermingle with the elastic network of the mesh, and are in turn attached, via connecting fibrils and specialized cell surface cytoskeletal modifications, to the endothelial cells of the inner wall of Schlemm's canal (Fig. 2). Thus, when the muscle contracts, the entire meshwork is expanded and Schlemm's canal dilated. This configurational change in the meshwork and Schlemm's canal somehow lessens their resistance to fluid flow from the anterior chamber through these tissues, so that outflow facility is increased. Various physiologic studies are consistent with this scenario, and have also indicated that this is the mechanism responsible for the outflow facility increase induced by cholinergic agonists (BÁRÁNY 1967; ROHEN et al. 1967; KAUF-MAN et al. 1984). In one such study performed in the laboratory of the late Dr. Ernst Bárány, cynomolgus monkeys had the iris of both eyes totally removed and the ciliary muscle of one eye disconnected from the scleral spur and trabecular meshwork over its entire 360 degree circumference (KAUFMAN and BARÁNY 1976). The muscle retracted posteriorly and reattached to the inner scleral wall well behind the scleral spur. In the surgically aniridic eyes, the response to pilocarpine was retained and was no different from that in surgically virgin eyes (KAUFMAN 1979). In contrast, the eyes with disconnected ciliary muscle showed no response to pilocarpine (Fig. 3), although they did respond to other agents which presumably act directly on the meshwork (KAUFMAN and BÁRÁNY 1977; KAUFAMAN and BÁRÁNY 1981).

It has been generally assumed that ciliary muscle contractility decreases very little if at all with age (SWEGMARK 1969; FISHER 1973). In fact, it is "common knowledge" that the age-related loss of acommodative amplitude, clinically called presbyopia, is consequent to a hardening or loss of elasticity of the crystalline lens, rather than to any diminution of ciliary muscle function (BITO and MIRANDA 1989). The quality of data on which this conclusion is based is marginal to say the least, but the lack of an animal model for presbyopia precluded more definitive experiments. Basically, subprimate species either do not accommodate or accommodate by mechanisms very different from the human (DUKE-ELDER 1958). However, the rhesus monkey has an accommodative mechanism very similar structurally and functionally to that of the human (BITO et al. 1982; LÜTJEN-DRECOLL et al. 1988 a, b; NEIDER et al. 1990).

In rhesus monkeys, the maximum accommodative amplitude induced by topical application of carbachol declines with age on a time scale relative to lifespan virtually identical to that exhibited by voluntary accommodation in the human (Fig. 4) (BITO et al. 1982). In a histologic study (LÜTJEN-DRECOLL et al. 1988b), one eye of

---

travenous and intracameral pilocarpine in the "disinserted" eyes, as opposed to the large facility increases in the opposite eyes. Note also the difference in the resting (pre-pilocarpine) facilities between the "disinserted" and opposite eye of monkey No. 79:74 following the initial perfusion and subsequent disinsertion operation. (From KAUFMAN and BÁRÁNY 1976).

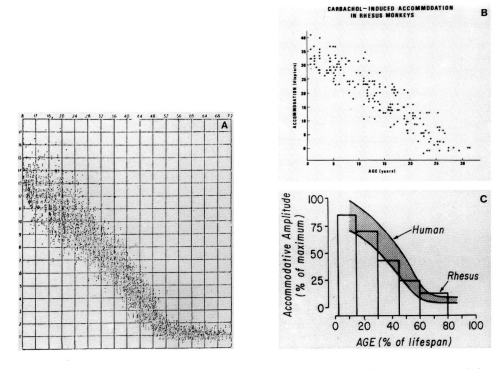

Fig. 4. Similarity of patterns of age-dependent loss of accommodative amplitude in humans and rhesus monkeys. Human data (A) from Duane 1922. Carbachol induced accommodation (B) in rhesus
monkeys from Bito and Miranda, unpublished. Composite (C) showing the mean accommodative
amplitude for each age group of rhesus monkeys (bars) superimposed on the time course of decrease
in accommodative amplitude in humans, shown by the shaded area that includes most normal human
cases. It is assumed that the lifespans of rhesus monkeys and humans are 35 and 80 years and that
their maximum accommodative amplitudes are 40 and 16 diopters, respectively. (From Bito and
Miranda 1987).

rhesus monkeys was treated with pilocarpine and the opposite eye with atropine
immediately before sacrifice. In young animals it was easy to tell which eye received which drug based on the difference in configuration of the ciliary muscle; ie,
the ciliary muscle of the eye receiving pilocarpine was contracted in contrast to the
relaxed ciliary muscle of the eye receiving atropine. However in old monkeys the
muscle configuration in the atropine and pilocarpine treated eyes was virtually the
same, appearing in a relatively "relaxed" topography (Fig. 5). This is not what one
would expect according to classic presbyopia theory; the pilocarpinized muscle
should assume a contracted configuration regardless of age if the problem is one of
lenticular hardening. In the elderly animals the muscle looked rather normal histo-

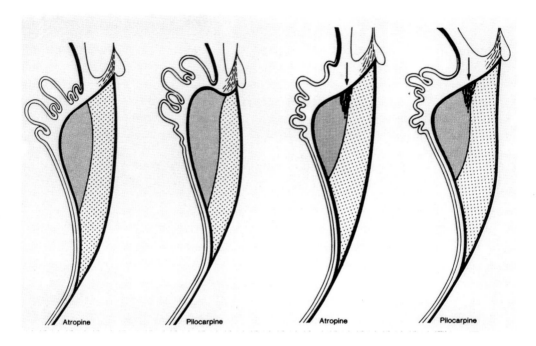

Fig. 5. Ciliary muscle topography and connective tissue distribution in rhesus monkeys. Representative sections are depicted schematically. Left, 8-year-old rhesus monkey exhibits essentially no intramuscular connective tissue. Right, 34-year-old rhesus monkey exhibits connective tissue (arrows) only anteriorly between longitudinal and reticular zones. Note configurational difference between atropine and pilocarpine treated muscle in young animal and absence of such difference in old animal. (From LÜTJEN-DRECOLL, TAMM and KAUFMAN 1988b).

logically; it was not markedly atrophic, there was no significant infiltration or replacement of muscle tissue by connective tissue, nor any other obvious reason why the muscle should be incapable of contracting. More careful light and electron microscopic studies in a group of these animals encompassing the entire species lifespan revealed a modest loss of muscle mass with age and some other age-related changes in muscle cell and intramuscular ciliary nerve structure (LÜTJEN-DRECOLL et al. 1988a,b) but these rather minor alterations should not render the muscle incapable of contracting.

The activity levels of the enzymes choline acetyltransferase and acetylcholinesterase, the biosynthetic and biodegradative enzymes for the cholinergic neurotransmitter acetylcholine, across the lifespan, showed no significant age-related change in the $K_m$ or the $V_{max}$ for either enzyme. Similarly, there was no change in either the affinity or the number of specific binding sites for the muscarinic receptor antagonist QNB, indicating no overall loss of muscarinic receptors in the ciliary muscle with age (Fig. 6) (GABELT et al. 1990). Although none of these studies absolutely ruled out the possibility of some structural or biochemical change within the muscle to explain its loss of mobility (for instance the loss of a specific muscarinic receptor subtype mediating most of the contractile function but accounting for only a small percentage of the overall muscarinic receptors), collectively they strongly suggested that the ciliary neuromuscular apparatus itself remained rather normal despite the apparently almost complete loss of the configurational response to cholinergic agonists.

Correlations between the histologic picture and the in vivo physiology were further investigated using two techniques developed specifically for that purpose.

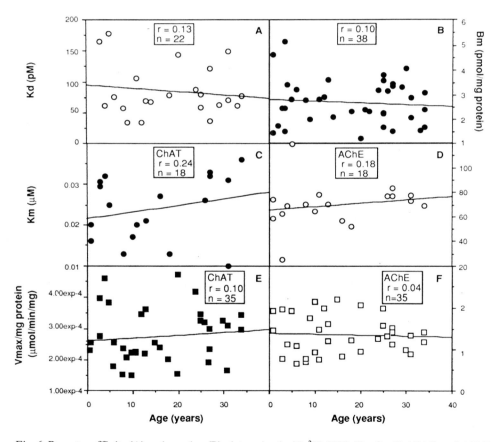

Fig. 6. Receptor affinity (A) and number (B), determined with $^3$H-QNB; Km for ChAT (C) and AChE (D); Vmax/mg protein for ChAT (E) and AChE (F) as a function of age in rhesus monkey ciliary muscle. No parameter correlates with age. (From GABELT, KAUFMAN and POLANSKY 1990).

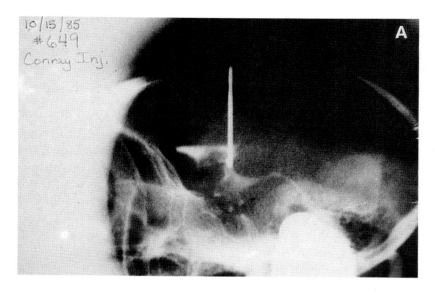

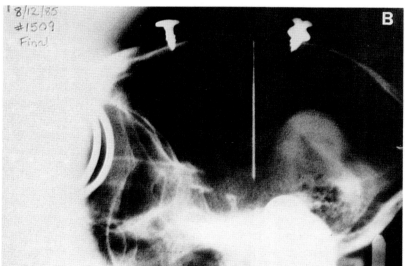

Fig. 7. Lateral radiographs showing placement of injection cannula (A) and stimulating electrode (B). Radiograph (A) was taken 30 s after injection of iothalamate meglumine into the foramen of Monroe. Radiograph (B) shows final electrode placement in Edinger-Westphal nucleus, resulting in maximum accommodation.

Contrast radioventriculography was used to localize the Edinger-Westphal nucleus and implant a permanent electrode into it (Fig. 7), permitting repeated, reproducible, bilaterally symmetric stimulation of accommodation via the normal efferent neuronal pathway (CRWAFORD et al. 1989). Modification of a Zeiss photo slit lamp and two different types of low light video cameras (Fig. 8) permitted Scheimpflug and gonioscopic real-time video imaging of the entire lens, the zonules, and the ciliary processes in previously totally iridectomized monkeys (NEIDER et al. 1990). Centrally stimulated accommodation declined with age on a time scale relative to lifespan virtually identical to that in the human. As predicted by "classical" accommodation-presbyopia teaching, during central stimulation the lens thickened and the ciliary processes moved forward and inward in young animals. Also as predicted by classical teaching, the lens in old presbyopic animals exhibited only a negligible shape change. However, in contravention of classical theory but consistent with the histologic studies in these animals, the ciliary muscle also moved only negligibly (Fig. 9) (NEIDER et al. 1990).

It is beyond the scope of this paper to discuss the pathophysiology of the age-related loss of ciliary muscle mobility in the rhesus monkey, and indeed, the story is far from complete. It suffices to say that an alteration in the extralenticular elastic components of the accommodative apparatus, and most specifically in the posterior tendons of the ciliary muscle and Bruch's membrane, by which the muscle is attached to the posterior sclera near the optic canal, is involved (TAMM et al. 1991). More relevant to the scope of this symposium are the potentially profound consequences of ciliary muscle immobility for aqueous dynamics.

Human visual experience involves frequent and rapid shifts of gaze among distant, intermediate and near objects of regard. Even when an individual spends long stretches of time working at one or another distance, there must still be very frequent, small accommodative shifts, mediated by microcontractions and relaxations of the ciliary muscle, to maintain focus on the object of regard. Given the intimate anatomic relationship between the ciliary muscle and the trabecular meshwork, these microcontractions and relaxations must generate tremendous distortional forces within the meshwork (KAUFMAN and GABELT 1992). Coupled with the flow of aqueous humor down the pressure gradient between the anterior chamber and the canal of Schlemm, these forces would promote washout of extracellular material and debris from the trabecular meshwork. This would be entirely consistent with Anders Bill's concept of the meshwork as a "self-cleaning filter" (BILL 1975), except that the self-cleaning would be by mechanical flushing as well as phagocytosis, and with Laszlo Bito's comment about the trabecular meshwork being "the sewer of the eye" (BITO, personal communication). The flushing and washout would represent the sewage flow, whereas the phagocytosis would perhaps represent the sewage treatment plant. A more pleasant analogy, for which we also credit Dr. Bito (personal communication), would be to a child sitting in a sandbox sifting sand through a strainer: when a clump won't go through, the child almost instinctively jiggles or shakes the strainer to promote disruption and dislodging of the clumped particles, allowing the sand to filter through (KAUFMAN 1991).

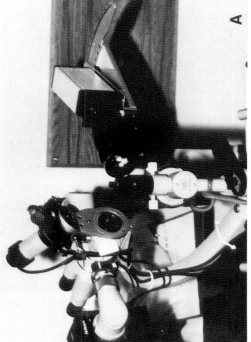

Fig. 8. Scheimpflug videography apparatus. Zeiss photo slit lamp fitted with low-light black and white video camera which pivots horizontally in relation to the zoom lens, allowing clear focusing of an optical section of the entire anterior segment in one plane on the video monitor and video tape. B. Goniovideography apparatus. Zeiss photo slit lamp fitted with low-light color video camera. Appropriate positioning of Swan-Jacob gonioscopy lens (C), slit projector, and microscope allows visualization, video monitoring, and video recording of the lens equator, zonule, and ciliary processes in the surgically aniridic monkey eye.

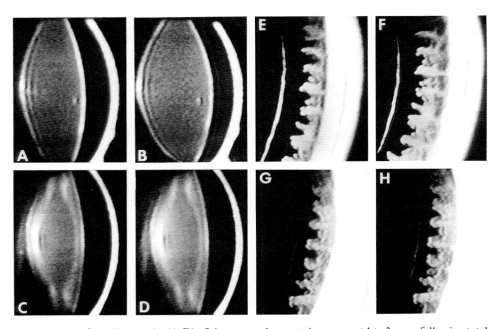

Fig. 9. Scheimpflug videography (A-D) of rhesus monkey anterior segment 1 to 3 years following total iridectomy and midbrain electrode implantation. A,B 4 years; C,D 24 years. A,C nonaccommodating; B,D accommodating maximally (14.0 and 1.5 diopters, respectively) in response to central electrical stimulation. Note: (1) decreasing overall transparency and increasing prominence of discontinuity zones of the lens with increasing age (A vs C); (2) lens thickening and anterior chamber shallowing during accommodation (A vs B, C vs D); and (3) loss of dissimilarity between nonaccommodating and accommodating eye with increasing age (A and B vs C and D). Goniovideography (E-H) of two rhesus monkey anterior segments following total iridectomy and midbrain electrode implantation. E and F, 4-year-old monkey, nonaccommodating and maximally accommodating (17.3 diopters, respectively; G and H, 24-year-old monkey, nonaccommodating and maximally accommodating (1.5 diopters), respectively. Note centripetal excursion of ciliary processes during accommodation in young animal (E vs F) and virtual absence of such excursion in the old animal attempting to accommodate (G vs H). Angle of observation unchanged from E to F, or from G to H. (Modified from NEIDER, CRAW-FORD, KAUFMAN and BITO 1990).

How would such a system respond to the loss of ciliary muscle mobility with age? In the normal young animal, extracellular material and other debris are dislodged, jiggled and washed through, etc., maintaining a "healthy" environment for the trabecular cells, promoting their normal function and in turn maitaining normal outflow resistance and intraocular pressure. When ciliary muscle mobility is lost, extracellular material and debris may accumulate. Additionally, such material could be toxic to the trabecular cells or sequester them from the aqueous humor which normally serves their metabolic needs, perhaps further compromising trabecular function. Such circumstances would all tend to increase outflow resistance and consequently to raise intraocular pressure.

This concept of glaucoma pathophysiology, depicted schematically in Fig. 10, is at least as consistent with the information available from glaucoma epidemiology and basic science research as the "trabeculocentric theory". As stated earlier, glaucoma is a disease of aging whose incidence begins to rise sharply, after age of 50 years (LESKE 1983; TIELSCH et al. 1991), at about the same time the last vestiges of accommodative amplitude are lost (DUANE 1922; ALPERN 1969; MOSES 1987). The disease is more prelevant in myopes (HOSKINS and KASS 1989), who perhaps do not need to accommodate as much as emmetropes and hyperopes, since they are already focused at near. Glaucoma is also more prelevant in diabetics (BECKER 1971), who lose their ability to accommodate at an earlier age than nondiabetics (MOSS et al. 1987), perhaps related to peripheral autonomic dysfunction. This theory would also be consistent with the age-related increase in the accumulation of extracellular material or "plaque material" within the meshwork, which occurs in both humans (LÜTJEN-DRECOLL et al. 1986) and monkeys (ROHEN 1990), and in humans is more pronounced in patients with primary open-angle glaucoma (LÜTJEN-DRECOLL et al. 1986) (although there are other possible explanations for that association). Even the age-related loss of trabecular cells, which again occurs in both species (ALVARADO et al. 1984; GRIERSON et al. 1982; ROHEN 1990) could be explained by hypothesizing as above that the accumulated debris is either toxic to the cells or sequesters them from their life-supporting aqueous humor, leading to cell death and depopulation.

Further support comes from studies of outflow facility measured by two-level constant pressure perfusion in pentobarbital-anesthetized rhesus monkeys encompassing the entire species lifespan. Resting facility declined with age as it does in the human. The facility response to intracameral pilocarpine also significantly declined with age (GABELT et al. 1991) albeit not to the same extent as the accommodative response (Fig. 11). The difference perhaps indicates that the mobility of the regions of the muscle mediating the different functions declines at different rates during the lifespan. In any case, neither resting facility nor the facility response to pilocarpine seemed to bottom out in the oldest animals, which suggests that if the animals had lived longer both might have declined further. In other words, if the animals live long enough, they might all get glaucoma. Although adequate prevalence data are not available for primary open angle glaucoma in elderly rhesus monkeys, the disease does exist in that population (Kaufman and Bito 1982). In this sense, the analogy to the human, where the prevalence of glaucoma reaches 5 – 10 % over the age of 80 years, is reasonable. Perhaps when we are all living to the age of 110 years, we will all get glaucoma – and it will not respond to pilocarpine. Although elderly glaucoma patients can indeed respond to pilocarpine, there has been no study of the age relationship of the magnitude of pilocarpine response, and such a study is certainly feasible with present tonographic technology.

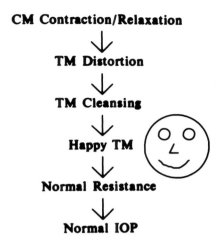

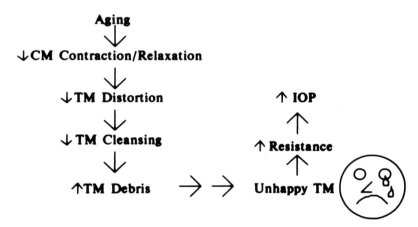

Fig. 10. Concept of glaucoma physiology whereby aging results in a decline in the ability of the ciliary muscle to contract/relax, consequently decreasing the distortional forces on the trabecular meshwork (TM) that normally create a cleansing action to prevent the build up of debris. Accumulation of debris with age increases resistance to outflow with a resultant increase in IOP.

## Summary

Recent data supporting a central role for the ciliary muscle in the pathophysiology of presbyopia and primary open angle glaucoma are discussed. The mecha-

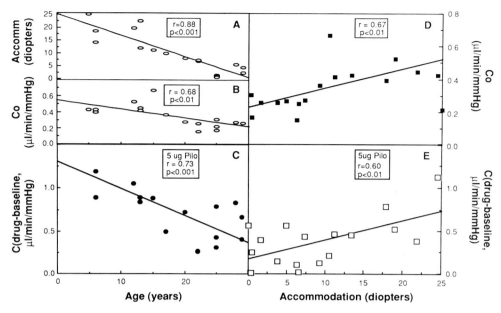

Fig. 11. Age vs maximal carbachol-induced accommodation (A), baseline outflow facility (B), or out-flow facility response to 5ug/ml intracameral pilocarpine HCl (C); maximum carbachol-induced accommodation vs baseline facility (D) or outflow facility response to 5ug/ml intracameral pilocarpine HCl (E) in 17 rhesus monkeys. (Modified from GABELT, CRAWFORD and KAUFMAN 1991).

nisms described contrast with but are as plausible as the classical lenticulocentric and trabeculocentric concepts of these diseases. Defects responsible for the lenticular immobility in presbyopia and the outflow resistance increase in glaucoma have not yet been found in the lens or in trabecular meshwork cells, despite extensive searches by many excellent laboratories. Perhaps such defects do not exist. We hope that this presentation will also reinforce the point that important insights can be gained from animal research and from keeping an open mind.

## Acknowledgement

Preparation of this chapter was supported by grants from the USPHS National Institutes of Health (EY02698) and the National Glaucoma Research Program of the American Health Assistance Foundation. The chapter is dedicated with gratitude to Professor Johannes W. Rohen, who has provided so much of our understanding of the functional morphology of accommodation, aqueous humor outflow and their relationship, on his 70th birthday.

# References

ALPERN, M. Accommodation (1969): In: H. Davson, (Ed.): The eye. Vol. 3, muscular mechanisms, pp 217–254. 2nd ed. New York: Academic Press, Inc.

ALVARADO, J., C. MURPHY, R. JUSTER (1984): Trabecular meshwork cellularity in primary open-angle glaucoma and nonglaucomatous normals. Ophthalmol. *91:* 564–579.

BÁRÁNY, E. H. (1967): The immediate effect on outflow resistance of intravenous pilocarpine in the vervet monkey. Cercopithecus ethiops. Invest. Ophthalmol. *6:* 373–380.

BECKER, B. (1971): Diabetes mellitus and primary open-angle glaucoma. The XXVII Edward Jackson Memorial Lecture. Am J Ophthalmol *71:* 1–16.

BILL, A. (1971): Aqueous humor dynamics in monkeys (*Macaca irus and Cercopithecus ethiops*). Exp. Eye. Res. *11:* 195–206.

BILL, A. (1975): The drainage of aqueous humor. Invest. Ophthalmol. *14:* 1–3.

BILL, A., C. I. PHILLIPS (1971): Uveoscleral drainage of aqueous humor in human eyes. Exp. Eye Res. *12:* 275– 281.

BITO, L. Z., C. J. DEROUSSEAU, P. L. KAUFMAN, J. W. BITO (1982): Age-dependent loss of accommodative amplitude in rhesus monkeys: an animal model for presbyopia. Invest. Ophthalmol. Vis. Sci. *23:* 23–31.

BITO, L. Z., O. C. MIRANDA (1987): Presbyopia: the need for a closer look. In: STARK, L. G. OBRECH (Eds.): Presbyopia: Recent Research and Reviews from the Third International Symposium, pp 411–429. New York: Churchill/Professional Press.

BITO, L. Z., O. C. MIRANDA (1989): Accommodation and presbyopia. In: Reinecke, RD. (Ed.): Ophthalmology Annual, pp 103–128. New York: Raven Press.

CRAWFORD, K., E. TERASAWA, P. L. KAUFMAN (1989): Reproducible stimulation of ciliary muscle contraction in the cynomolgus monkey via a permanent indwelling midbrain electrode. Brain Research *503:* 265–272.

DUANE, A. (1922): Studies in monocular and binocular accommodation and their clinical implications. Am. J. Ophthalmol. *5:* 865–877.

DUKE-ELDER, S. (1958): In System of Ophthalmology, The Eye in Evolution, Vol. 1. St. Louis: C. V. Mosby.

FISCHER, R. F. (1973): Presbyopia and the changes with age in the human crystalline lens. J. Physiol. (Lond) *228:* 765–779.

GABELT, B. T., K. CRAWFORD, P. L. KAUFMAN (1991): Outflow facility and its response to pilocarpine decline in aging rhesus monkeys. Arch. Ophthalmol. *109:* 879–882.

GABELT, B. T., P. L. KAUFMAN, J. R. POLANSKY (1990): Ciliary muscle muscarinic binding sites, choline acetyltransferase, and acetylcholinesterase in aging rhesus monkeys. Invest. Ophthalmol. Vis. Sci. *31:* 2431–2436.

GRIERSON, I., Q. WANG, P. G. MCMENAMIN, W. R. LEE (1982): The effects of age and antiglaucoma drugs on the meshwork cell population. Res. Clin. Forums 69–92.

HOSKINS, H. D. JR, M. A. KASS (1989): Becker-Schaffer's diagnosis and therapy of the glaucomas, p 279. 6th edition. St. Louis: CV Mosby.

KAUFMAN, P. L. (1979): Aqueous humor dynamics following total iridectomy in the cynomolgus monkey. Invest. Ophthalmol. Vis. Sci. *18:* 870–875.

KAUFMAN, P. L. (1987): Aging and aqueous humor dynamics. In: DiVincentis, M. (Ed.): The Fundamental Aging Processes of the Eye, pp 41–46. Florence: Baccini and Chiappe.

KAUFMAN, P. L. (1991): Physiology and pharmacology of aqueous humor outflow: Implications for treatment. Ophthalmology Clinics of North America, *4:* 781–802.

KAUFMAN, P. L., E. H. BÁRÁNY (1976): Loss of acute pilocarpine effect on outflow facility following surgical disinsertion and retrodisplacement of the ciliary muscle from the scleral spur in the cynomolgus monkey. Invest. Ophthalmol. *15:* 793–807.

KAUFMAN, P. L., E. H. BÁRÁNY (1977): Cytochalasin B reversibly increases outflow facility in the eye of the cynomolgus monkey. Invest. Ophthalmol. Vis. Sci. *16:* 47–53.

KAUFMAN, P. L., E. H. BÁRÁNY (1981): Adrenergic drug effects on aqueous outflow facility following ciliary muscle retodisplacement in the cynomolgus monkey. Invest. Ophthalmol. Vis. Sci. *20:* 544 – 651.

KAUFMAN, P. L., L. Z. BITO (1982): The occurence of senile catarcts, ocular hypertension, and glaucoma in rhesus monkeys. Exp. Eye Res. *34:* 287 – 291.

KAUFMAN, P. L., B. T. GABELT (1992): Cholinergic mechanisms and aqueous humor dynamics. In: DRANCE, S. M., M. VAN BUSKIRK, A. H. NEUFELD (Eds.): Pharmacology of Glaucoma, pp 64 – 92. Baltimore: Williams & Wilkins.

KAUFMAN, P. L., T. WIEDMAN, J. R. ROBINSON (1984): Cholinergics. In: Sears ML, ed. Pharmacology of the eye. Handbook of experimental pharmacology. Berlin: Springer-Verlag, *69:* 149 – 191.

LESKE, M. C. (1983): The epidemiology of open-angle glaucoma: A review. Am. J. Epidemiol. *118:* 161 – 191.

LÜTJEN-DRECOLL, E., R. FUTA, J. W. ROHEN (1981): Ultrahistochemical studies on tangential sections of the trabecular meshwork in normal and glaucomatous eyes. Invest. Ophthalmol. Vis. Sci. *21:* 563 – 573.

LÜTJEN-DRECOLL, E., R. SHIMIZU, M. ROHRBACH, J. W. ROHEN (1986): Quantitative analysis of "plaque material" in the inner and outer wall of Schlemm's canal in normal and glaucomatous eyes. Exp. Eye Res. *42:* 443 – 455.

LÜTJEN-DRECOLL, E., E. TAMM, P. L. KAUFMAN (1988a): Age changes in rhesus monkey ciliary muscle: light and electron microscopy. Exp. Eye Res. *47:* 885 – 899.

LÜTJEN-DRECOLL, E., E. TAMM, P. L. KAUFMAN (1988b): Age-related loss of morphologic responses to pilocarpine in rhesus monkey ciliary muscle. Arch. Ophthalmol. *106:* 1591 – 1598.

MOSES, R. A. (1987): Accommodation. In: MOSES, R. A., W. M. JR. HART (Eds.): Adler's physiology of the eye, clinical application, pp 291 – 310. 8th ed. St. Louis: CV Mosby.

MOSS, S. E., R. KLEIN, B. E. K. KLEIN (1987): Accommodative ability in younger onset diabetics. Arch. Ophthalmol. *105:* 508 – 512.

NEIDER, M. W., K. CRAWFORD, P. L. KAUFMAN, L. Z. BITO (1990): In vivo videography of the rhesus monkey accommodative apparatus. Arch. Ophthalmol. *108:* 69 – 74.

ROHEN, J. W. (1982): The evolution of the primate eye in relation to the problem of glaucoma. In: LÜTJEN-DRECOLL, E. (Ed.): Basic Aspects of Glaucoma Research, pp 3 – 33. Stuttgart: F. K. Schattauer.

ROHEN, J. W. (1990): Ageing and non-ageing processes in the anterior segment of the eye. Proc. Int. Soc. Eye Res. *6:* 1.

ROHEN, J. W., E. FUTA, E. LÜTJEN-DRECOLL (1981): The fine structure of the cribriform meshwork in normal and glaucomatous eyes as seen in tangential sections. Invest. Ophthalmol. Vis. Sci. *221:* 574 – 585.

ROHEN, J. W., E. LÜTJEN, E. BÁRÁNY (1967): The relation between the ciliary muscle and the trabecular meshwork and its importance for the effect of miotics on aqueous outflow resistance. Graefes Arch. Klin. Exp. Ophthalmol. *172:* 23 – 31.

SHIOSE, Y., Y. KAWASE (1986): A new approach to stratified normal intraocular pressure in a general population. Am. J. Ophthalmol. *101:* 714 – 721.

STIEVE, R. (1949): Über den Bau des menschlichen Ciliarmuskels, seine Veränderungen während des Lebens und seine Bedeutung für die Akkommodation. Anat. Anz. *97:* 69 – 79.

SWEGMARK, G (1969): Studies with impedance cyclography on human ocular accommodation at different ages. Acta Ophthalmologica *47:* 1186 – 1206.

TAMM, E., E. LÜTJEN-DRECOLL, W. JUNGKUNZ, J. W. ROHEN (1991): Posterior attachment of ciliary muscle in young, accommodating old, presbyopic monkeys. Invest. Ophthalmol. Vis. Sci. *32:* 1678 – 1692.

TIELSCH, J. (1991): Epidemiology of blindness and glaucoma: racial variations. In: COWAN, C. L. JR. (Ed.): The third Caribbean glaucoma symposium, pp 4 – 7. New York: Lawrence DellaCorte Publications.

TIELSCH, J. M., A. SOMMER, J. KATZ, R. M. ROYAL, H. A. QUIGLEY, J. JAVITT (1991): Racial variations in the prevalence of primary open angle glaucoma: the Baltimore Eye Survey. JAMA *266:* 369 – 374.

TOWNSEND, D. J., R. F. BRUBAKER (1980): Immediate effect of epinephrine on aqueous formation in the normal human eye as measured by fluorophotometry. Invest. Ophthalmol. Vis. Sci. *19:* 256 – 266.

*Departments of Ophthalmology[1] and Neurology[2]*
*Harvard Medical School*
*Boston, MA*

# The effects of endothelin, atrial natriuretic factor, and nitroglycerin on outflow facility in the primate eye

K. A. ERICKSON-LAMY[1] and J. A. NATHANSON[2]

## Introduction

It has long been spectulated that sensory mechanisms might be present in the conventional outflow pathways to regulate intraocular pressure via changes in the resistance to aqueous flow. There is considerable sensory innervation within the trabecular meshwork of the primate eye (STONE and LATIES 1987). Furthermore, in the rhesus monkey, the demonstrated neuroendocrine nature (STONE et al. 1984; STONE and LATIES 1987) of the Schwalbe line cells (RAVIOLA 1982) suggests that these cells may play a key role in a putative IOP-regulating function either by acting as baroreceptors, or by elaborating regulatory peptide hormones. It is notable that similar cell populations have not been identified in human eyes.

However, it may not be necessary to invoke the presence of specific baro or stretch receptors for the existence of a pressure-regulating system within the conventional outflow pathways. Notably, it is now well documented that the vascular endothelia are capable of local regulation of the contaction of underlying vascular smooth muscle cells by secreting numerous chemical substances including prostaglandins, endothelium-derived relaxing factor (EDRF), and constricting factors including endothelins in response to a wide range of stimuli including muscarinic agonists, ATP and ADP, substance P, bradykinin, norepinephrine, VIP, and mechanical stretch (see: VANHOUTTE 1988, for a comprehensive review). Further, the atriopeptins (atrial natriuretic factor (ANF)) are apparently released by atriomyocytes in response to changes in tissue architecture (induced by either transmural pressure or atrial wall stress) independent of sensory neural mechanisms (NEEDLEMAN et al. 1989).

The reported presence of smooth muscle-like cells in the trabecular meshwork (GIPSON et al. 1979; DEKATER et al. 1990) has spurred speculation about the possible role of these smooth muscle-like cells in mediating changes in outflow resistance. A functional physiologic role for these cells remains to be proven. However, the close proximity of smooth muscle-like cells and endothelial cells in the trabecular meshwork raises the possibility that, like the cardiovascular system, these cell populations might interact in response to changes in intracameral volume or intraocular pressure.

During the past few years, our laboratories have investigated the hypothesis that outflow facility in the primate eye might be regulated by locally produced autocoids via an action on the smooth muscle like cells in the outflow pathways and/or the ciliary muscle. To date our studies have been limited to the analysis of the physiologic effects of several autocoids which influence vascular tone; namely, atriopeptin, endothelin, and nitroglycerin (which mimics the effects of EDRF) on outflow facility in the primate eye. In related biochemical electrophysiological (KORBMACHER et al. 1989), and physiological studies, we have also obtained preliminary information about the possible mechanisms by which these vasoactive substances affect outflow resistance. A summary of these findings follows.

## Endothelin

Endothelins are a group of vasoconstrictor polypeptides which were originally isolated from cultured endothelial cells (YANAGISAWA et al 1988). The effects of endothelin on the cardiovascular system are similar to those of angiotensin II, but endothelin is far more potent. Endothelin also contracts nonvascular smooth muscle cells (UCHIDA et al. 1988; KOZUKA et al. 1989; MAGGI et al. 1989).

## Effect on outflow facility in the living monkey eye

Total outflow facility, (determined by two-level constant pressure perfusion (BÁRÁNY 1964)) was measured in the living cynomolgus monkey eye before and after perfusion with endothelin (ERICKSON-LAMY et. al 1991). Endothelin-1 caused a statistically significant dose-related increase in outflow facility in concentrations ranging from $10^{-9}$ to $10^{-7}$ M with a maximal increase of approximately 70 % occuring at a concentration of $10^{-8}$ M (Table 1).

## Mechanism of action on outflow facility: Contraction of the ciliary muscle?

Endothelin-1 induces a marked depolarization of cultured human ciliary muscle cells accompanied by a rise in intracellular calcium (KORBMACHER et al. 1989). Similar depolarizations occur in cultured cells derived from the human trabecular meshwork (CORONEO et al. 1991). Endothelin has also been reported to cause iso-metric contractions of bovine ciliary muscle and reticular meshwork strips (LEPPLE-WIENHUES et al. 1991). Collectively, the results of these studies support the

Table 1: Effect of endothelin on facility of outflow and accommodation in the monkey eye in vivo.

| ENDO (M) | n | Co | Cd | Cd/Co | Accommodation (diopters) |
|---|---|---|---|---|---|
| $10^{-10}$ | 5 | $0.158 \pm .020$ | $0.189 \pm .022$ | $1.22 \pm .12$ | $0.8 \pm .4$ |
| $10^{-9}$ | 5 | $0.158 \pm .020$ | $0.229 \pm .038$ | $1.45 \pm .16^a$ | $1.6 \pm .5^a$ |
| $10^{-8}$ | 5 | $0.173 \pm .024$ | $0.285 \pm .050$ | $1.69 \pm .24^a$ | $2.2 \pm .5^b$ |
| $10^{-7}$ | 5 | $0.173 \pm .024$ | $0.291 \pm .045$ | $1.71 \pm .20^b$ | $2.4 \pm .4^c$ |

Endothelin-1 (ENDO) was administered to the monkey eye intracamerally, giving the indicated approximate anterior chamber concentrations. Outflow facility ($\mu l/min/mmHg$) was measured unilaterally before (Co) and after (Cd) two sequential doses of ENDO. On a separate occasion, the two remaining doses were administered to the fellow eye. All post drug facilities were adjusted downward by 15 % to compensate for "washout" (KAUFMAN et al. 1988). Accommodation (the refraction after drug treatment-baseline refraction) was determined after each successive intracameral dose. Data are the mean $\pm$ SEM of the indicated measurements in n eyes. Cd/Co significantly differed from 1.0 by the two-tailed paired t-test. $^a p < 0.05$; $^b p < 0.02$; $^c p < 0.01$. From Invest. Ophthalmol. Vis. Sci. 32: 492 – 495, 1991.

presence of functional endothelin receptors in both the ciliary muscle and the tra-becular meshwork, and the possibility that endothelin's effect on outflow facility might be mediated by effects on one or both of these two tissues.

We measured the accommodative response to intracameral endothelin in the monkey eye in vivo (ERICKSON-LAMY et al. 1991) in order to determine whether ciliary muscle contraction occurs in response to endothelin. As shown in Table 1, endothelin caused a dose related increase in accommodation at concentrations ranging from $10^{-9}$ M to $10^{-7}$ M with a maximal effect of 2.4 diopters at $10^{-7}$ M. Similar to the effects with cholinergic agonists, the dose-related changes in outflow facility induced by endothelin were highly correlated with changes in accommodation ($r = 0.9$; $P < 0.002$). Furthermore, a comparison of the diopters of endothelin-induced accommodation corresponding to the percent change in outflow facility with previously published results using pilocarpine and aceclidine (ERICKSON-LAMY and SCHROEDER 1990) showed that the relationship between outflow facility increase and accommodative amplitude induced by endothelin was similar to that obtained with aceclidine (Fig. 1). The in vitro demonstration of the responsiveness of ciliary muscle cells to endothelin along with the demonstration of an accommodative response to endothelin in vivo suggest that at least a portion of the endothelin effects on outflow facility is mediated through a contraction of the ciliary muscle resulting in a mechanical alteration of the outflow pathway. It is not yet known to what degree endothelin may affect the trabecular meshwork directly.

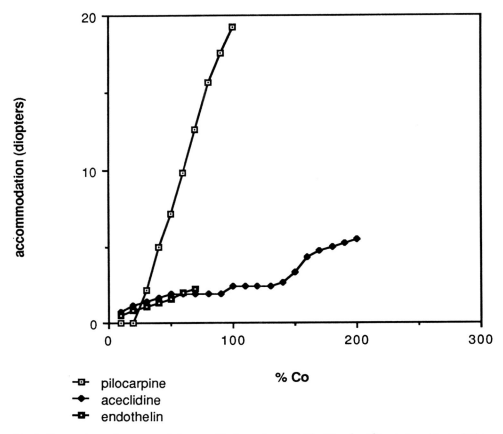

Fig. 1. Comparison of accommodative amplitudes vs increased facility of outflow induced by endothelin, aceclidine, and pilocarpine. Data points represent the mean calculated diopters of accommodation
in n = 5 eyes for each drug occuring at calculated mean drug concentrations necessary to induced indicated facility increase in separate groups of eyes treated with endothelin (n = 5), aceclidine (n = 5), or
pilocarpine (n = 6). From Invest. Ophthalmol. Vis Sci. *32:* 492 – 495, 1991.

## Vasoactive hormones that stimulate cGMP

*Atrial natriuretic peptide (ANF):* Atrial natriuretic peptides, first isolated from
cardiac atrial myocytes (CANTIN and GENEST 1985; DEBOLD 1985) are a group of
polypeptides involved systemically in the regulation of body fluid homeostasis.
These peptides also cause smooth muscle relaxation.
*Nitroglycerin:* The organic nitrates are a class of chemicals which have been used
for many years in the treatment of certain cardiovascular disorders. Glyceryl trini-
trate (nitroglycerin) is an organic nitro-ester with the active moiety ultimately being

the released nitric oxide. It is thought that all organic nitrates share the same pharmacological effects and have mechanism of action. In the cardiovascular system, nitroglycerin has a biphasic action, dilating the venous capacitance system at low concentrations and dilating the arterial vasculature at higher concentrations (FLAHERTY 1989). Organic nitrates induce smooth muscle relaxation via stimulation of cytoplasmic cGMP. This leads to a reduction in cytoplasmic calcium (AHLNER and AXELSON 1987) and may also affect substrate phosphorylation through stimulation of cGMP-dependent protein kinase (MITTAL and MURAD 1982).

Organic nitrates mimic the action of EDRF, and EDRF (FURCHGOTT and ZAWADZKI 1980) has been identified as nitric oxide (NO) (PALMER et al. 1987). Like other organic nitrates, EDRF is synthesized and released by generator cells, and stimulates cytoplasmic guanylate cyclase in target smooth muscle cells as well as other cell types.

## The role of cyclic GMP in aqueous dynamics

Investigations into a possible role of cGMP in regulation of aqueous humor dynamics have until recently been relatively few. NEUFELD (1978) reported little effect of intracameral 8-bromo-cGMP on outflow facility in vervet monkeys. In another study, KRUPIN (1977) found an increase in IOP after topical administration of high (1-2%) concentrations of sodium nitroprusside (which indirectly elevate cGMP).

More recently, NATHANSON (1987) suggested that cGMP may play a role in the regulation of IOP. The observation that rat ANF reduces the formation rate of cerebrospinal fluid (STEARDO and NATHANSON 1987) led to investigations on possible effects of ANF on the ciliary processes of the eye. In the rabbit eye, intravitreal administration of ANF results in reduced intraocular pressure (NATHANSON 1987; MITTAG et al. 1987; KORENFELD and BECKER 1989) in association with a reduction in the rate of aqueous humor formation (KORENFELD and BECKER 1989). ANF stimulation of membrane preparations from ciliary processes (NATHANSON 1987; MITTAG et al. 1987) and from homogenates of the ciliary body (KORENFELD and BECKER 1989) results in increased cyclic GMP.

Organic nitrates which, like EDRF, stimulate cyclic GMP production through activation of soluble guanylate cyclase also lower intraocular pressure in the rabbit eye (NATHANSON 1988) and the monkey eye (SCHUMAN et al. 1991).

*Effects of ANF and nitroglycerin on outflow facility in the living monkey eye*

*ANF:* ANF was administered unilaterally to the eye of 6 cynomolgus monkeys as bolus injections of 10 microliters resulting in approximate anterior chamber concentrations of $10^{-9}$ M, $10^{-8}$ M, or $10^{-7}$ M. ANF administration was associated in all six eyes with a decrease from baseline in facility of outflow at an anterior chamber concentration of $10^{-8}$ M (Table 2). At the other concentrations tested, facility also

Table 2: Effect of Atrial Natriuretic Factor (ANF) on outflow facility in the monkey eye in vivo.

| ANF ($\times 10^{-9}$M) | n | Co | Cd | Cd/Co |
|---|---|---|---|---|
| 1 | 6 | $0.44 \pm .11$ | $0.47 \pm .13$ | $0.96 \pm .13$ |
| 10 | 6 | $0.44 \pm .11$ | $0.31 \pm .08$ | $0.67 \pm .11$[a] |
| 100 | 6 | $0.49 \pm .10$ | $0.42 \pm .09$ | $1.00 \pm .10$ |

Facility of outflow ($\mu$l/min/mmHg) was measured unilaterally in monkey eyes by two-level constant pressure perfusion. After determination of a baseline facility (Co) ANF was administered intracamerally in a 10 $\mu$l bolus injection giving the indicated approximate anterior chamber concentrations. A post drug facility (Cd) was then determined, and a paired comparison was made for each eye between pre and post drug treatment measurements (Cd/Co). All post drug facilities were adjusted downward by 15 % to compensate for "washout" (KAUFMAN et al. 1988). Data are mean $\pm$ SEM outflow facilities or outflow facility ratios for the indicated number of eyes. Facility ratios are significantly different from 1.0 by the two-tailed paired t-test: [a]$p < 0.05$.

decreased in 4 of 6 eyes by average of 22 % and 30 % at $10^{-9}$ M and $10^{-7}$ M respectively. In contrast, there was an increase in facility of outflow in the other two eyes at these dosages. Three eyes were perfused with the ANF vehicle (0.25 mM ascorbate and 0.01 % bovine serum albumin in the normal perfusion medium) without added ANF to verify that the vehicle did not itself change the facility. In the eyes, facility increased an average of 11 % which is consistent with the 15 % increase in facility generally seen over the same period with unmodified perfusion medium (KAUFMAN et al. 1988).

*Nitroglycerin:* The effects of nitroglycerin were biphasic, depending upon concentration. Perfusion of the monkey eye in vivo with a constant concentration of nitroglycerin ($10^{-7}$ M) resulted in a 42 % reduction in outflow facility. Bolus injections of higher anterior chamber concentrations resulted in increased outflow facility (SCHUMAN et al. 1991). In the rabbit, nitroglycerin applied topically also increased outflow facility (NATHANSON 1992)

*Mechanism of the ANF and nitroglycerin-induced decrease in outflow facility: Relaxation of the ciliary muscle?* The observation of a decrease in aqueous humor outflow facility by ANF and both an increase and decrease with nitroglycerin indicated that agents which elevate cyclic GMP may have complex pharmacological

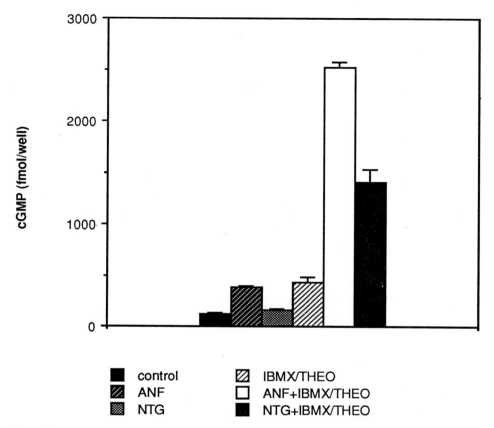

Fig. 2. Stimulation of cyclic GMP by atrial natriuretic factor (ANF) and nitroglycerin (NTG) in cultured ciliary muscle cells. Duplicate confluent cultures of ciliary muscle cells were incubated with ANF, NTG, theophylline (THEO) and IBMX, or ANF or NTG in combination with THEO and IBMX in parallel with duplicate control cultures incubated in culture medium only. After drug incubation, a triplicate RIA determination for cyclic GMP content was conducted on each of the cultures. Data are mean cyclic GMP content of the duplicate cultures. Error bars represent the standard deviation of the mean.

effects in the eye. In vascular and some non-vascular smooth muscle, bothANF and nitroglycerin mediate muscle ralaxation. Therefore, we wondered if ciliary muscle relaxation could possibly play a role in the observed facility decrease due to ANF and to the complex biphasic effect of nitroglycerin. A decrease in facility similar to that occurring with ANF and certain concentrations of nitroglycerin is noted in monkey eyes perfused with atropine (which is apparently due to ciliary muscle relaxation) (BÁRÁNY and CHRISTENSEN 1967).

In preliminary experiments we measured by radioimmunassay the accumulation of cGMP in broken cell preparations of cultured ciliary muscle cells. At a concentration of $10^{-7}$ M ANF stimulation increased cyclic GMP accumulation approximately 3 fold (Fig. 2). The combination of the phosphodiesterase inhibitors IBMX (1mM) and theophylline (10mM) resulted in an approximate 4 fold increase in cyclic GMP. Incubation of the cell cultures with ANF plus the phosphodiesterase inhibitors resulted in a 21 fold increase in cyclic GMP over baseline 6.6 and 5.5 fold increase over incubation with ANF alone and phosphodiesterase inhibitors alone respectively. In a second identical experiment, the pattern of drug responsiveness was the same (data not shown). These data provide evidence for the probable existence of functional ANF receptors on the ciliary muscle. The potentation of the cyclic GMP response to ANF in the presence of theophylline and IBMX further indicates an action on guanylate cyclase rather than on phosphodiesterase activity. These data thereby supply indirect support to the hypothesis that the observed ANF reduction in outflow facility may have been in part mediated by ciliary muscle relaxation.

Incubation of ciliary muscle cells with nitroglycerin resulted in a 12-fold increase in cyclic GMP over baseline, and a 9 fold increase over nitroglycerin alone (Fig. 2). These data support the possibility of a nitroglycerin-mediated relaxation of the ciliary muscle which could be responsible for the reduced outflow facility seen at certain concentrations of nitroglycerin.

On the other hand, the increased outflow facility at other concentrations of nitroglycerin suggests additional sites of action mediating nitroglycerin's effects on facility. One possibility would be a dilation of outflow resistance channels which would be expected to lead to increased outflow facility. (Of course, these agents may have additional effects on aqueous humor secretion which alter the overall effect on IOP).


## Conclusion

Collectively the findings of these studies support the possibility of a localized regulatory mechanism for aqueous outflow resistance. Biochemical and electrophysiological evidence points to the ciliary muscle as one potential target for smooth muscle-active peptides and hormones. It is not unreasonable to assume that the ciliary muscle could be involved in a regulatory mechanism as it is well documented that in the primate eye contraction of the ciliary muscle induced by voluntary accommodation (ARMALY 1958) and exogenously administered cholinergic agonists (ROHEN et al. 1967; ARMALY 1959a) results in increased facility of outflow, while ganglionic blocking agents increase outflow resistance (ARMALY 1959b; LAZENBY and GRANT, 1963; BÁRÁNY and CHRISTENSEN 1967). Evidence that these changes are mediated by the ciliary muscle and are not direct effects on the outflow pathways is provided by studies showing that disinsertion of the ciliary muscle from it's proximal attachment at the scleral spur in the monkey eye virtually eliminates changes in outflow facility induced by exogenous cholinergic agents (KAUFMAN and BÁRÁNY 1976).

We are currently undergoing combined biochemical and physiological studies in our laboratories using the perfused human ocular anterior segment (ERICKSON-LAMY et al. 1991; ERICKSON-LAMY 1992) to determine a potential direct action of these hormones on the conventional outflow pathways. Regardless of the ultimate target for these hormones, verification of the presence of a local regulatory mechanism requires the demonstration of the synthesis and release of regulatory hormones by anterior ocular tissues. To date, pharmacologic levels of ANF have been demonstrated in the aqueous humor of the rabbit eye (NATHANSON 1987). In the rat eye, endothelin-1 mRNA and binding sites have been identified in the iris (LOVENBERG and MILLER 1990). The mRNA for endothelin has also been identified in the corneal endothelium (MACCUMBER et al. 1989).

Hopefully, additional physiological, histochemical, and receptor mapping studies in the primate eye may help to determine if these hormones play a physiological role in the control of aqueous humor outflow, and if so, the nature of that role.

# References

AHLNER, J., K. L. AXELSSON (1986): Nitrates: mode of action at a cellular level. Drugs *33* (Suppl VI): 17–25.

ARMALY, M. F. (1959a): Studies on intraocular effects of the orbital parasympathetics. I. Technique and effects on morphology. Arch. Ophthalmol. *61:* 14–29.

ARMALY, M. F. (1959b): Studies on intraocular effects of the orbital parasympathetics. II. Effects on intraocular pressure. Arch. Ophthalmol. *62:* 117–124.

ARMALY, M. F., H. M. BURIAN (1958): Changes in the tonogram during accommodation. Arch. Ophthalmol. *60:* 60–68.

BÁRÁNY, E. H. (1964): Simultaneous measurement of changing intraocular pressure and outflow facility in the vervet monkey by constant pressure infusion. Invest. Ophthalmol. *3:* 135–143.

BÁRÁNY, E. H., R. E. CHRISTENSEN (1967): Cycloplegia and outflow resistance. Arch. Ophthalmol. *77:* 757–760.

CANTIN, M., J. GENEST (1985): The heart and the atrial natriuretic factor. Endocr. Rev. *6:* 107–127.

CORONEO, M. T., K. A. ERICKSON-LAMY, M. WIEDERHOLT (1991): Membrane voltage recordings in a cell line (HTM) derived from human trabecular meshwork. Invest. Ophthalmol. Vis. Sci. *32* (ARVO Suppl): 942.

DEBOLD, A. J. (1985): Atrial natriuretic factor: A hormone produced by the heart. Science *230:* 767–770.

DEKATER, A. W., S. J. SPURR-MICHAUD, I. K. GIPSON (1990): Localization of smooth muscle myosin-containing cells in the aqueous outflow pathway. Invest. Ophthalmol. Vis. Sci. *31:* 347–353.

ERICKSON-LAMY, K. A. (1992): The perfused human ocular anterior segment as a model for aqueous outflow physiology. J. of Glaucoma, in Press.

ERICKSON-LAMY, K. A., J. W. ROHEN, W. M. GRANT (1991): Outflow facility studies in the perfused human ocular anterior segment. Exp. Eye Res. *52:* 723–731.

ERICKSON-LAMY, K. A., C. KORBMACHER, J. S. SCHUMAN, J. A. NATHANSON (1991): Effect of endothelin on outflow facility and accommodation in the monkey eye in vivo. Invest. Ophthalmol. Vis. Sci. *32:* 492–495.

FLAHERTY, J. T. (1989): Nitrate Tolerance. A review of the Evidence. Drugs *37:* 523–550.

FURCHGOTT, R. F., J. V. ZAWADZKI (1980): The obligatory role of endothial cells in the relaxation of arterial smooth muscle by acetylcholine. Nature *288:* 373–376.

GIPSON, I. K., R. A. ANDERSON (1979): Actin filaments in cells of human trabecular meshwork and Schlemm's canal. Invest. Ophthalmol. Vis. Sci. *18:* 547–561.

KAUFMAN, P. L., E. H. BÁRÁNY (1986): Loss of acute pilocarpine effect on outflow facility following surgical disinsertion and retrodisplacement of the ciliary muscle from the scleral spur in the cynomolgus monkey. Invest. Ophthalmol. *15:* 793–807.

KAUFMAN, P. L., B. A. TRUE-GABELT, K. A. ERICKSON-LAMY (1988): Time-dependence of perfusion outflow facility in the cynomolgus monkey. Curr. Eye Res. *7:* 721–726.

KORBMACHER, C., H. HELBIG, H. HALLER, K. A. ERICKSON-LAMY, M. WIEDERHOLT (1989): Endothelin depolarizes membrane voltage and increases intracellular calcium concentration in human ciliary muscle cells. Biochem. Biophys. Res. Comm. *164:* 1031–1039.

KORENFELD, M. S., B. BECKER (1989): Atrial natriutretic peptides. Invest. Ophthalmol. Vis. Sci. *30:* 2385–2392.

KOZUKA, M., T. ITO, S. HIROSE, K. TAKAHASHI, H. HAGAWARA (1989): Endothelin induces two types of contractions of rat uterus: phasic contractions by way of voltage dependent calcium channels and developing contractions through a second type of calcium channel. Biochem. Biophys. Res. Commun. *159:* 317–323.

KRUPIN, T., A. WEISS, B. BECKER, N. HOLMBERG, C. FRITZ (1977): Increased intraocular pressure following topical azide or nitroprusside. Invest. Ophthalmol. Vis. Sci. *16:* 1002–1007.

LAZENBY, G. W., J. W. REED, W. M. GRANT (1968): Short term tests of anticholinergic medication in open angle glaucoma. Arch. Ophthalmol. *80:* 443–448.

LEPPLE-WIENHUES, A., F. STAHL, U. WILLNER, M. WIEDERHOLT (1991): Endothelin: Possible regulator of aqueous humour outflow by ciliary muscle and trabecular meshwork contraction. Invest. Ophthalmol. Vis. Sci.*32* (ARVO Suppl): 788.

LOVENBERG, W., R. C. MILLER (1990): Endothelin: A review of its effects and possible mechanism of action. Neurochem. Res. *15:* 407–417.

MACCUMBER, M. W., C. A. ROSS, B. M. GLASSER, S. H. SNYDER (1989): Endothelin: Visualization of mRNAs by in situ hybridization provides evidence for local action. Proc. Natl. Aca. Sci. USA *86:* 7285–7289.

MAGGI, C. A., S. GIULIANI, R. PATACCHINI, P. SANTICIOLI, D. TURINI, G. BARBANTI, A. MELI (1989): Potent contractile activity of endothelin on the human isolated urinary bladder. Br. J. Pharmacol. *96:* 755–757.

MITTAG, T. W., A. TORMAY, M. ORTEGA, C. SEVERIN (1987): Atrial natriuretic peptide (ANP), guanylate cyclase, and intraocular pressure in the rabbit eye. Curr. Eye Res. *6:* 1189–1196.

MITTAL, C., F. MURAND (1982): Guanylate cyclase: regulation of cGMP metabolism. In: NATHANSON, J., J. KEBABIAN (Eds.): Handbook of Exp. Pharmacol. *58:* 225–260.

NATHANSON, J. A. (1987): Atriopeptin-activated guanylate cyclase in the anterior segment. Invest. Ophthalmol. Vis. Sci. *28:* 1357–1364.

NATHANSON, J. A. (1988): Direct application of a guanylate cyclase activator lowers intraocular pressure. Eur. J. Pharmacol. *147:* 155–157.

NATHANSON, J. A. (1992): Nitrovasodilators as a new class of ocular hypotensive agents. J. Pharmacol. Exp. Therap., in Press.

NEEDLEMAN, P., E. H. BLAINE, J. E. GREENWALD, M. L. MICHENER, C. B. SAPER, P. T. STOCKMAN, H. E. TOLUNAY (1989): The biochemical pharmalogy of atrial peptides. Ann. Rev. Pharmacol. and Tox. *29:* 23–54.

NEUFELD, A. H. (1978): Influences of cyclic nucleotides on outflow facility in the vervet monkey. Exp. Eye Res. *27:* 387–397.

PALMER, R. M. J., A. G. FERRIDGE, S. MONCADA (1987): Nitric oxide release accounts for the biological activity of endothelium-derived relaxing factor. Nature *327:* 524–526.

RAVIOLA, G. (1982): Schwalbe line's cells: A new cell type in the trabecular meshwork of Macaca mulatta. Invest. Ophthalmol. Vis. Sci. *22:* 45 – 56.

ROHEN, J. W., E. LÜTJEN-DRECOLL, E. H. BÁRÁNY (1967): The relation between the ciliary muscle and the trabecular meshwork and its importance for the effect of miotics on aqueous outflow resistance. Graefes Arch. Klin. Exp. Ophthalmol. *172:* 23 – 47.

SCHUMAN, J. S., J. A. NATHANSON, K. ERICKSON-LAMY (1991): Nitroglycerin lowers intraocular pressure and increases outflow facility in cynomolgus monkeys. Invest. Ophthalmol. Vis. Sci. *32* (ARVO Suppl): 871.

STEARDO, L., J. NATHANSON (1987): Brain-barrier tissues: End organs for atriopeptins. Science *235:* 470 – 473.

STONE, R. A., Y. KUWAYAMA, A. M. LATIES, P. J. MARANGOS (1984): Neuronspecific enolase-containing cells in the rhesus monkey trabecular meshwork. Invest. Ophthalmol. Vis. Sci. *25:* 1332 – 1334.

STONE, R. A., A. M. LATIES (1987): Neuroanatomy and neuroendocrinology of the chamber angle. In: Glaucoma Update III, Krieglstein, G. K. (Ed.): Springer-Verlag, Berlin.

UCHIDA, Y., H. NINOMIYA, M. SAOTOME, A. NOMURA, M. OHTSUKA, M. YANAGISAWA, K. GOTO, T. MASAKI, S. HASEGAWA (1988): Endothelin, a novel vasoconstrictor peptide, as potent bronchoconstrictor. Eur. J. Pharmacol. *154:* 227 – 228.

VANHOUTTE, P. M. (Ed.) (1988): Relaxing and Contracting Factors, The Humana Press, Clifton, NJ.

YANAGISAWA, M., H. KURIHARA, S. KIMURA, Y. TOMOBE, M. KOBAYASHI, Y. MITSUI, Y. YAZAKI, K. GOTA, T. MASAKI (1988): Endothelin: A novel potent vasoconstrictor peptide produced by vascular endothelial cells. Nature *322:* 411 – 415.

*Institut für Klinische Physiologie, Klinikum Steglitz, Freie Universität Berlin, 1000 Berlin 45, FRG*

# Contractile properties of trabecular meshwork and ciliary muscle

M. Wiederholt, A. Lepple-Wienhues and F. Stahl

It has been well established, especially by Rohen and his group (Rohen 1964; Rohen et al. 1981; Rohen and Lütjen-Drecoll 1982; Rohen and Jikihara 1988), that contraction of the ciliary muscle via its insertion at the scleral spur and its tendons is able to expand and spread the trabecular lamellae and increase the filtrating area of the cribriform meshwork. The cribriform layer accounts for most of the outflow resistance (Bill and Svedbergh 1972). Thus, the ciliary muscle is directly involved in the regulation of aqueous humor outflow and intraocular pressure. This concept has been supported by the obeservation that pilocarpine reduced outflow resistance by ciliary muscle contraction (Barany 1967; Rohen and Lütjen-Drecoll 1982) and induced a distension of the cribriform meshwork (Grierson et al. 1978; Lütjen-Drecoll et al. 1981). In addition, the experimental model of ciliary muscle disinsertion suggested that pilocarpine increased outflow facility entirely by drug-induced contraction of the ciliary muscle with no direct effect on the trabecular meshwork (Kaufman and Barany 1976; Kaufman 1984).

Bárány (Barany 1962) was probably the first author to consider a direct pharmacological effect (pilocarpine) on the cells of the trabecular meshwork. Morphological studies have demonstrated that pilocarpine may directly affect trabecular meshwork cells and may modify the geometry of the intertrabecular spaces (Flocks and Zweng 1957; Holmberg and Barany 1966; Lütjen-Drecoll et al. 1981). Morphological (Tripathi and Tripathi 1980) and electrophysiological (Coroneo et al. 1991 a) techniques in cultured trabecular meshwork cells have revealed evidence for contractility and excitability of these cells. The data were consistent with a smooth muscle-like function of the meshwork . More recently, contractile filaments have been demonstrated in trabecular meshwork tissue and cultured meshwork cells (Coroneo et al. 1991 a; De Kater et al. 1990; Flügel et al. 1991; Grierson et al. 1986; Iwamoto and Tamura 1988; Ringvold 1978; Tripathi and Tripathi 1980). All these data suggest a direct effect of trabecular meshwork on outflow regulation in addition to the indirect effect of ciliary muscle.

The present paper summarizes our experiments with cultured trabecular meshwork and ciliary muscle cells and compares the contractile properties of isolated trabecular meshwork (TM) with those of ciliary muscle (CM).

## 1.0 Excitability of cultured trabecular meshwork and ciliary muscle cells

Primary cultures of bovine TM cells were grown by established techniques (ANDERSON et al. 1980; GRIERSON et al. 1985) and characterized by electron micros-copy and histochemistry (CORONEO et al. 1991 a). Human Tm cell cultures were pre-pared from donor eyes as described by others (ALVARADO et al. 1982; POLANSKY et al. 1979; ROHEN et al. 1978). Some human TM cells were kindly supplied by Dr. A. Clark (Alcon Laboratories, Fort Worth, TX). Experiments on ciliary muscle cells were performed with our established cell line H7CM (KORBMACHER et al. 1989, 1990) and primary cultures. Continuous membrane voltage (V) recordings were obtained using microelectrodes in subconfluent and confluent monolayers of cul-tured cells. The experimental setup has been described in detail (JENTSCH et al. 1984; HELBIG et al. 1989).

### 1.1 Bovine trabecular meshwork cells

Table 1 summarizes our morphological and electrophysiological evidence (CORONEO et al. 1991 a) that cultured bovine TM cells possess properties of smooth muscle cells. In particular, the spontaneous fluctuations of membrane voltage and action potentials induced by extracellular barium (1 – 10 mmol/l) are typical for

Table 1. Characterization of smooth muscle-like spindle cells of the bovine trabecular mesh-work

**Morphology**

- parallel alignement of intracellular smooth muscle-specific α-isoactin filaments
- cytoplasmic processes, abundant intermediate filaments and microfilaments

**Electrophysiology**
- resting voltage (V)      $-50$ to $-70$ mV
- K transference number      0.71
  (relative $K^+$      (71%)
  permeability)
- excitability      spontaneous fluctuations of V, "abortive" and "overshooting" action potentials (induced by $Ba^{2+}$) action potentials dependent on extracellular $Ca^{2+}$, blockable by nifedipine, not blockable by tetrodotoxin

Data from (CORONEO et al. 1991 a; FLÜGEL et al. 1991), and unpublished observations by Lepple-Wienhues, Stahl, Wiederholt

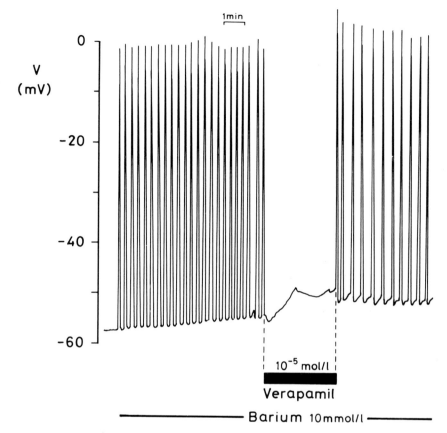

Fig. 1. Membrane voltage (V) in a cultured bovine trabecular meshwork cell. Repetitive overshooting action potentials are induced by addition of extracellular $Ba^{2+}$ and are abolished in the presence of the calcium-channel blocker verapamil.

smooth muscle cells. These action potential are dependent on extracellular calcium and can be totally blocked by calcium channel blockers such as verapamil (Fig. 1). Action potentials could also be induced by barium in other contractile cells such as cultured ciliary muscle cells (KORBMACHER et al. 1990) and retinal pericytes (HELBIG et al. 1991). We never found them to be induced, however, in cultured epithelial cells of corneal endothelium and ciliary epithelium even at high barium concentrations. Thus, the excitability of cultured TM cells strongly indicates that they function as smooth muscle cells and are probably contractile.

## 1.2 Human trabecular meshwork cells

A variety of different cell cultures from human trabecular meshwork have been used to perform experiments similar to those in bovine cultures (ref. Coroneo et al. 1991 b, and unpublished data by Lepple-Wienhues, Stahl and Wiederholt). The mean membrane voltage under resting conditions ($-63.1 \pm 1.0$ mV), the K transference number for $K^+$ (0.65) and the depolarization induced by ouabain were similar in human cells to those obtained in bovine cells (Coroneo et al. 1991 a, 1991 b). Action potentials could be induced by 10 mmol/l $Ba^{2+}$ in all of the 7 cell lines successfully obtained from different donors (Table 2). Again, the fact that the action potentials were dependent on extracellular calcium and could be blocked by the calcium channel blocker nifedipine $10^{-6}$ mol/l (n = 5, Fig. 2) but not by tetrodotoxin $10^{-6}$ mol/l (n = 4) suggests that we are dealing here with smooth muscle-like cells.

In at least 2 cell lines (H1TM, n = 5; BER 62, n = 6), acetylcholine $10^{-5}$ to $10^{-4}$ mol/l caused depolarization in V (Fig. 3A). This effect could be blocked by atropine $10^{-4}$ mol/l. At low concentrations of $10^{-9}$ to $10^{-7}$ mol/l, the β-adrenergic agonist isoproterenol had no effect on baseline V (H1TM, n = 4). At a concentration of $10^{-6}$ to $10^{-4}$ mol/l, however, isoproterenol dose-dependently depolarized the membrane voltage in the BER 62 cells (n = 22), and this effect could be partially inhibited by metipranolol $10^{-5}$ mol/l (Fig. 3 A and B). Thus, the smooth muscle-like human trabecular meshwork cells express functional muscarinic and β-adrenergic receptors.

Table 2: Cultured human trabecular meshwork cells

| Source of material | Age of donor (years) | Action potentials induced by barium |
|---|---|---|
| ALC A > ALC 4 | 18 | + (n=7) <br> + (n=2) |
| ALC B > ALC 2 | 76 | + (n=3) <br> + (n=3) |
| ALC 10 B | 54 | + (n=3) |
| H1TM | 16 | + (n=7) |
| BER 62 | 29 | + (n=9) |

The cells "ALC" were supplied by Alcon Laboratories (Dr. Clark), the cells "H1TM" by Dr. Erikson Lamy (Coroneo et al. 1991 b), and the cells "BER" are from our own cultures. "H1TM" is a spontaneously transformed cell line; all other cells are subcultures from primary cultures. "ALC B" and "ALC 2" are cultures from a glaucomatous eye; all other cultures are from normal eyes.

Action potentials could also be induced in human ciliary-muscle cells (Korbmacher et al. 1989, 1990), but were never observed in cultured epithelial cells such as human non-pigmented ciliary cells and bovine pigmented ciliary and corneal endothelial cells (unpublished observations).

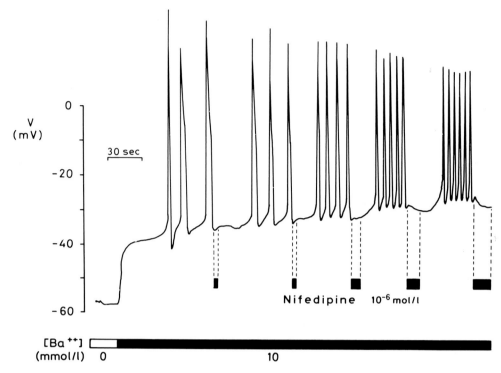

Fig. 2. Effect of repeated nifedipine application on membrane voltage (V) in a cultured human trabecular meshwork cell. $Ba^{2+}$-induced action potentials are totally suppressed by the calcium channel blocker.

### 1.3 Human ciliary muscle cells

A smooth muscle cell line (H7CM) was established from human ciliary muscle and characterized by electrophysiological and morphological techniques (KORBMACHER et al. 1990). As in cultured TM cells, calcium-dependent action potentials could be induced, and steady-state membrane voltage could be depolarized by muscarinic agonists (acetylcholine, carbachol, and, to a lesser extent, pilocarpine). The regulation of intracellular $Ca^{2+}$ and $H^+$ could be describd by measurements of intracellular calcium and pH (intracellularly trapped dyes) (STAHL et al. 1991). Recently, an electrogenic $Na^+/HCO_3^-$ cotransproter which moves 2 or 3 $HCO_3^-$ ions together with 1 $Na^+$ ion and thus carries net negative charge across the cell membrane was demonstrated in these ciliary muscle cells (STAHL et al. 1992). This cotransporter was also present in our primary cultures of human ciliary muscle as well as in primary cultures supplied by Drs. Tamm and Lütjen-Drecoll (Universität

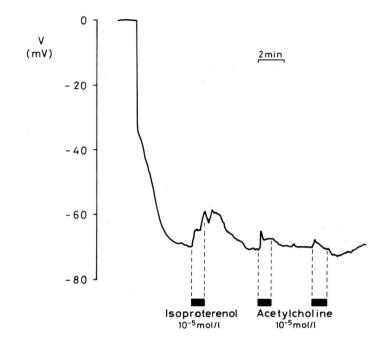

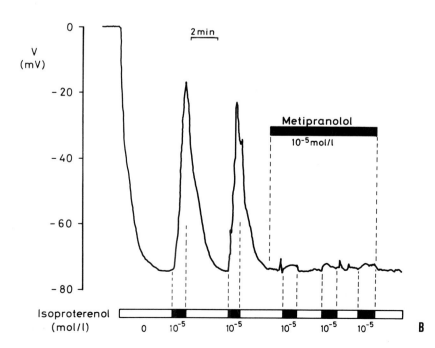

Erlangen). It is the first description of an electrogenic $Na^+/HCO_3^-$ cotransporter in contractile cells. This cotransporter also seem to be present in the human TM cells we tested (BER 62, ALC 2, ALC B, ALC 10 B, Table 2).

Besides these similarities (action potentials, steady-state V, transporter) between the cultured smooth muscle-like cells of ciliary muscle and trabecular meshwork, we found some noteworthy differences (Table 3). Most interestingly, isoproterenol-induced depolarization was observed in a TM cell line but never in CM cells. This functional test thus differentiates the smooth muscle-like cells of TM and CM.

## 2.0 Contractility of isolated trabecular meshwork and ciliary muscle strips

The contractility of isolated ciliary muscle strips has been measured in several mammalian species including man (ITO and YOSHITOMI 1986; LOGRANO and REIBALDI 1986; SUZUKI 1983). In view of the smooth muscle-like properties of cultured trabecular meshwork cells, we attempted to obtain direct contractility measurements in isolated trabecular meshwork strips and compare them with those in ciliary muscle strips. To obtain isometric recordings at very small forces (F) in the micronewton (μN) range, we developed (LEPPLE-WIENHUES et al. 1991 a) a force-length-transducer system similar to that described by Brutsaert et al. (BRUTSAERT et al. 1988). Basically, contractions of the isolated strips are electrically counteracted via a lever/magnetic coil system and an optoelectronic device. This results in a "position clamp" behaviour with length changes of less than 10 μm in the tissue strips.

Because of the anatomical proximity of ciliary muscle and trabecular meshwork in the eyes of higher primates, we chose to use the bovine eye as a model. Since the ciliary muscle is rudimentary and posteriorly located in this species (FLÜGEL et al. 1991; ROHEN 1964; TRIPATHI 1974), it could be prepared separately from the trabecular meshwork, which here more closely resembles a reticular meshwork, (FLÜGEL et al. 1991; ROHEN 1964). The bovine chamber angle has recently been examined in detail (FLÜGEL et al. 1991). The bovine meshwork was ultrastructurally and immunocytochemically different from the ciliary muscle. Both regions contained α-smooth muscle actin; but the ciliary muscle was desmin- and vimentin-positive, while the meshwork only stained for vimentin. The described myofibroblasts (FLÜGEL et al. 1991) are probably the morphological substrate responsible for the contractile activity of the bovine meshwork.

◄ Fig. 3. Response of membrane voltage (V) on superfusion of acetylcholine (Fig. 3A) and isoproterenol (Fig. 3A and Fig. 3B) in human trabecular meshwork cells. The magnitude of depolarization induced by the drugs varied considerably. In all experiments, however, voltage changes induced by acetylcholine could be partially blocked by atropine, and those induced by isoproterenol were sensitive to the β-blocker metipranolol.

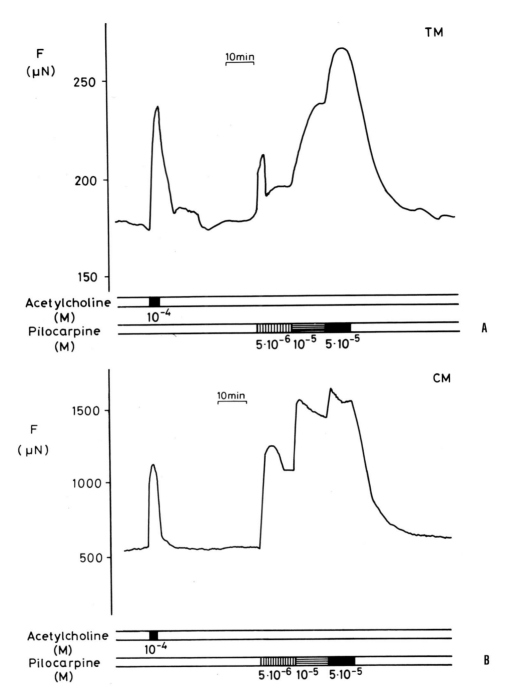

Fig. 4. Isometric force response (F) of isolated bovine trabecular meshwork (Fig. 4 A) and ciliary muscle strips (Fig. 4 B). Administration of cholinergic agonists resulted in dose-dependent contractions of both tissues.

Table 3: Comparison of electrical properties of cultured human ciliary muscle (CM) and trabecular meshwork (TM) cells

| Action potentials | |
|---|---|
| – induced by $Ba^{2+}$ | CM = TM |
| – dependent on $Ca^{2+}$ | CM = TM |
| – insensitive to TTX | CM = TM |
| **Steady-state voltage** | |
| – depolarization induced by $Na^+$ removal | CM = TM |
| – V changes induced by muscarinic agonists | CM ~ TM (depolarization in CM cells ~ 30–50 mV, and in TM cells ~ 10–20 mV) |
| – oscillation of V on removal of $Na^+$ | only in TM |
| – depolarization induced by β-adrenergic agonists (isoproterenol, partially inhibited by metipranolol) | only in TM |

Data from (CORONONEO et al. 1991 b) and unpublished observations by Lepple-Wienhues, Stahl, Wiederholt

## 2.1 Cholinergic agents

A large number of cholinergic nerve terminals have been described in the ciliary muscle, while the trabecular meshwork contains fewer nerve endings (ISHIKAWA 1962; ROHEN 1964; RUSKELL 1982). Superfusion of cholinergic agonists resulted in an immediate dose-dependent force development in both TM and CM (Fig. 4). Atropine reduced the contractile response of TM and CM, indicating that muscarinic receptors are involved in both tissues (LEPPLE-WIENHUES et al. 1991 a). It is noteworthy that both resting tension and drug-induced contraction were lower in TM than in CM. Furthermore, depolarization induced by a raised extracellular potassium concentration resulted in a consistently lower contractile response of TM than of CM (LEPPLE-WIENHUES et al. 1991 a). Following perfusion with $10^{-5}$ mol/l atropine, the contractile response to potassium was completely abolished in CM and markedly reduced in TM. The data are consistent with the observation of different number of cholinergic nerve terminals in the two tissues and provide first evidence for a direct influence of trabecular meshwork contractility on outflow regulation.

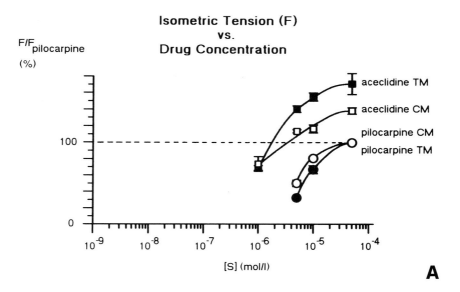

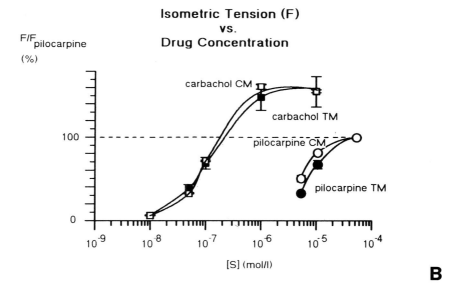

Fig. 5. Cumulative concentration-response curves for aceclidine (Fig. 5A) and carbachol (Fig. 5 B) on contraction in isolated bovine tranbecular meshwork and ciliary muscle strips. Values are given as percentage of the maximal pilocarpine ($5 \times 10^{-5}$ mol/l) response. Each point shows mean values $\pm$ s. e. m. of 4–9 experiments.

Fig. 5 A summarizes the dose-dependent contractions of TM and CM in response to pilocarpine and aceclidine. The contractions could be completely inhibited by atropine $10^{-5}$ mol/l. The dose-response relation and maximal response of TM and CM differed significantly, however. Compared to pilocarpine, aceclidine evoked a maximal response of 172.5 ± 12.6% in TM (n = 7) and 138.9 ± 4.0% in CM (n = 8, p < 0.05). The fact that aceclidine was more effective in eliciting contractions in TM than in CM strips could explain the clinical observation that aceclidine is more effective in lowering intraocular pressure and has less effect on accommodation than pilocarpine (ERICKSON-LAMY and SCHROEDER 1990; KEREN and TREISTER 1980). Fig. 5 B demonstrates the contractility response to various doses of carbachol. Maximal contractions could be induced in both CM and TM by carbachol at concentrations one to two orders of magnitude lower than pilocarpine (shift of dose-response curve to the left). In contrast to aceclidine, carbachol elicited the same dose-response relation in TM and CM.

Our data with isolated strips indicate that cholinergic agonists can act on outflow facility by both ciliary muscle contraction and a direct effect of the cholinomimetics on the trabecular meshwork itself. It is not yet known what the quantitative differences in the influence (Table 4) of the cholinomimetics on TM and CM signify with respect to the regulation of intraocular pressure and how the geometry of trabecular meshwork/cribriform layer is modified by contraction of the meshwork.

## 2.2 Adrenergic agents

Epinephrine and dipivefrin (dipivalyl epinephrine) have long been used to lower intraocular pressure. Besides reducing aqueous humor secretion by stimulating β-receptors of the ciliary epithelium, the adrenergic agents are though to exert vascular actions and facility-increasing effects (KAUFMAN 1984; LEOPOLD and DUZMAN 1986). However, the precise sites and mechanisms of action of adrenergic agonists have not been established. Furthermore, there is no explanation for the observation that both agonists and antagonists of the β-adrenergic system reduce intraocular pressure.

Our contracility measurements in isolated bovine TM and CM strips permit some preliminary statements (Table 4). Confirming the results from cultured human TM cells (see above), functional β-receptors could be verified in TM strips. As shown in Fig. 6, β-stimulation by isoproterenol induced a relaxation in TM strips precontracted by pilocarpine. This relaxation could be inhibited by the β-blocker metipranolol. As in TM strips, isoproterenol relaxed precontracted CM tissues. Epinephrine ($10^{-4}$ mol/l) contracted CM but not TM (Fig. 6). Stimulation with the more selective α-agonist phenylephrine evoked contractions in CM strips. These contractions could be blocked by the $\alpha_1$-antagonist prazosin. Phenylephrine had

Table 4: Functional differences in contractile properties of trabecular meshwork and ciliary muscle

|  | Ciliary Muscle | Trabecular Meshwork |
|---|---|---|
| 1) maximal isometric tension, F ($\mu$N) | 500 – 2000 | 50 – 500 |
| 2) $K^+$-induced contractions (120 mmol/l $K^+$, atropine-sensitive) | +++ (59% of max. acetylcholine response) | (+) (19% of max. acteylcholine response) |
| 3) relative contractions induced by acaclidine vs. pilocarpine | + (139% of max. pilocarpine response) | ++ (173% of max. pilocarpine respone) |
| 4) relative contractions induced by carbachol vs. pilocarpine | ++ (165% of max. pilocarpine) | ++ (164% of max. pilocarpine) |
| 5) functional receptors | $\alpha$, $\beta$ | $\alpha$, $\beta$ |
| stimulation of $\alpha$ ($\alpha_1$) stimulation of $\beta$ inhibition of $\beta$ | contraction relaxation contraction | (contraction) relaxation contraction |
| 6) relative contractions induced by endothelin vs. carbachol | + (73% of max. carbachol) | + (52% of max. carbachol) |
| 7) $Ca^{2+}$-dependence of contractions evoked by endothelin or cholinergic agonists | complete | partial |

Data from (LEPPLE-WIENHUES et al. 1991a, 1991b, 1991c)

only a small effect on TM strips. Thus, both TM and CM possess relaxing $\beta$-receptors. However, CM expresses a contracting $\alpha_1$-receptor, while the effect of $\alpha$-stimulation is rather weak in TM strips.

### 3.0 Possible role of endothelin in regulation of aqueous humor

Endothelin-1 (ET-1) belongs to the familiy of peptides comprising the most potent vasoconstrictive agents yet described (YANAGISAWA et al. 1988). The iris of the rabbit eye has been found to contain high levels of mRNA for ET-1 (MACCUMBER

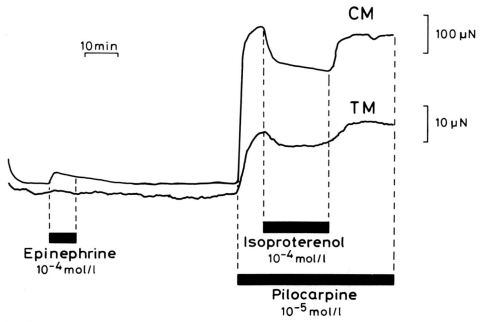

Fig. 6. Original recordings of force development (F) in a trabecular meshwork and a ciliary muscle strip. Epinephrine induced a small contraction only in CM, while isoproterenol induced relaxation in pilocarpine-precontracted strips of both tissues.

et al. 1989). The effects of endothelin on membrane voltage and intracellular calcium in human ciliary muscle cells led us to postulate a functional endothelin receptor in the human eye (KORBMACHER et al. 1989). Recently, conflicting data have been reported on the effect of endothelin on intraocular pressure and outflow facility (ERICKSON-LAMY et al. 1991; GRANSTAM et al. 1991; MACCUMBER et al. 1991).

### 3.1 Membrane voltage and intracellular calcium

In cultured human ciliary muscle and human and bovine trabecular meshwork cells, endothelin dose-dependently induced a reversible membrane voltage depolarization and a rise in intracellular calcium (Table 5). In some experiments, oscillations of intracellular calcium and membrane voltage could be induced by endothelin. The data provide further evidence that the cultured ciliary muscle and trabecular meshwork cells are smooth muscle-like and that both express functional endothelin receptors. Second messenger systems are involved in mediating cellular responses on application of endothelin. In the cultured cells, ET-1 increased intra-

Table 5: Effect of endothelin on cultured cells and isolated strips of ciliary muscle (CM) and trabecular meshwork (TM)

| Cultured cells | Human CM | Human TM | Bovine TM |
|---|---|---|---|
| - resting membrane voltage (mV) | $-67 \pm 1$ (n = 125) | $-62 \pm 5$ (n = 17) | $-55 \pm 1$ (n = 191) |
| - Depolarization induced by endothelin ($10^{-10}$ to $10^{-6}$ mol/l) | + | + | + |
| - Biphasic increase in intracellular calcium induced by endothelin | + | not tested | + |
| **Isolated bovine strips** | | CM | TM |
| - Contraction (F) induced by endothelin | | + | + |
| - EC$_{50}$ endothelin | | $5 \times 10^{-9}$ mol/l | |
| - $F_{endothelin}/F_{carbachol}$ | | $52 \pm 6\%$ (n = 5) | $73 \pm 5\%$ (n = 7) |
| - Endothelin-induced F remaining after removal of extracellular calcium | | 0% | 23% |

Data from (CORONEO et al. 1991a, 1991b; KORBMACHER et al. 1989, 1990; LEPPLE-WIENHUES et al. 1991b, 1991c).

cellular calcium by calcium release from intracellular stores and by increased calcium influx via activation of unspecific cation channels. In TM cells, these channels were insensitive to dihydropyridines (LEPPLE-WIENHUES et al. 1991 b, 1991 c).

## 3.2 Contractility

Application of ET-1 to isolated CM and TM strips (Table 5) led to dose-dependent contractions. The development of force was slower in both tissues with endothelin than with cholinergic agonists (Fig. 7 A, B). The relaxation after removal of ET-1 was very slow compared to the washout of cholinomimetics. Both observations are typical for endothelin-induced contractions. Saturation of the contraction was reached at $8 \times 10^{-9}$ mol/l, half-maximal effective contraction (EC$_{50}$) was $5 \times 10^{-9}$ mol/l for endothelin. The tension evoked by ET-1 was 73% of the maximal carbachol-elicited contraction in trabecular meshwork and 52% in ciliary muscle

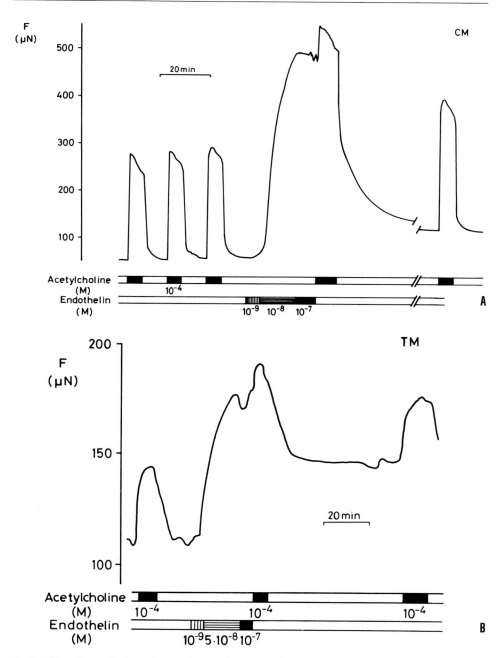

Fig. 7. Effect of endothelin on isometric force in a trabecular meshwork (Fig. 7 A) and a ciliary muscle strip (Fig. 7 B). Endothelin in low doses induced a longer-lasting contracting than acetylcholine. Data from (LEPPLE-WIENHUES et al. 1991 b).

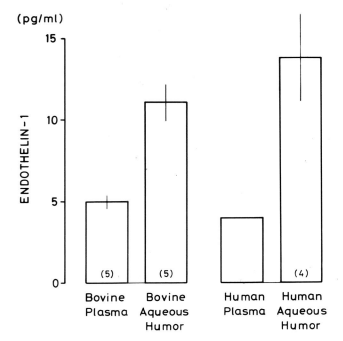

Fig. 8. Endothelin-1 concentration determined by radioimmunoassay in bovine and human plasma and aqueous humor. For an individual measurement of ET-1 in aqueous humor samples were pooled from 3–5 bovine and 7–9 human eyes. The ET-1 concentration in human plasma represents the mean value of more than 50 measuremetns under identical conditions. Data from (LEPPLE-WIENHUES et al. 1991 d).

(Table 5). The TM retained 23 % of the endothelin-induced force response after removal of extracellular calcium, while the CM contraction was totally dependent on extracellular calcium. It must thus be postulated that the trabecular meshwork possesses an additional mechanism of endothelin action independent of extracellular calcium. These results provide further evidence of functional differences between the contractile region of TM and CM.

### 3.3 Synthesis of endothelin

A commercial immunoassay was used to determine ET-1 after extraction in bovine and human plasma and aqueous humor and in the supernatant of cultured cells (LEPPLE-WIENHUES et al. 1991 d). At $11.1 \pm 0.98$ pg/ml, ET-1 was significantly higher in bovine aqueous humor than in plasma ($5.0 \pm 0.27$ pg/ml, n = 5, p < 0.01). ET-1 concentrations were similar in bovine and human plasma under identical con-

## CULTURED NONPIGMENTED CILIARY EPITHELIAL CELLS

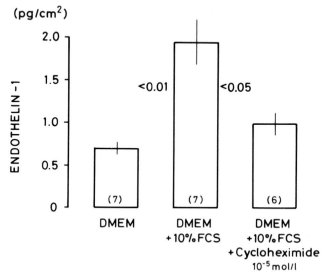

Fig. 9. Endothelin synthesis of cultured human non-pigmented cells of the ciliary epithelium. Endothelin was determined by radioimmunoassay in the supernatant of cultured cells incubated for 24 hours. Addition of fetal calf serum stimulated endothelin release which could be inhibited by cycloheximide.

ditions (Fig. 8). Preliminary experiments with aqueous humor pooled from 30 patients (approximately 100 μl taken at the beginning of cataract surgery) show that ET-1 in human aqueous humor also exceeds the plasma concentration (Fig. 8). This supports the notion that endothelins may be secreted into the aqueous humor and may act as transmitters or modulator substances in the eye.

ET-1 syntheis has previously been demonstrated in cultured human retinal microvascular endothelial cells (MacCumber et al. 1989). ET-1 synthesis was tested in various cultured cells and found in a well-described cell line of human non-pigmented ciliary epithelial cells (Lepple-Wienhues et al. 1991 d). After subculturing, the cells reached their maximal ET-release 5 days after seeding. The basal ET-release 1 day after incubation with Dulbecco's Minimal Essential Medium (DMEM) was $0.69 \pm 0.06$ pg/cm$^2$ (Fig. 9). The synthesis could be significantly stimulated by fetal calf serum. This stimulated synthesis was decreased by cycloheximide, an inhibitor of translation. Cell lines of human ciliary muscle and bovine corneal endothelium showed only small productions of ET-1 (Lepple-Wienhues et al. 1991 d). ET-1 synthesis by non-pigmented ciliary epithelial cells could be an important source of this peptide found in aqueous humor. Though unlikely to be an important circulating vasoregulatory hormone, ET-1 may represent a local humoral factor involved in regulation of aqueous humor dynamics. Release of ET is increased by stretch of vascular endothelial cells (SUMPIO and WIDMAN 1990) and by stimulation of the fluid flow rate (MILNER et al. 1990). Thus, ET release could be changed by an increase in aqueous humor secretion and/or intraocular pressure. The ET concentration in aqueous humor could then act as a counterbalancing force by influencing outflow facility via stimulation of contractile elements of the ciliary muscle and trabecular meshwork. Finally, it may be speculated on the dysfunction of such a feedback system in a diesease such as glaucoma.

## Acknowledgement

Supported by Deutsche Forschungsgemeinschaft, grant Wi 328/11 and Dr. Mann Pharma, Berlin.

## References

ALVARADO, J. A., I. WOOD, J. R. POLANSKY (1982): Human trabecular cells. II. Growth pattern and ultrastructural characteristics. Invest. Ophthalmol. Vis. Sci 23: 464–478.

ANDERSON, P. J., J. WANG, D. L. EPSTEIN (1980): Metabolism of calf trabecular (reticular) meshwork. Invest. Ophthalmol. Vis. Sci. 19: 13–20.

BÁRÁNY, E. H. (1962): The mode of action of pilocarpine on outflow resistance in the eye of a primate. Invest. Ophthalmol. 1: 712–727.

BÁRÁNY, E. H. (1967): The immediate effect on outflow resistance of intravenous pilocarpine in the vervet monkey, Cercopithecos ethiops. Invest. Ophthalmol. Vis. Sci. 6: 373–380.

BILL, A., B. SVEDBERGH (1972): Scanning electron microscopic studies of the trabecular meshwork and the canal of Schlemm – an attempt to localize the main resistance to outflow of aqueous humor in man. Acta Ophthalmol. 50: 295–320.

BRUTSAERT, D., A. MEULEMANS, K. SIPIDO, S. SYS (1988): Effects of damaging the endocardial surface on the mechanical performance of isolated cardiac muscle. Circ. Res. 62: 358–366.

CORONEO, M. T., C. KORBMACHER, B. STIEMER, C. FLÜGEL, E. LÜTJEN-DRECOLL, M. WIEDERHOLT (1991 a): Electrical and morphological evidence for heterogeneous populations of cultured bovine trabecular meshwork cells. Exp. Eye Res. 52: 375–388.

CORONEO, M. T., K. A. ERICKSON-LAMY, M. WIEDERHOLT (1991 b): Membrane voltage recordings in a cell line (H₁TM) derived from human trabecular meshwork. Invest. Ophthalmol. Vis. Sci. 32: 942.

DEKATER, A., S. SPURR-MICHAUD, I. GIPSON (1990): Localisation of smooth muscle myosin-containing cells in the aqueous outflow pathway. Invest. Ophthalmol. Vis. Sci. 31: 347–353.

ERICKSON-LAMY, K., A. SCHROEDER (1990): Dissociation between the effect of aceclidine on outflow facility and accommodation. Exp. Eye Res. 50: 143–147.

ERICKSON-LAMY, K., C. KORBMACHER, J. S. SCHUMAN, J. A. NATHANSON (1991): Effect of endothelin on outflow facility and accommodation in the monkey eye in vivo. Invest. Ophthalmol. Vis. Sci. 32: 492–495.

FLOCKS, M., H. C. ZWENG (1957): Studies on the mode of action of pilocarpine on aqueous outflow. Am. J. Ophthalmol. 44: 380–388.

FLÜGEL, C., E. TAMM, E. LÜTJEN-DRECOLL (1991): Different cell populations in bovine trabecular meshwork: an ultrastructural and immunohistochemical study. Exp. Eye Res. 52: 681–690.

GRANSTAM, E., L. WANG, A. BILL (1991): Ocular response to endothelin-1 in the rabbit and the cat. Invest. Ophthalmol. Vis. Sci. 32: 757.

GRIERSON, I., W. R. LEE, S. ABRAHAM (1978): Effects of pilocarpine on the morphology of the human outflow apparatus Brit. J. Ophthalmol. 62: 302–313.

GRIERSON, I., E. ROBINS, W. UNGER, L. MILLAR, A. AHMED (1985): The cells of the bovine outflow system in tissue culture. Exp. Eye Res. 40: 35–46.

GRIERSON, I., L. MILLAR, J. DeYONG, J. DAY, N. McKECHNIE, C. HITCHINS, M. BOULTON (1986): Investigations of cytoskeletal elements in cultured bovine meshwork cells. Invest. Ophthalmol. Vis. Sci. 27: 1318–1330.

HELBIG, H., C. KORBMACHER, J. WOHLFAHRT, M. COCA-PRADOS, M. WIEDERHOLT (1989): Electrical membrane properties of a cell clone derived from human nonpigmented ciliary epithelium. Invest. Ophthalmol. Vis. Sci. 30: 882–884.

HELBIG, H., S. KORNACKER, A. LEPPLE-WIENHUES, F. STAHL M. WIEDERHOLT (1991): Smooth muscle-like electrical membrane properties of bovine retinal capillary pericytes. Invest. Ophthalmol. Vis. Sci 32: 976.

HOLMBERG, A., E. H. BÁRÁNY (1966): The effect of pilocarpine on the endothelium formed on the inner wall of Schlemm's Canal; Schlemm's Canal, an electronmicroscopic study in the monkey. Invest. Ophthalmol. 5: 53–58.

ISHIKAWA, T. (1962): Fine structure of the human ciliary muscle. Invest. Ophthalmol. 1: 587–608.

ITO, Y., T. YOSHITOMI (1986): Membrane and contractile properties of the dog ciliary muscle. Br. J. Pharmacol. 88: 629–638.

IWAMOTO, Y., M. TAMURA (1988): Immunocytochemical study of intermediate filaments in cultured human trabecular cells. Invest. Ophthalmol. Vis. Sci. 29: 244–250.

JENTSCH, T. J., M. KOCH, H. BLECKMANN, M. WIEDERHOLT (1984): Effect of bicarbonate, methazolamide and stilbenes on the intracellular potentials of cultured bovine corneal endothelial cells. J. Membr. Biol. 78: 103–107.

KAUFMAN, P., E. BÁRÁNY (1976): Loss of acute pilocarpine effect on outflow facility following surgical disinsertion and retrodisplacement of the ciliary muscle from the scleral spur in the cynomolgus monkey. Invest. Ophthalmol. Vis. Sci. 15: 793–807.

KAUFMAN, P. (1984): Aqueous humor outflow. Curr. Top. Eye Res. 4: 97–138.

KEREN, G., G. TREISTER (1980): Effect of aceclidine (+) isomer and pilocarpine on the intraocular pressure decrease and the miosis in glaucomatous eyes. Effect on accommodation in normal eyes of young subjects. Ophthalmologica 180: 181–187.

KORBMACHER, C., H. HELBIG, H. HALLER, K. A. ERICKSON-LAMY, M. WIEDERHOLT (1989): Endothelin depolarizes membrane voltage and increases intracellular calcium concentration in human ciliary muscle cells. Biochem. Biophys. Res. Commun. 164: 1031–1039.

KORBMACHER, C., H. HELBIG, M. T. CORONEO, K. A. ERICKSON-LAMY, B. STIEMER, E. TAMM, E. LÜTJEN-DRECOLL, M. WIEDERHOLT (1990): Membrane voltage recordings in a primary cell line derived from human ciliary muscle. Invest. Ophthalmol. Vis. Sci. 31: 220–230.

LEOPOLD, I. H., E. DUZMAN (1986): Observations on the pharmacology of glaucoma. Ann. Rev. Pharmacol. Toxicol. 26: 401–426.

LEPPLE-WIENHUES, A., F. STAHL, M. WIEDERHOLT (1991a): Differential smooth muscle-like contractile properties of trabecular meshwork and ciliary muscle. Exp. Eye Res. 53: 33–38.

LEPPLE-WIENHUES, A., F. STAHL, U. WILLNER, R. SCHÄFER, M. WIEDERHOLT (1991b): Endothelin-evoke contractions in bovine ciliary muscle and trabecular meshwork: interaction with calcium, nifedipine and nickel. Current Eye Res. 10: 983–989.

LEPPLE-WIENHUES, A., F. STAHL, D. WUNDERLING, U. WILLNER, U. SCHNEIDER, M. WIEDERHOLT (1991c): Membrane properties of trabecular meshwork endothelial cells – action of barium and endothelin. Pflügers Arch. 418 (Suppl. 1): R76

LEPPLE-WIENHUES, A., F. STAHL, J. HENSEN, M. BECKER, M. WIEDERHOLT (1991d): Endothelin-1 synthesis in nonpigmented ciliary body epithelial cells. Pflügers Arch. 419 (Suppl. 1): R94

LOGRANO, M., A. REIBALDI (1986): Receptor responses in fresh human ciliary muscle. Br. J. Pharmac. *87:* 379 – 385

LÜTJEN-DRECOLL, E., R. FUTA, J. W. ROHEN (1981): Ultrahistochemical studies on tangential sections of the trabecular meshwork in normal and glaucomatous eyes. Invest. Ophthalmol. Vis. Sci. *21:* 563 – 573.

MACCUMBER, M. W., C. A. ROSS, B. M. GLASER, S. H. SNYDER (1989): Endothelin: Visualization of mRNAs by in situ hybridization provides evidence for local action. Proc. Natl. Acad. Sci., USA *86:* 7285 – 7289.

MACCUMBER, M. W., H. D. JAMPEL, S. H. SNYDER (1991): Ocular effects of the endothelins: Abundant peptides in the eye. Arch. Opthalmol. *109:* 705 – 709.

MILNER, P., P. BODIN, A. LOESCH, G. BURNSTOCK (1990): Rapid release of endothelin and ATP from isolated aortic endothelial cells exposed to increased flow. Biochem. Biophys. Res. Commun. *170:* 649 – 656.

POLANSKY, J. R., R. N. WEINREB, J. D. BAXTER, J. ALVARADO (1979): Human trabecular cells. I. Establishment in tissue culture and growth characteristics. Invest. Ophthalmol. Vis. Sci. *18:* 1043 – 1049.

RINGVOLD, A. (1978): Actin filaments in trabecular endothelial cells in eyes of the vervet monkey. Acta Ophthalmologica *56:* 217 – 227.

ROHEN, J. (1964): Das Auge und seine Hilfsorgane, Bd. III/2, „Haut und Sinnesorgane". In: Handbuch der mikroskopischen Anatomie des Menschen (Eds. v. Möllendorff, W. and W. Bargmann), Springer Verlag, Berlin, pp. 189 – 328.

ROHEN, J. W., D. O. SCHACHTSCHNABEL, H. FIGGE, B. BIGALKE (1978): Morphological and biochemical studies of the human trabecular meshwork in tissue culture. Invest. Opthalmol. Vis. Sci. *17* (Suppl.): 207.

ROHEN, J., R. FUTA, E. LÜTJEN-DRECOLL (1981): The fine structure of the cribriform meshwork in normal and glaucomatous eyes. Invest. Ophthalmol. Vis. Sci. *21:* 574 – 585.

ROHEN, J. W., E. LÜTJEN-DRECOLL (1982): Biology of the trabecular meshwork. In: Basic aspects of glaucoma research (Ed. E. Lütjen-Drecoll), Schattauer Verlag, Stuttgart, pp. 141 – 166.

ROHEN, J., S. JIKIHARA (1988): Morphologie des Kammerwasserabflußsystems bei verschiedenen Glaukomformen. Fortschr. Ophthalmol. *85:* 15 – 24.

RUSKELL, G. (1982): Innervation of the anterior segment of the eye. In: Basic aspects of glaucoma research (Ed. E. Lütjen-Drecoll), Schattauer Verlag, Stuttgart, pp. 211 – 220.

STHAL, F., A. LEPPLE-WIENHUES, M. KUPPINGER, U. SCHNEIDER, M. WIEDERHOLT (1991): Measurements of intracellular calcium and contractility in human ciliary muscle. Pflügers Arch. *418:* 531 – 537.

STAHL, F., A. LEPPLE-WIENHUES, M. KUPPINGER, E. TAMM, M. WIEDERHOLT (1992): Electrogenic sodium-bicarbonate cotransport in human ciliary muscle cells. Am. J. Physiol. *262:* C427 – C435.

SUMPIO, B. E., M. D. WIDMANN (1990): Enhanced production of an endothelium-derived contracting factor by endothelial cells subjected to pulsatile stretch. Surgery *108:* 277 – 282.

SUZUKI, R. (1983): Neuronal influence on the mechanical activity of the ciliary muscle. Br. J. Pharmac. *78:* 591 – 597.

TRIPATHI, R. C. (1974): Comparative physiology and anatomy of the aqueous outflow pathway. In: The Eye, Vol. 5 (Eds. H. Davson and L. Graham) Academic Press, New York, pp. 163 – 356.

TRIPATHI, B. J., R. C. TRIPATHI (1980): Contractile protein alteration in trabecular endothelium in primary open-angle glaucoma. Exp. Eye Res. *31:* 721 – 724.

YANAGISAWA, M., H. KURIHARA, S. KIMURA, Y. YAZAKI, K. GOTO, T. MASAKI (1988): A novel potent vasoconstrictor peptide produced by vascular endothelial cells. Nature *332:* 411 – 415.

*Cellular Pharmacology Laboratories, Department of Ophthalmology,*
*University of California, Medical Center, San Francisco*

# HTM cell culture model for steroid effects on intraocular pressure: Overview

J. R. POLANSKY

## Introduction

The human trabecular meshwork (HTM) is the principal drainage pathway for aqueous humor, and represents a potentially important site for physiologic and pharmacologic regulation of outflow facility. Earlier studies of the biology of the trabecular meshwork had supported the view that HTM cells participate in pathologic alterations leading to reduced outflow facility (see review by ROHEN and LÜTJEN- DRECOLL 1982). A quanative loss of cells in the meshwork occurs in aging, primary open-angle glaucoma (POAG), and possibly other types of glaucoma, implicating a variety of possible cellular mechanisms which could participate in glaucoma pathogenesis (ALVARADO et al. 1984, POLANSKY et al. 1984a). For these reasons, studies of the homeostatic properties of HTM cells, as well as the responses of these cells to stimuli which might influence outflow facility, have constituted a major area for our research.

Studies of trabecular meshwork cells were given substantial impetus by the development of effective tissue culture methods for this cell type. Reports on monkey trabecular meshwork (ROHEN 1975; SCHACHTSCHABEL, BIGALKE, ROHEN 1977; GRIERSON 1980) showed some success in serial cultures. However, there were reservations expressed regarding the ability to maintain the cells without morphological alterations, and the split ratios employed were often quite low (1 : 2), limiting the amount of defined experimental material which could be obtained. Beginning in the late 1970's, our laboratory and others were successful in isolating and propagating HTM cells at high split ratios (1 : 10 to 1 : 20) which retained their original culture appearance and distinguishing ultrastructured features using pretested fetal calf serum and bFGF (e.g. see POLANSKY et al. 1979, 1984; POLANSKY, WEINREB, ALVARADO 1981; ALVARADO, WOOD, POLANSKY 1982). Morphologically differentiated HTM cells from the same cryopreserved stock of cells could be grown and evaluated over many years, enabling repeated experimental evaluations to be performed under reproducible conditions. Since HTM lines from separate individuals could be examined in the same study, the generality of a given HTM cell property or response of interest could be confirmed, and potential intersubject variations verified.

The possibility that glucocorticoids (GCs) might alter the properties and/or functions of HTM cells provided one of our first research directions in the field of glaucoma. The recent biochemical and molecular biological discoveries we have made on this system have shown potentially important clinical correlates.

Previously, there has been considerable interest regarding potential mechanisms for GC effects on intraocular pressure, especially since a "steroid glaucoma" can be observed in some patients receiving topical corticosteroid eyedrops. The original case reports occurred during the course of topical GC anti-inflammatory therapy (FRANCOIS 1954), but approximately ten years went by before the generality of steroid effects on IOP was confirmed by testing populations of patients with dexamethasone phosphate or betamethasone phosphate eyedrops (ARMALY 1963a,b; BECKER and MILLS 1963a,b; KITAZAWA 1976). Progressive increases of intraocular pressure (IOP) and decreased outflow facility were observed in a relatively large percentage of the normal population receiving these eyedrops three to four times a day for periods of three to six weeks. Individuals who showed sufficiently large increases of IOP were classified as "high responders", and this type of response was reported to occur with a high prevalence in patients with POAG or with pigment dispersion (for reviews see EPSTEIN 1989; POLANSKY and WEINREB 1984). The reasons for these different GC responses have not yet been adequately explained, and we are currently considering both environmental and genetic factors in evaluating cultured HTM cells for steroid effects.

## Development of the HTM cell model system to explore prolonged GC effects

The ability to obtain large numbers of HTM cells facilitated several studies including those proven useful in other steroid-responsive systems. Initial studies included evaluations of GC receptor binding using $^3$H-dexamethasone, with and without unlabeled competitors. Scatchard analysis of this binding showed a single class of high affinity GC receptors, and evidence for the expected receptor translocation to the cell nucleus was obtained. Appropriate specificity for steroid analogues was demonstrated in competition studies (WEINREB et al. 1981). In separate investigations, inhibition of thymidine uptake (POLANSKY, WEINREB, ALVARADO 1981) and decreased metabolism of arachidonic acid into prostaglandins (PGs) were demonstrated (WEINREB, MITCHELL and POLANSKY 1983; WEINREB, POLANSKY and MITCHELL 1988) using 1 to 2 day dexamethasone (DEX) exposures. However, only minor changes in specific protein synthesis and equivocal effects on

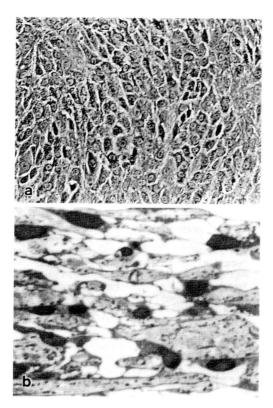

Fig. 1. a. Confluent cultures of human trabecular meshwork (HTM) cells propagated *in vitro* from a 30-year-old subject, at the fourth passage according to Methods. b. HTM from the corneoscleral meshwork of a young individual (from POLANSKY et al. 1984 a).

phagocytosis were observed. This was surprising because the HTM cells showed a greater than normal sensitivity compared to other cell types we had evaluated for the DEX inhibition of PG production, and 24 to 48 hours has always been considered sufficient for GCs to bind to their receptor(s) and produce maximal effects.

One possibility was HTM cells might show larger effects on specific protein synthesis and phagocytosis with longer hormone exposures (as suggested by Dr. L. Bito, personal communication), which appeared plausible because of the progressive effects on IOP noted in the topical steroid testing protocols in patients. Since GC-induced IOP elevations often require several weeks to become pronounced, we examined one and three week DEX treatments compared to a one day treatment. Before evaluating the time course for DEX effects, the HTM cultures were maintained approximately 7 days after confluency to eliminate as much as possible GC effects on cell division. The typical monolayered appearance of an HTM cell culture used in the experiments is shown in Fig. 1a. A cross section of HTM cells from the corneoscleral meshwork *in situ* is shown in Fig. 1b. The amount of DEX added to the cultures was based on the concentrations of active hormone (approximately 100 nM DEX equivalents) in the anterior chamber measured by radioreceptor assay following 0.1% dexamethasone phosphate eyedrops in rabbits (POLANSKY and ALVARADO 1985).

Three week GC treatments demonstrated a large induction of proteins near 55 kDa on SDS polyacrylamide gel electrophoresis [PAGE] using brief $^{35}$S-methionine labeling as a measure of specific protein synthesis. The induced proteins showed substantially more labeling at three weeks than at one week or one day when the HTM cultures were treated with 10 nM or 100 nM DEX (POLANSKY et al. 1984b, 1985, 1989; KONAMI et al. 1986). Although such progressive GC-induced changes in protein synthesis did not have any precedent to our knowledge, the effect certainly appeared worthy of further investigation. Studies on three additional HTM cell lines confirmed the original observation that progressive alterations in protein synthesis were occuring in the same region of the gel, while neighboring ocular fibroblasts used as controls did not show this effect. Based on these observations, we proposed prolonged GC exposure to HTM cells could provide a "model system" for exploring cellular alterations relevant to steroid glaucoma and perhaps other forms of glaucoma (POLANSKY 1984b, 1985).

Using this information, SHIRATO et al. (1988) and YUN et al. (1989) found long-term DEX-induced changes in HTM cell phagocytosis and cell associated connective tissues, respectively. TRIPATHI et al. (1990a) have reported a GC-induced protein/glycoprotein in porcine trabecular meshwork cells similar to our findings in human cells, which could be of substantial interest for transgenic studies. The parameters we have defined in the HTM system regarding the dose and timing of DEX-induced changes in specific protein synthesis could prove useful in examining the varied proposals made by other investigators concerning cellular and connective tissue mechanisms for steroid effects on IOP (e.g. see BARANY 1956; BILL 1975; CLARK et al. 1990; HAJEK et al. 1983, 1984; HERNANDEZ et al. 1985; HIGBEE et al. 1989; PARTRIDGE et al. 1989; RICHARDSON 1981; ROHEN und LÜTJEN-DRECOLL 1982; RICHARDSON 1981; TRIPATHI, TRIPATHI and SWIFT 1989; TRIPATHI, MILLARD and TRIPATHI 1990a,b). The steroid glaucoma feline model developed by Bito (ZAHN, MIRANDA and BITO 1989) could also be useful to evaluate.

Within our own laboratory, we have placed an emphasis on both biochemical and molecular biological approaches to consider the various long-term DEX-induced alterations of HTM cells (e.g. see KONAMI et al. 1986; POLANSKY et al. 1989, 1990, 1991; NGUYEN et al. 1991).

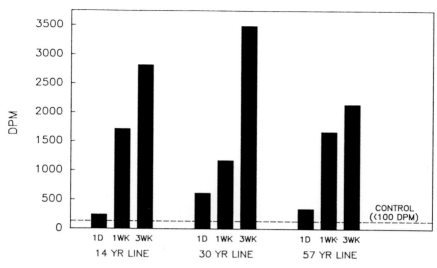

Fig. 2. Time-course for the induction of 55 kDa proteins from two-dimensional gels. HTM cells were exposed to 100 nM DEX for the time periods indicated, and the major inductions at approximately 52 to 55 kDa (pI range, 5.4 to 5.8) were examined. The gels were quantitated using two-dimensional autoradiograms with the PDQuest system for automated computer analysis in which the domain of the HTM GC response was evaluated. (J. R. POLANSKY and R. KURTZ, unpublished data). Values expressed are in disintegrations per minute normalized to internal standards (from POLANSKY et al. 1989).

## Biochemical correlates to IOP changes

A number of different biochemical assays are being used to evaluate the major GC-induced proteins/glycoproteins in HTM cells. A summary of this work and some new findings are presented by Fauss et al. (1992) in this volume. In this section, we review some of the evidence regarding the time course and dose-response for the major protein inductions in HTM cells which supports the concept of a link between *in vitro* findings and *in vivo* observations in patients.

To perform these evaluations, we considered it essential to obtain as much quantitative information as possible regarding GC effects on the specific inductions. $^{35}$S-methionine pulse labeling provides a reasonable estimate of specific mRNA changes following GC treatment to cells, in which the intensity of labeling on two-dimensional (2-D) gels is determined by the protein's synthetic rate (IVARIE and O'FARRELL 1978). This technique helps to define the specificity of the GC responses in differentiated cell types and to understand the "domain" of the response (i.e. since only 2% to 4% of the proteins on 2-D gels are typically regulated by GCs, and these are different for different cell types, it is crucial to know which are being affected in HTM cells).

Quantitative 2-D gels were used to examine individual HTM cell protein inductions as a function of time after brief and prolonged DEX treatments. The domain of the response shows a number of cellular proteins are regulated by DEX. Here, we emphasize the major progressive cellular induction at 52 to 55 kDa (55 kDa). The 55 kDa induction on one-dimensional SDS-PAGE was examined by 2-D gel quantitation as shown in Figure 2. In all subjects evaluated, the levels of the 55 kDa induction increase substantially between one day and one week, and also from one week to three weeks. Some HTM cell lines appear to show the induction sooner than others at the 100 nM dose tested.

The protein inductions were also quantitated for their dose-response characteristics using 2-D gels. Qualitative observations for several years on SDS-PAGE had suggested that a higher than expected DEX dose might be required to see a maximal 55 kDa induction, in that 60 to 100 nM DEX treatments characteristicly produced a substantially higher induction compared to 3 to 30 nM treatments. Use of quantitaive 2-D gels confirmed this impression, as shown in Fig. 3. Following ten-day DEX treatments, the half-maximal ($C_{50}$) response occured at approximately 30 nM DEX (assuming a 100 nM DEX maximal effect), which is substantially higher than that expected for DEX binding to the GC receptor ($K_D = 3$ nM). The dose of DEX required to induce the 55 kDA protein(s) was substantially higher than the dose required for PG inhibition in the same cultures (the observed $C_{50}$ for PG inhibition was approximately 4 nM).

Current evidence indicates that the progressive cellular inductions have a short half life, at least in part due to the transport of the protein(s) out of the cytosol and into the media or onto the cell surface. Interestingly, the dose-response for media inductions in HTM cells (POLANSKY et al. 1990, 1991) appears to be shifted even further to right, and it may be that 100 nM DEX has not yet reached a maximum for GC-induced glycoproteins (see chapter in this volume by FAUSS et al. 1993). It is possible that the high GC requirement to produce these cellular and media changes may help to explain the requirement for relatively high aqueous humor levels following typical corticosteroids to produce substantial IOP elevations (based on our interpretations of the studies of ARMALY [1965] and KITAZAWA [1976]).

By conducting further biochemical evaluations, it should be possible to learn more about the mechanisms of the prolonged GC inductions as well as the life cycle of the major GC protein/glycoproteins (i. e. the steps in the synthesis, export, function, and degradation of the molecules). Such an approach may provide clues concerning the clinical correlations with steroid effects on IOP and glaucoma. If it is found that the GC alterations in HTM cells play some role in IOP effects, then it might be possible to consider interventions to prevent selected molecular processes.

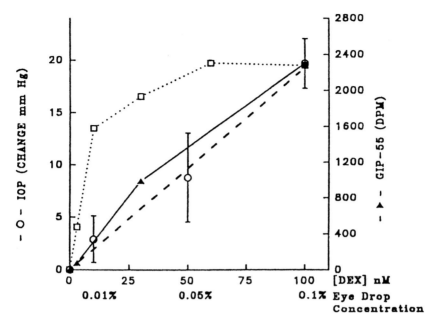

Fig. 3. Dose-response for the DEX induction of the 55 kDA proteins from two dimensional gels compared with the dose-response for IOP changes in patients. Data from our studies is plotted along with IOP results obtained by ARMALY (1965) using different concentrations of topical dexamethasone phosphate assessed in steroid responders. The values for aqueous humor GC activity in the graph were calculated based on DEX radioreceptor assays we conducted in rabbits after dexamethasone phosphate eyedrops (POLANSKY and ALAVARADO 1985). The IOP response is shown by the open circles. The dose-response of 55 kDa protein in HTM cells is indicated by the closed triangles. The dose-response of %-maximal PGE2 inhibition in HTM cells by DEX is indicated by the open squares. As shown, there is a marked diminution of the IOP effect (mm Hg) when the 0.1 % dexamethasone phosphate eyedrops are diluted to 0.05 % and 0.01 % concentrations (aqueous humor levels are presented as nM DEX "eqivalents" of glucocorticoid activity above these values). The DEX effect on IOP appears to increase substantially between 50 and 100 nM DEX activity in the aqueous humor, a dose-response consistent with that observed for the induced proteins/glycoproteins in HTM cells. Oral corticosteroid therapies with moderate GC doses (e. g. prednisone, 15 mg/po; or dexamethasone, 3 mg/po) would be expected to produce a maximum of 20 nM DEX activity in the aqueous humor (assuming the unbound hormone in the plasma is free to equilibrate with the aqueous humor), possibly explaining the relatively low incidence of major IOP elevations in patients receiving oral vs topical corticosteroids.

## Molecular biology approaches

Molecular biology methods have provided confirmation of the progressive GC-inductions in the HTM cell model, and an approach to obtain information regarding the identities of the gene products regulated. As mentioned later in this volume, NGUYEN et al. (1991) obtained cDNA clones from subtraction screening protocols, isolating and sequencing a major GC-induced novel mRNA that has characteristics

## HTM CELL MODEL FOR GLUCOCORTICOID- EFFECTS ON IOP

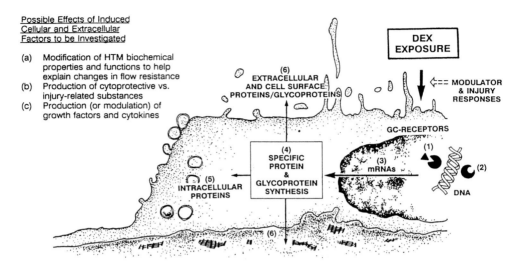

Possible Effects of Induced
Cellular and Extracellular
Factors to be Investigated

(a)  Modification of HTM biochemical
      properties and functions to help
      explain changes in flow resistance
(b)  Production of cytoprotective vs.
      injury-related substances
(c)  Production (or modulation) of
      growth factors and cytokines

Fig. 4. Schematic of HTM cell model for steroid effects in glaucoma: Possible molecular mechanisms for alterations in specific mRNAs and protein/glycoproteins that are observed following prolonged DEX treatment of the cells. Such effects may be modulated separately by other mediators and injury (e. g. oxidative stress, phagocytic stress) effects in addition to direct GC actions. The diagram shows in the DEX (triangle) associated with the GC-receptor (1) which binds as a complex to regulatory sequences on the DNA which then influences the production of specific mRNAs. A role for other trans-acting factors is shown by the open circle (2), which could involve other hormone receptors or cell mediators/growth factors as indicated on the left (a – c). These factors could be separately regulated through a GC responsive mechanism. Together these concepts will be investigated in attempts to explain the progressive nature of the GC inductions in HTM cells and explaining the coordinate effects of the other hormones and "stress factors" on the regulation of the induced and deinduced mRNAs (3) and HTM cell protein/glycoproteins (4). Progressive mRNA inductions with prolonged DEX exposure could also involve mRNA stabilization. The well-known steps involved in the GC-receptor binding, activation of the receptor, and the binding of the receptor hormone complex to promoter sites in the HTM genome are shown schematically Changes in some GC receptors after chronic DEX exposure may also be involved in the dose-response observations. The induced proteins and glycoproteins may act (5) intracellularly or on (6) the cell surface and/or in the extracellular space to influence HTM cell properties. If this external site proves relevant, then the steps involved in glycosylation and transport out of the cell, as well as cell surface binding, could be quite important.

compatible with the secreted glycoprotein identified by biochemical methods. Additional applications of molecular biology methods should also permit us to understand the molecular basis for the progressive inductions, to identify regulatory sites for hormones and transacting factors, and to screen for the effects of other factors which could be influencing the cells. The diagram in Fig. 4 presents some of these concepts in a simplified model of GC-induced changes of mRNA and protein expression in HTM cells.

Efforts are also being made to understand the molecular mechanisms for progressive mRNA changes (e. g. messenger stabilization vs a variety of direct transcription controls) as well as to investigate the possible role of endogenous growth factor activity. Quantitative PCR methods to evaluate mRNA levels in both HTM cells and meshwork tissues treated with DEX are being developed which should be applicable to organ culture perfusion and surgical specimens (from individuals with POAG and other types of glaucoma). Such studies could help to examine multiple hormone and modulator effects on the major GC regulated molecules in HTM cells, and should help in the preparation of required probes and antibodies for *in vivo/in vitro* correlations.

Oligonucleotide probes are being synthesized to follow-up on the different leads provided by the library subtraction from control and ten-day DEX-treated HTM cultures. Other probes are also being used to assay for GC inductions known in the literature from different cell types. One of the reduced clones from the HTM subtraction screening has led us into another major area of investigation based on its sequence homology with insulin-like growth factor (IGF) binding proteins. Specific probes have already been made by our collaborators for the IGF family of agonists, receptors and binding proteins. Initial results have demonstrated that a reduction in IGF-1 activity in HTM cells occurs following DEX treatment, which might provide a stress to this cell type if this growth factor plays an essential role in HTM homeostasis.

## Summary and conclusion

Biochemical and molecular biological methods are helping to explore the HTM cell model system for glucocorticoid (GC)-induced elevations of intraocular pressure (IOP). The HTM cell type not only shows unique properties, but demonstrates progressive changes in gene regulation with prolonged GC exposure that may be specific for this cell type. Major, long-term changes in protein/glycoproteins and mRNAs are detected by comparing brief (1 to 2 day) to prolonged (1 to 3 week) DEX treatments using confluent HTM cultures. The dose-response and time course for some of the DEX-induced changes in HTM cells correlate with observed IOP effects of topical steroid eyedrops, especially for the largest GC inductions. Other GC-induced changes, including a marked inhibition of HTM cell division and the effects of growth factors, are also being examined. An understanding of alterations which occur in HTM cells following prolonged DEX treatment, and knowledge of environmental and endogenous factors which modulate these effects, could provide new therapeutic avenues.

## Acknowledgements

Supported by NIH grant EY02477 and AHAF, National Glaucoma Research

## References

ALVARADO, J. A., I. WOOD, J. R. POLANSKY (1982): Human trabecular cells II: ultrastructural characteristics of cultured trabecular cells. Invest. Ophthalmol. Vis. Sci. *23:* 464 – 478.

ALVARADO, J. A., C. MURPHY, R. JUSTER (1984): Trabecular meshwork cellularity in primary open-angle glaucoma and non-glaucomatous normals. Ophthalmology *91:* 564 – 79.

ARMALY, M. F. (1963 a): Effect of corticosteroids on intraocular pressure and fluid dynamics. 1. The effect of dexamethasone in the normal eye. Arch. Ophthalmol. *70:* 98 – 105.

ARMALY, M. F. (1963 b): Effect of corticosteroids on intraocular pressure and fluid dynamics. II. The effects of dexamethasone in the glaucomatous eye. Arch. Ophthalmol. *70:* 492 – 499.

ARMALY, M. F. (1965): Statistical attributes of the steriod hypertensive response in the clinically normal eye. Invest. Ophthalmol. *4:* 187 – 197.

BARANY, E. H. (1956): The action of different kinds of hyaluronidase on the resistance to flow through the angle of the anterior chamber. Acta Ophthalmol. *34:* 403 – 497.

BAXTER, J. D., G. G. ROUSSEAU (1979): Glucocorticoid Hormone Action. Springer-Verlag, Berlin and New York (BAXTER, J. D., G. G. ROUSSEAU, Eds.).

BECKER, B., D. W. MILLS (1963 a): Corticosteroids and intraocular pressure. Arch. Ophthalmol. *70:* 500 – 507.

BECKER, B., D. W. MILLS (1963 b): Elevated intraocular pressure following corticosteroid eyedrops. J.A.M.A. *185:* 170 – 172.

BILL, A. (1975): The drainage of aqueous humor. Invest Ophthalmol. Vis. Sci *14:* 1 – 3.

CLARK, A., K. WILSON, M. KUNKLE, W. HOWE (1990): Effect of glucocorticoids on the cytoskeleton of cultured human trabecular cells. Invest. Ophthalmol. Vis. Sci. (Suppl) *31:* 338.

EPSTEIN, D. L. (1989): Pigment dispersion and pigmentary glaucoma. In: Chandler and Grant's Glaucoma, Third Edition, Lea and Febiger, Philadelphia pp. 201 – 210.

FRANCOIS, J., V. VICTORIA-TRONCOSO (1977): Corticosteroid glaucoma. Ophthalmologica *174:* 195 – 209.

GRIERSON, I., E. ROBINSON, R. C. HOWES (1980): Preliminary observations on human trabecular meshwork cells *in vitro.* Albrecht von Graefe's Arch. Klin. Exp. Ophthalmol. *212:* 173 – 86.

HAJEK, A., N. SOSSI, G. SOSSI, P. PALMBERG (1983): Dexamethasone phosphate increases accumulation of collagen in the cell layer of cultured human trabecular endothelial cells. Invest. Ophthalmol. Vis. Sci. (Suppl) *24:* 136.

HAJEK, A., S. NUNZI, G. SOSSI, P. PALMBERG (1984): Glucocortiocoids cause human trabecular endothelial cells in culture to accumulate hyaluronic acid even at confluency. Invest. Ophthalmol. Vis. Sci. (Suppl) *25:* 100.

HERNANDEZ, M., B. WEINSTEIN, M. DUNN, G. GORDON, A. SOUTHREN (1985): The effect of dexamethasone on the synthesis of collagen in the normal human trabecular meshwork explants. Invest. Ophthalmol. Vis. Sci. *26:* 1784 – 88.

HIGBEE, R. G., K. HAGGARD, H. MOLL, A. CLARK, W. GOOSSENS, M. G. HRIZD, P. A. KNEPPER (1989): Biochemical markers in aqueous humor of increased IOP. Invest. Ophthalmol. Vis. Sci. (Suppl) *30:* 29.

IVARIE, R., P. O'FARRELL (1978): The glucocorticoid domain: steroid-mediated changes in the rate of synthesis of rat hepatoma proteins. Cell *13:* 41 – 55.

KITAZAWA, Y. (1976): Increased intraocular pressure induced by corticosteroids. Am. J. Ophthalmol. *82:* 492 – 495.

KONAMI, D., J. A. ALVARADO, R. KIM, R. KURTZ, J. R. POLANSKY (1986): Steroid-induced changes in specific protein synthesis of human trabecular meshwork cells: long-term vs. short-term responses. Invest. Ophthalmol. Vis. Sci. (Suppl) *27:* 165.

NGUYEN, T. D., W. D. HUANG, A. WANG, E. BLOOM, D. FAUSS, W. SHANDS, J. R. POLANSKY (1991): Molecular biology studies of steroid-induced glaucoma model using cultured human trabecular meshwork (HTM) cells. Invest. Ophthalmol. Vis. Sci., in press.

PARTRIDGE, C., B. WEINSTEIN, A. SOUTHREN, M. GERRITSEN (1989): Sectreted proteins in human trabecular meshwork cells. Invest. Ophthalmol. Vis. Sci. *30:* 1843–47.

POLANSKY, J. R., R. WEINREB, J. BAXTER, J. A. ALVARADO (1979): Human trabecular cells I: estab-lishment in tissue culture and growth characteristics. Invest. Ophthalmol. Vis. Sci. *18:* 1043–9.

POLANSKY, J. R., R. WEINREB, J. A. ALVARADO (1981) Studies on human trabecular cells propagasted *in vitro*. Vision Res. *21:* 155–60.

POLANSKY, J. R., I. WOOD, M. MAGLIO, J. ALVARADO (1984 a): Trabecular meshwork cell culture in glaucoma research: Evaluation of biological activity and structural properties of human trabecular cells *in vitro*. Ophthalmol. *91:* 580–595.

POLANSKY, J. R., E. BLOOM, D. KONAMI, R. WEINREB, J. A. ALVARADO (1984 b): Cultured human trabecular cells: evaluation of hormonal and pharmacological responses *in vitro*. In: Recent advances in glaucoma. Elsevier Sciences Publishers. Tel Aviv (TICHO, U., R. DAVID, Eds.).

POLANSKY, J. R., R. WEINREB (1984): Steroids as anti-inflammatory agents. In: Ocular Pharmacology. Springer-Verlag, New York and Berlin (SEARS, M., Eds.). Handbook of Exp. Pharm. *69:* 461–538.

POLANSKY, J. R., J. A. ALVARADO (1985): Isolation and evaluation of target cells in glaucoma research: hormone receptors and drug resonses. Curr. Eye Res. *4:* 267–279.

POLANSKY, J. R., D. KONAMI, R. KIM, J. A. ALVARADO (1985): Glucocorticoid regulation of cultured human trabecular meshwork cells: A model system to study the effects of steroids on IOP. Invest. Ophthalmol. Vis. Sci. (Suppl) *26:* 5.

POLANSKY, J. R., R. KURTZ, J. A. ALAVARDO, R. WEINREB, M. MITCHELL (1989): Eicosanoid produc-tion and glucocorticoid regulatory mechanisms in cultured human trabecular meshwork cells. Prog. Clin. Biol. Res. *312:* 113–138.

POLANSKY, J. R., R. M. KURTZ, T. D. NGUYEN (1990) et al.: *In vitro* model for steroid effects on IOP: characterization of HTM protein/glycoprotein changes and molecular cloning approaches. Invest. Ophthalmol. Vis. Sci. (Suppl). *31:* 377.

POLANSKY, J. R., R. M. KURTZ, D. J. FAUSS, R. Y. KIM, E. BLOOM (1991): *In vitro* correlates of gluco-corticoid effects on intraocular pressure. In: Glaucoma Update. (KRIEGLSTEIN, G. K., Eds.) Sprin-ger-Verlag, Berlin, New York.

RICHARDSON, T. (1981): The effct of topical steroids on the synthesis of glycosaminogly-cans in the trabecular meshwork. Invest. Ophthalmol. Vis. Sci. (Suppl.) *20* (3): 30.

ROHEN, J. W., E. LÜTJEN-DRECOLL (1982): Biology of the trabecular meshwork. In: Basic aspects of glaucoma research. Schattauer, F. K. Verlag (LÜTJEN-DRECOLL, E., Ed.). Stuttgart, New York.

ROHEN, J. W., SCHACHTSCHABEL, P. MATTHIESSEN (1975): *In vitro* studies on the trabecular meshwork of the primate eye. Graefe's Arch. Klin. Exp. Ophthalmol. *193:* 95–107.

SCHACHTSCHABEL, D. O., B. BIGALKE, J. W. ROHEN (1977): Production of glycosaminoglycans by cell cultures of the trabecular meshwork of the primate eye. Exp. Eye Res. *24:* 71–80.

SHIRATO, S., E. BLOOM, J. R. POLANSKY, J. A. ALAVARDO (1988): Phagocytic properties of confluent cultures HTM cells. Invest. Ophthalmol. Vis. Sci. (Suppl) *29:* 125.

TRIPATHI, B. J., R. C. TRIPATHI, H. H. SWIFT (1989): Hydrocortisone-induced DNA endoreplication in human trabecular cells in vitro. Exp. Eye Res. *49:* 259–70.

TRIPATHI, B. J., C. B. MILLARD, R. C. TRIPATHI (1990 a): Corticosteroids induce a sialated glycopro-tein (Cort-GP) in trabecular cells in vitro. Exp. Eye Res. *51:* 735–737.

TRIPATHI, B. J., E. BLOOM, J. D. BAXTER, J. ALVARADO, N., LAN, J. O'DONNELL, J. R. POLANSKY (1981): Detection of glucocorticoid receptors in cultured human trabecular cells. Invest. Ophthal-mol. Vis. Sci. *21:* 403–407.

TRIPATHI, B. J., C. B. MILLARD, R. C. TRIPATHI (1990 b): Sialoglycoproteins of human trabecular meshwork and Schlemm's canal. Invest. Ophthalmol. Vis. Sci. (Suppl) *31:* 377.

WEINREB, R. N., E. BLOOM, J. D. BAXTER, J. ALVARADO, N. LAN, J. O'DONNEL, J. R. POLANSKY
  (1981): Detection of glucocorticoid receptors in cultured human trabecular cells. Invest. Ophthalmol. Vis. Sci. *21:* 403 – 407.
WEINREB, R. N., M. D. MITCHELL, J. R. POLANSKY (1983): Prostaglandin production by human trabecular cells: in vitro inhibition by dexamethasone. Invest. Ophthalmol. Vis. Sci. *24:* 1541 – 1545.
WEINREB, R. N., J. R. POLANSKY, M. D. MITCHELL (1988): Arachidonic acid metabolism in human
  trabecular meshwork cells. Invest. Opthalmol. Vis. Sci. *29:* 1708 – 171.
YUN, A., C. MURPHY, J. R. POLANSKY, D. NEWSOME, J. A. ALVARADO (1989): Dexamethasone
  induced proteins secreted by trabecular cells. Invest. Ophthalmol. Vis. Sci. *30:* 2012 – 2022.
ZHAN, G. L., O. C. MIRANDA, L. Z. BITO (1989): Steroid-induced ocular hypertension in cats. Invest.
  Ophthalmol. Vis. Sci. (Suppl) *30:* 445.

*Cellular Pharmacology Laboratories, Department of Ophthalmology,*
*University of California Medical Center,*
*San Francisco, CA*

# Glucocorticoid (GC) effects on HTM cells: Biochemical approaches and growth factor responses

D. J. Fauss, E. Bloom, G. M. Lui, R. M. Kurtz and J. R. Polansky

## Introduction

The effects of glucocorticoid (GC) hormones on human trabecular meshwork (HTM) cells have been a longstanding interest of our laboratories and those of our collaborators (e.g. see reviews, Polansky and Weinreb 1984; Polansky et al. 1989). The mechanisms by which GC hormones produce decreased outflow facility are unknown, although clinical and basic studies have encouraged a variety of suggestions regarding alterations in different parts and functions of the outflow pathway. Many different effects on HTM cells have been proposed, as mentioned in the prior chapter. We have attempted to gain as broad a perspective as possible in examining GC effects on the properties of HTM cells, using the clinical evidence as a guide for cell biological and biochemical investigations.

Our working assumption has been that evaluations of specific gene regulation would help to explain (directly or indirectly) changes in HTM cells that could be related to steroid effects on the outflow pathway. This mechanism is recognized as the major one by which GCs produce their clinical effects and side-effects in other systems (Baxter and Rousseau 1979; Polansky and Weinreb 1984). Methods to evaluate the gene regulation mechanism through changes in the synthesis of individual labeled proteins provided the sufficiently general approach we desired. While other mechanisms were possible (including direct GC membrane effects), it appeared less likely to us that they would be playing a role relevant to HTM cell responses *in vivo*.

Using $^{35}$S-methionine labeling and one dimensional SDS-PAGE, minor inductions (e. g. a protein at approximately 30 kDa) were found following a 24 hour DEX treatment, but different inductions became prominent (especially a group near 55 kDa) following a 1 week treatment (Polansky et al. 1989). A progressive increase in the 55 kDa inductions was also noted between 1 and 3 weeks of DEX treatment to HTM cell cultures. Our findings did not appear to be an artifact of growing the cells in culture, since a collaborative study with Johnson et al. (1989) showed that trabecular meshwork tissues *in situ* exposed to long-term, but not 24 hours of DEX resulted in protein inductions at 55 kDa.

In the current paper we describe some of the recent evidence concerning the long-term DEX inductions in confluent HTM cells. GC inhibition of HTM cell division was also evaluated as another potentially relevant cellular response of prolonged DEX treatments.

## Methods

### *Cell culture and cell growth experiments*

HTM cells which had been established and characterized previously were used for the current experiments. Third to fifth passage HTM cultures were removed from cryopreserved stocks and grown employing methods similar to those we described previously (POLANSKY et al. 1984). Protein synthesis studies were conducted using confluent, stable HTM cultures, with cells plated originally at 10,000 cells/cm$^2$. Cell growth studies were conducted by plating at 2,500 cells/cm$^2$, with cell counts performed during log phase of growth (7 days) and approximately one week after the control cultures had reached confluency (3 to 5 weeks, depending on the HTM cell line). Recombinant bFGF (Intergen) was used rather than the partially purified G-75 bFGF we have previously described for routine HTM culture. The cloned bFGF showed optimal dose-responses for HTM cell division in the 0.5 to 1 ng/ml range as opposed to 50 ng/ml observed with the G-75 preparation. For evaluating bFGF and TGFß effects, treatments were made with media changes every 2 days.

### *Gel electrophoresis and tunicamycin experiments*

Methods for one-dimensional (SDS-PAGE) and two-dimensional (2-D) gel electrophoresis and analyses were those we have published previously (POLANSKY et al. 1989). To evaluate tunicamycin effects (e. g. see YOKOMORI et al. 1989) on secreted proteins, HTM cells were grown in 35 mm dishes and treated with 500 nM DEX every 2 days for 10 days. The cultures were then changed to methionine-free medium with 10% fetal calf serum (FCS) containing tunicamycin (1 µg/ml). After two hours, the cultures were placed in methionine-free medium containing 500 uCi/ml translation grade $^{35}$S-methionine (New England Nuclear) for 10 minutes, rinsed twice, and then placed into new medium containing 1mg/ml dl-methionine. Collections of the medium and cell layers were performed from 30 minutes to 4 hours after removal of the $^{35}$S-methionine. Immediately after collection, each sample was exposed to lysis buffer (20 mM Tris HCl, pH 7.6; 10 mM MgS04; 0.1% Triton X100; chymostatin, 2 ug/ml; Leupeptin, 4 ug/ml; Bacitracin, 25 ug/ml; PMSF, 1 mM) at

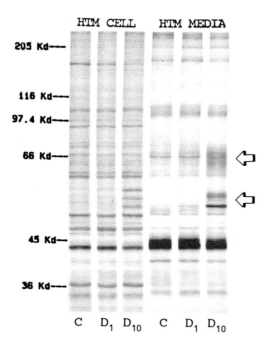

Fig. 1. Effects of dexamethasone (DEX, 60 nM) on the proteins and glycoproteins labeled with $^{35}$S-methionine in the HTM cell fraction (left) and HTM media fraction (right), as described in Methods. Control (C), 1 day DEX (D$_1$) and 10 day DEX (D$_{10}$) treated cultures are compared. Major inductions are shown by arrows. Results are from HTM cells cultured from a 30-year-old individual (POLANSKY et al. 1991).

4°C. The trichloroacetic acid precipitable counts of the cell lysates were used to normalize the amounts of media added to the gel electrophoresis lanes. SDS-PAGE was performed using 11% acrylamide gels as we described previously (POLANSKY et al. 1989)

## Results

### Protein/glycoprotein studies

Following our initial observations of the time course and dose response of the GC inductions in the HTM system, we then concentrated on media and cell surface changes. The 55 kDa protein(s) induced in the cell layer were observed to have a short half life after labeling, in large part due to their secretion into the HTM medium.

Fig. 1 demonstrates GC effects on HTM proteins and glycoproteins labeled with $^{35}$S-methionine in which the cytosol and media fractions are compared from a 30 year-old individual, for control (non-steroid treated), one-day, and ten-day 60 nM DEX treatments. The 55 kDa induction was observed in both cytosol and media fractions of ten-day DEX-treated HTM cultures as a series of bands between 52 and 58 kDa (this gel shows an improved resolution of the 40 to 70 kDa region). The somewhat diffuse 65-72 kDa induction observed in the media fraction of ten-day DEX treatments is not seen in the cytosol fractions, although it may sometimes be observed as a faint set of spots with long-term 500 nM DEX treatments in the cytosol of 2-D gels. In the media, it is possible to see very small amounts of labeling for the 65-72 kDa proteins after one day of DEX treatment, corresponding to a small one-day induction in the cytosol which can be observed on 2-D gels but not 1-D gels (unpublished observations).

Fig. 2 demonstrates the DEX dose-response for induction of HTM cell proteins/ glycoproteins in the cell layer (above) and media (below) after ten days of DEX

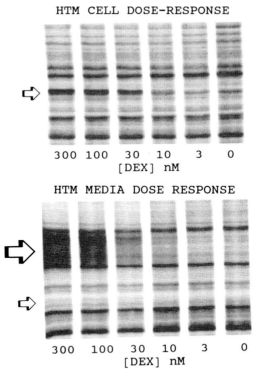

Fig. 2. Dexamethasone (DEX) dose-response effects on HTM cell proteins/glycoproteins in the HTM cell fraction (above) and the HTM media fraction (below) evaluated after 10 days of glucocorticoid treatment. Major inductions are shown with arrows. Results are from HTM cells cultured from a 14-year-old individual (from POLANSKY et al. 1991).

treatment evaluated by SDS-PAGE. The responses of HTM cells from the 14 year-old individual are shown. Compared to the HTM cell line from the 30 year-old individual, this cell line has a somewhat more prominent DEX-induction at 55 kDa in the cytosol, and a substantially larger 65 – 72 kDa relative to 55 kDa inductions in the media. The half-maximal ($C_{50}$) response for the major glucocorticoid inductions is approximately 30 nM DEX in the cytosol, and between 30 to 100 nM in the media. The $C_{50}$ for DEX inhibition of prostaglandin (PG) production in these cells was approximately 4 nM, similar to results we reported previously (WEINREB, MITCHELL, POLANSKY et al. 1983).

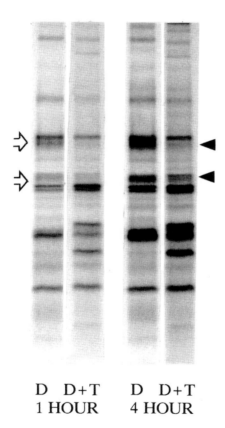

D   D+T      D   D+T
1 HOUR      4 HOUR

Fig. 3. Tunicamycin effect on secreted proteins/glycoproteins in ten-day dexamethasone (500 nM)-treated HTM cells. The media fractions were collected one hour and four hours after pulse labeling. with $^{35}$S-methionine, according to Methods. The GC inductions produced by DEX ("D") are shown by the open arrows at 66 kDa and 55 kDa to the left; the loss of labeling in these bands following tunica-mycin treatment of these samples is shown by the solid arrowheads to the right. Results are from HTM cells cultured from a 57-year-old individual, a cell line which shows a balance between the 66 and 55 kDa media inductions.

The 65 – 72 kDa inductions were considered to be glycoproteins based on their appearance on 2-D gels and based on the results of our neuraminidase (an enzyme which cleaves sialic acid linkages) digestions (POLANSKY et al. 1990). Two-dimensional gel studies of these inductions reveal a group of proteins within a rather wide range of isoelectric values and molecular weights (65 to 72 kDa and pI 4.8 to 5.3), and neuraminidase treatment reduces these to a lower molecular weight and a more restricted isoelectric range just above the 55 kDa proteins on the gels. This evidence suggested that we were dealing with sialated glycoproteins which were likely to contain a variety of carbohydrate residues. For this reason, we evaluated whether tunicamycin would affect the media inductions in the ten-day DEX-treated samples.

Fig. 3 presents the 1 hour and 4 hour media collections with and without addition of tunicamycin according to Methods. A marked decrease in the 66 kDa inductions was observed, and the upper band in the 55 kDa region was also decreased. A possible increase of labeling is observed in the lower 55 kDa band, along with a clear increase in some lower molecular weight species. These findings supported the concept that the major long-term GC inductions in the HTM cells are secreted proteins/glycoproteins, since tunicamycin has been reported to act preferentially on N-glycosylation linkages which are associated with extracellular transport of glycoproteins. It remains to be determined whether or not the lower molecular weight species are degradation products or otherwise related to the major inductions.

A possible link between long-term DEX treatments compared with other "stress" conditions was explored in other studies conducted over the past two years. We have confirmed that changes in proteins synthesis are observed following mild injury (1 hour 0.3 mM $H_2O_2$, or 1 µM TPA) to HTM cells, some of which closely resemble the major cell media inductions seen after DEX treatments (but at a lower level than the GC effect). An even smaller induction is seen with heat shock, and none is seen with bradykinin treatment. These findings may indicate a link between GC-related and oxidative stress-related effects on the meshwork of potential importance.

### Growth effects

Although we have proposed that studies of confluent monolayers of HTM cells are the most relevant model for evaluating the GC effects on IOP, it also appeared reasonable to test the hormonal effects on HTM cell growth. HTM cells are not regarded as a cell population which divides very often *in vivo*, but the cells may have a capacity for division after damage or stress. It is conceivable that a decreased ability of the cells to undergo effective mitosis could play a role in the long-term

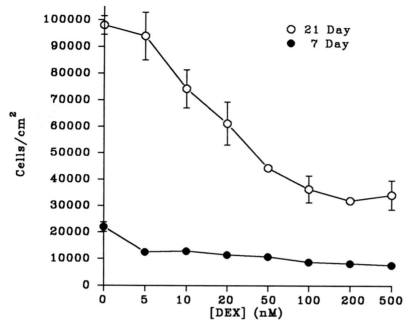

Fig. 4. Dose-response of dexamethasone (DEX) on HTM cell number evaluated after seven days (log phase of growth) and twenty-one days of DEX treatment (ten days following initial confluency of the untreated cultures). DEX treatment of growing HTM cells results in enlarged, poorly-dividing cells which show evidence of increased vacuolization and other alterations characteristic of senescent cell populations. The experiment was conducted in Dulbecco's Modified Eagle's (DME) medium using 10% fetal calf serum (FCS). Results are from HTM cells cultured from a thirty-year-old individual. Cells were plated originally at 2,500 cells/cm² according to Methods.

loss of HTM cells associated with aging and POAG. Tripathi et al. (1989) had this idea in mind when they showed an effect of high levels of hydrocortisone on HTM cell division. However, the levels employed ($10^{-4}$ to $10^{-6}$M) suggested a suprapharmacologic effect (see disscusion of detergent vs receptor-mediated effects by POLANSKY and WEINREB 1984, pp. 510–511), rather than one which could reasonably occur in the eye. We decided to explore GC effects on HTM cell growth under more physiologic conditions, and also using DEX which is a more potent and more specific GC hormone for our experimental evaluations.

As shown in Fig. 4, DEX treatment of HTM cells in log phase of growth produces a substantial inhibition of cell division, beginning at low DEX concentrations. Control cultures contained approximately 22,000 cells/cm² compared to 5 nM DEX-treated ones which contained approximately 12,500 cells/cm². An additional dose effect up to 500 nM DEX was observed (approximately 8,000 cells/cm²). The GC effects on HTM cell growth appeared even more marked when 21 day

DEX treatments were evaluated, by which time the control HTM cells had already formed their normal, confluent monolayer. In this case, the half-maximal DEX effect occured at approximately 30 to 50 nM, which was certainly well below membrane "stabilizing" levels. Our findings demonstrate a major influence on HTM cell division which is compatible with known physiological responses through the GC receptor. The shift to the right of the dose-response with the longer DEX treatments did suggest a possible correlation for the higher doses required for long-term GC-induced protein/glycoprotein changes in the HTM cells. We are currently using biochemical methods to evaluate GC effects on growing HTM cells to see whether the same changes occur as those found in the confluent cultures.

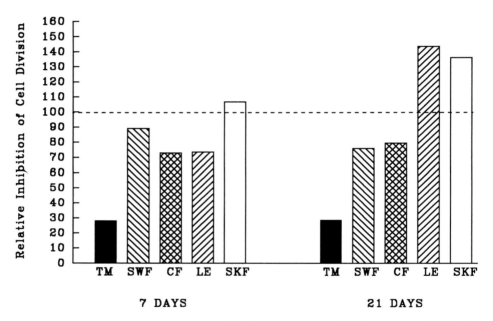

Fig. 5. Relative inhibition of cell division by 500 nM dexamethasone (DEX) comparing HTM cells to other cell types in culture. A pronounced inhibition of TM cell growth is observed which is substantially greater than that seen with scleral fibroblasts (SWF), corneal fibroblasts (CF, keratocytes), lens epithelium (LE), and skin fibroblasts (SKF) is shown at both 7 days (log phase) and 21 days (stable, confluent TM cultures). Cells were plated originally at 2,500 cells/cm$^2$ according to Methods.

The effects of DEX on HTM cell growth appeared to be more pronounced than other cell types evaluated under the same conditions. For example, in studies of skin fibroblasts from patients with POAG vs controls, we previously observed only a minor GC inhibition in growing cultures, and a rather large GC-stimulation of fibroblast cell division when confluency was approached (POLANSKY et al. 1985 b).

In Fig. 5, DEX effects on other cells from our laboratory were tested in parallel with HTM cells. As shown, DEX treatment produces a greater inhibition of HTM cell growth compared to the other cell lines. A minor inhibition to a slight stimulation is observed in the different cell types. Fibroblasts from the scleral wall and cornea (keratocytes) show inhibitions in the range of 10 to 20% during growing and late stages of confluency. Lens epithelium and ciliary epithelium show some stimulatory DEX effects. The marked inhibition of cell division by DEX on HTM cells has now been confirmed in HTM cultures established from two additional subjects. It is clear, however, that the percent and type of serum used are variables that need to be considered in evaluating the mechanisms involved in HTM growth responses, including the roles of different growth factors.

Recent studies of growth factor effects on HTM cells have shown an ability of bFGF to overcome much of the DEX-induced inhibition of cell division unless TGFß is also present. TGFß, which is found in the aqueous humor, may play a role in magnifying some GC-induced alterations in HTM cells. This could be important if only moderate GC levels reach the HTM cell in normal physiology, especially if required growth factors (or their receptors) were present in diminished amounts. Although ideas regarding growth factor effects on HTM cells in vivo remain speculative, it is possible that they may be involved in regulating GC effects on HTM cells. In this regard, preliminary studies have shown bFGF is able to partially reverse the 55 kDa induction in confluent cultures, in addition to overcoming growth inhibition in growing cultures. It did not, however, fully reverse some of the detrimental effects of DEX on HTM cell morphology in growing cultures. Combinations of different growth factors will be considered in both growing and confluent HTM cells in our future work on the system.

## Discussion

Methods to detect progressive changes in HTM cell gene expression and cell division following DEX treatment have helped in characterizing the HTM cell model system. In both cases, dose and time relationships have been observed which might be related to clinical observations. Each method has provided new leads to investigate specific structural and functional changes in the HTM cells.

The alterations in the proteins/glycoproteins produced by prolonged, relatively high dose DEX observed in this model could potentially play a role in the reduction in outflow facility (i) because the correlations in time course and dose-response for the inductions of the proteins and glycoproteins in HTM cells correspond to those expected for IOP effects, and (ii) because other changes in HTM cells involving cell surface labeling, cell division, and phagocytosis could be related to the specific protein inductions. Although short-term lower-dose GC effects on HTM cells may also play a role in some effects on meshwork cells (e. g. the inhibition of prosta-glandin production), it appears that the model system defined (i. e. 100 to 500 nM DEX treatments for 1 to 3 weeks) may be more useful to explore the mechanisms for reduced outflow facility.

The media and cell surface changes appear to correspond to the cellular induc-tions insofar as they show the longer time period and higher dose requirements for GC effects. However, it has not yet been proven definitely that the cell surface changes are directly related to the other changes. GC agonist and antagonist stu-dies, as well as the lack of agonist effects of progesterone and other inactive stero-ids, support the view that some type of GC-receptor is involved in the HTM response (FAUSS, BLOOM, POLANSKY unpublished observation). To explain the unusual properties of the major GC induction, it will probably be necessary to uncover new mechanisms. One possibility for the altered dose-response is a recep-tor modification influencing a subclass of GC receptors with prolonged DEX, lowering their affinity for the agonist.

Quantitative evaluations of the GC-regulated changes in HTM cells and media proteins/glycoproteins are currently being performed. The media inductions cen-tered around 66 kDa may be of particular interest because of patient/patient differ-ence in their prominence following DEX treatments. It appears that the media inductions may involve post-translational modifications of the major 55 kDa induc-tion, and that the modifications include sialic acid and other carbohydrate residues based on the neuraminidase digestions reported previously and the tunicamycin experiment presented in this paper. Sialation and tunicamycin sensitivity have been associated with secreted glycoproteins, implicating extracellular and/or cell surface sites of action, which may be the site of action for the major long-term HTM DEX inductions. Glycoprotein changes could, for example, contribute to alterations in the permeability of the intertrabecular spaces and the juxtacanalicular tissue, as well as to shape changes and other modifications of HTM cell properties.

The induced proteins/glycoproteins in HTM cells could also help to explain the DEX-mediated changes in HTM cell surface labeling, phagocytosis, binding of other proteins and/or other cellular changes associated with prolonged GC expo-sure (see discussion, POLANSKY et al. 1991). Of potential interest, TRIPATHI et al. (1990) has recently reported GC-induced species from porcine meshwork which may have similar characteristics to our HTM media protein/glycoproteins. The report by PARTRIDGE et al. (1989) of short-term GC-induced secreted proteins from HTM cells do not appear related to our findings.

The major GC effects we have demonstrated on HTM cell division have opened up the area of growth factors and growth regulators, in addition to providing a potentially relevant resonse which might be related to reduced meshwork cellular-ity in POAG. Growth factor effects on confluent as well as growing HTM cells are currently being explored for their effects on specific cell properties and functions.

# Summary

Use of biochemical and cell biological approaches to GC effects in the HTM cell model have provided new information regarding induced extracellular proteins and glycoproteins, and have demonstrated a marked inhibition of HTM cell division. Attention can now be focussed on individual alterations which appear most promising in providing a link between cell culture observations and structural/functional changes which may take place *in vivo*. Growth factor effects may be a particularly fruitful area to explore for understanding pathogenic mechanisms and for developing new therapeutic approaches.

# Acknowledgements

Supported by NIH grants EY02477 (JP), EY08973 (EB), AHAF, National Glaucoma Research, and That Man May See.

# References

BAXTER, J. D., G. G. ROUSSEAU (1979): Glucocorticoid Hormone Action. Springer-Verlag, Berlin and New York (BAXTER, J. D., G. G. ROUSSEAU, Eds).

JOHNSON, D. H., J. M. BRADLEY, T. S. ACOTT, D. J. FAUSS, J. R. POLANSKY (1989): The effect of steroids on human trabecular meshwork in perfusion organ culture. Invest. Ophthalmol. Vis. Sci. (Suppl) *30:* 223.

PARTRIDGE, C., B. WEINSTEIN, A. SOUTHREN, M. GERRITSEN (1989): Secreted proteins in human trabecular meshwork cells. Invest. Ophthalmol. Vis. Sci. *30:* 1843–47.

POLANSKY, J. R., I. WOOD, M. MAGLIO, J. ALVARADO (1984): Trabecular meshwork cell culture in glaucoma research: Evaluation of biological activity and structural properties of human trabecular cells *in vitro*. Ophthalmol. *91:* 580–595.

POLANSKY, J. R., R. WEINREB (1984): Steroids as anti-inflammatory agents. In: Ocular Pharmacology. Springer-Verlag, New York and Berlin (SEARS, M., Ed.). Handbook of Exp. Pharm. *69:* 461–538.

POLANSKY, J. R., D. KONAMI, R. KIM, J. A. ALVARADO (1985a): Glucocorticoid regulation of cultured human trabecular meshwork cells: A model system to study the effects of steroids on IOP. Invest. Ophthalmol. Vis. Sci. (Suppl) *26:* 5.

POLANSKY, J. R., P. PALMBERG, D. MATULICH, N. LAN, S. HAJEK, A. HAJEK, B. BECKER, J. BAXTER (1985b): Cellular sensitivity to glucocorticoids in patients with POAG. Invest. Ophthalmol. Vis. Sci. *26:* 805–809.

POLANSKY, J. R., R. KURTZ, J. A. ALVARADO, R. WEINREB, M. MITCHELL (1989): Eicosanoid production and glucocoticoid regulatory mechanisms in cultured human trabecular meshwork cells. Prog. Clin. Biol. Res. *312:* 113–138.

POLANSKY, J. R., R. M. KURTZ, T. D. NGUYEN, et al. (1990): *In vitro* model for steroid effects on IOP: characterization of HTM protein/glycoprotein changes and molecular cloning approaches. Invest. Ophthalmol. Vis. Sci. (Suppl) *31:* 377.

POLANSKY, J. R., R. M. KURTZ, D. J. FAUSS, R. Y. KIM, E. BLOOM (1991): *In vitro* correlates of glucocorticoid effects on intraocular pressure. In: Glaucoma Update. (KRIEGLSTEIN, G. K., Ed.) Springer-Verlag, Berlin, New York.

TRIPATHI, B. J., R. C. TRIPATHI, H. H. SWIFT (1989): Hydrocortisone-induced DNA endoreplication in human trabecular cells *in vitro*. Exp. Eye Res. *49:* 259 – 70.

TRIPATHI, C.B. MILLARD, R. C. TRIPATHI (1990): Corticosteroids induce a sialated glycoprotein (Cort-GP) in trabecular cells *in vitro*. Exp. Eye Res. *51:* 735 – 737.

WEINREB, R. N., M. D. MITCHELL, J. A. POLANSKY (1983): Prostaglandin production by human trabecular cells:*in vitro* inhibition by dexamethasone. Invest. Ophthalmol. Vis. Sci. *24:* 1541 – 1545.

YUN, A., C. MURPHY, J. R. POLANSKY, D. NEWSOME, J. A. ALVARADO (1989): Dexamethasone induced proteins secreted by trabecular cells. Invest. Ophthalmol. Vis. Sci. *30:* 2012 – 2022.

YOKOMORI, K., N. LAMONICA, S. MAKINO, C. K. SHIEH, M. M. C. LAI (1989): Biosynthesis, structure, and biological activities of envelope protein gp65 of murine coronavirus. Virology *173:* 683 – 691.

*Cellular Pharmacology Laboratories and The Department of Opthalmology, University of California Medical Center San Francisco, CA*

# Glucocorticoid (GC) effects on HTM cells: Molecular biology approaches

T. D. NGUYEN, W. HUANG, E. BLOOM and J. R. POLANSKY

## Introduction

We have been employing gene cloning and other molecular biology approaches to help characterize the human trabecular meshwork (HTM) cell model system for prolonged glucocorticoid (GC) effects (see recent abstract, NGUYEN et al. 1991). Prior to our studies, steroid inductions have been evaluated for a wide range of proteins, including tyrosine aminotransferase (TAT) (OLSON and GRANNER 1980), glutamine synthetase (CROOK et al. 1978), tryptophan oxygenase (SCHUTZ et al. 1975), $\alpha_1$-antichymotrypsin (BERMAN et al. 1988), secreted glycoproteins (BAUMAN and HELD 1981), $\alpha_1$-acid glycoprotein (AGB) (REINKE and FIEGELSON 1985), non specific sequences (SUN and FRANKEL 1986), housekeeping genes such as metallothionein (KARIN and HERSCHMAN 1979), and for growth hormone and other endocrine factors (BAXTER and ROUSSEAU 1979). Cloning studies of glucocorticoid (GC) inductions in other systems have been performed mainly to evaluate short-term inductions to understand the basis for steroid effects and regulatory controls over these inductions. However, it was apparent that important clinical side-effects are only observed after weeks of therapy (BAXTER and TYRRELL 1981; POLANSKY and WEINREB 1984). By evaluating genes regulated by long-term GC treatment in specific cell types it might be possible to understand more concerning the clinical effects and side-effects of steroid therapy.

GC effects on HTM cells were examined by us because steroid-induced glaucoma appeared to be an excellent model to investigate a sustained steroid side-effect. Elevated intraocular pressure (IOP) due to both local and systemic GC therapy is known to be a progressive but usually reversible condition. The induced proteins in DEX-treated HTM cells were reversible and showed time characteristics and a concentration dependence which suggested clinical relevance to IOP changes in patients (POLANSKY et al. 1985). In this study we report the molecular cloning approach undertaken in our laboratory to isolate a highly induced mRNA (2 – 4 % total cellular mRNA) coding for a unique secretory glycoprotein, which has a similar time course and abundance as described for the induced proteins. In addition, we also obtained other molecular probes (a minor induction of $\alpha_1$-antichymotryp-sin and a reduction of IGF-BP4) which might provide additional leads to understand the molecular basis of steroid glaucoma.

## Methods

1) *Cell Culture and Treatments:* HTM cells were propagated in tissue culture by techniques described previously (POLANSKY et al. 1984). Stress treatments were conducted on confluent HTM cells using 0.3 mM $H_2O_2$ in PBS, 1 $\mu$M TPA in DME, and heat shock at 42 °C for 1 hour, followed by an incubation in normal DME culture medium at 37 °C for 3 hours. Cycloheximide (from 1–10 $\mu$g) was added to confluent HTM cultures in the presence or absence of DEX to investigate the role of protein synthesis in the major GC-induction.

2) *cDNA Library Construction and Differential Screening:* A ten-day DEX-treated cDNA library was constructed in our laboratory using Lamda Zap II, and bacterial strain XL-1 from Stratagene (San Diego, California). Thirty to fifty $\mu$g purified poly $A^+$ mRNA were obtained from 5 x $10^7$ DEX-treated cells using the Fast Track preparation of Invitrogene (San Diego, California). Complimentary strands were synthesized from 3 to 5 $\mu$g mRNA incubated with 250 units of MMLV (BRL) reverse transcriptase at 32 °C for 1 hour. The cDNA-mRNA duplex was then digested with RNase H to randomly nick the mRNA, generating primers for DNA polymerase synthesis of the second strands. This reaction employed DNA polymerase I for 1 hour at 37 °C, as described by GUBLER and HOFFMAN (1983). The double-stranded DNAs were ligated to Not-ECoRI adapters (Invitrogene) by $T_4$ ligase at 12 °C for overnight incubation. After the ligation, the Not-ECoRI-DNA inserts are subcloned to ECoRI Zap II vectors of Stratagene by a similar ligation reaction as above. From 50 ng to 150 ng of the DNA inserts are used to ligate to 1 $\mu$g of Zap II vector to obtain a favorable concatamer (i. e. a vector-ligated vector or an insert-ligated insert) for high efficiency packaging. Packaging was performed using Gigapak Plus extracts from Stratagene. The unamplified cDNA library was titrated to 5 x $10^6$ phages/$\mu$g DNA; the amplified library obtained was $10^{11}$–$10^{12}$ phages/ml. We screened approximately 4 x $10^4$ phages in two separate schedules from the 10-day DEX-treated cDNA library. Approximately $10^3$ phages were grown on 100 mm NZY agar plates using the phage titration method to avoid overcrowded phages for later signal examination. About 20 plates were needed to screen the 2 x $10^4$ phages for each schedule. The plates were double lifted by nitrocellulose membranes, which were then treated with 0.5 M NaOH, 1.5 M NaCl on 3 MM paper for 5 min, then in 3 M Na Acetate for 5 min, and washed (2 x SSC, 0.2 M Tris HCl, pH 8) for 15 to 30 min with gentle shaking. The membranes were partially air dried and the phage DNAs crosslinked to the membranes using a UV crosslinker Stratalinker

1800 (Stratagene) at 1200 joules for 90 seconds. One set of membranes was hybridized to [$\alpha$-$^{32}$P]-labeled cDNA made from the control; the duplicate membrane was hybridized to the labeled cDNA of the ten-day DEX-treated cells. These probes were synthesized from the total cellular mRNA as described for the cDNA synthesis except that $^{32}$PdCTP (3000 Ci/mM) was used and the cold dCTP was reduced to 12 $\mu$M. The hybridization protocol was performed using a similar method as that described for Southern analysis (GATTI et al. 1984).

Northern analysis was performed with 10 $\mu$g total RNA using glycoxal (McMASTER and CARMICHEAL 1977). RNA was transferred to the membrane and hybridized to $^{32}$P labeled II.2 probe as detailed above for the screening procedure.

3) *Sequencing:* Plasmid DNA was prepared using the quick method of Krieg and Melton (1989) which is sufficient to obtain abundant, clean DNA for sequencing. Sequencing was performed with the double-stranded DNAs by denaturing in 0.2N NaOH prior to the primer template annealing in the standard sequencing procedure for single stranded DNA (SANGER et al. 1977) using the Sequenase Kit (USB Corp., Cleveland, Ohio with $^{35}$S dATP for labeling of the reaction.

4) *Dot Blot Analysis:* The 1.2, II.2 and V.4 clones were used in dot blot analyses to quantitate their relative changes in one-day and ten-day DEX treatments. One $\mu$g DNA of each clone was diluted in a series of three-fold dilutions in 20 x SSC. The DNA solutions were heat denatured at 95 °C for 15 min and fixed on nitrocellulose membranes using HYBRI-DOT (BRL). The membrane was then denatured, neutralized, and washed according to standard procedures (GATTI et al. 1984); the DNAs were then crosslinked to the membranes by UV treatments as described above. A total of three membranes were required; one membrane was hybridized to the control and the others to the 1-day and 10-day $^{32}$P labeled cDNAs.

5) *RT-PCR Quantitation:* PCR was performed for 30 cycles on the Perkin Elmer Cetus automated thermal cycler. Each cycle included denaturation of DNA at 94 °C/1′, primer-template annealing at 55 °C/1′ and enzymatic extension at 72 °C/1′. The quantitative PCR was performed in collaboration with Alice Wang (Cetus Corp.) who has been instrumental in the development of this technique for other systems (WANG et al. 1990). A two-step procedure for the amplication was used to assure that the PCR products were not saturated. The first step involved using a series of two-fold dilutions of cDNA samples to determine the exponential range for the amplification of specific primers. Concentrations within the exponential range were used in step two for the amplification as described above. In addition, actin primer was used for normalization of the RNA content. Specific primer sequences for amplification were obtained from the published cDNA sequences for MT, $\alpha_1$ AGP, TAT, actin. Primers for clone II.2 and V.4 (IGF-BP4) were obtained from our sequencing results.

## Results

*Library subtraction screening and dot blot verification:*

Two independent screening of 20,000 phages each were conducted according to Methods. A total of 23 clones that showed differential expression in the 10-day DEX-treated condition compared to the control were selected. Induced and reduced (de-induced) clones were detected by observing the cDNA hybridization signals. Particular emphasis was given to clones present in the treated condition, but absent, or expressed in significantly lower levels in the untreated condition. The reverse criteria were used for selection of reduced clones. The diagram presented in Fig. 1 shows the scheme employed for the library subtraction screening performed on DEX-treated HTM cells, with the selection of the candidate clone of a relative induction as indicated.

Dot blot analysis verified the mRNA changes and the estimated the level of specific mRNA for each clone as shown in Fig. 2. Both ten-day and one-day DEX treatments were included in the dot blot and compared to control levels to evaluate short-term vs long-term GC effects. Based on the different signal intensities observed, the clones obtained were classified into three groupings: a major induction group (30–50 fold, 8 clones), a minor induction group (3–5 fold, 8 clones), and a major reduction group, of the total cellular (approximately 20 fold, 3 clones). Labeled $^{32}$P-cDNA of the total cellular mRNA of control, one-day and ten-day treated cells was used in dot blot hybridizations. As shown in the figure, clone 1.2 increased somewhat between day 1 and day 10 of DEX treatment while, clone II.2 was poorly induced at 1-day but progressively and highly induced at 10-day. In addition, PCR quantitation was used to confirm the progressive nature of II.2 induction under different test conditions using 24 well multiwells. Clone V.4 was highly expressed at control and 1-day, but was suppressed after 10-day DEX treatment.

Sequencing analysis revealed that clone 1.2 was $\alpha_1$-antichymotrypsin which has been shown in other systems to be regulated by GC and clone V.4 was identified as the recently reported IGF binding protein 4 (IGF-BP4) (LATOUR et al. 1991, KIEFER et al. 1991). Clone II.2 has been shown to be a unique sequence. Nothern blot analysis using II.2 probe showed a size of 2.5 Kb suggesting the clone is nearly complete, since the ECoRI insert of the clone is over 2.3 Kb. Sequencing analyses of clone II.2 has revealed an open reading frame (ORF) of 483 aa coding for a typical hydrophobic signal peptide sequence of 20 aa, an N-linked glycosylation sequence in the hydrophobic amino terminal region, and nine putative leucine zipper units distributed throughout the molecule.

## STEPS OF HYBRIDIZATION SUBTRACTION SCREENING

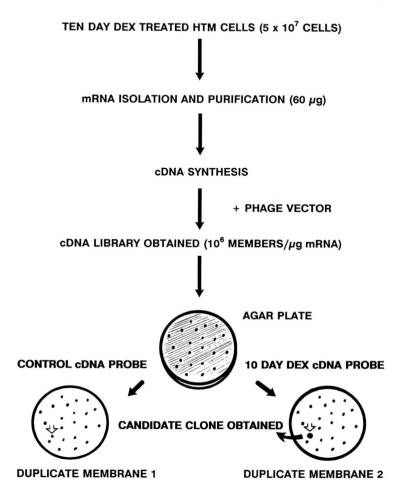

**TEN DAY DEX TREATED HTM CELLS ($5 \times 10^7$ CELLS)**

**mRNA ISOLATION AND PURIFICATION (60 $\mu$g)**

**cDNA SYNTHESIS**

**+ PHAGE VECTOR**

**cDNA LIBRARY OBTAINED ($10^6$ MEMBERS/$\mu$g mRNA)**

**AGAR PLATE**

**CONTROL cDNA PROBE**       **10 DAY DEX cDNA PROBE**

**CANDIDATE CLONE OBTAINED**

**DUPLICATE MEMBRANE 1**       **DUPLICATE MEMBRANE 2**

Fig. 1. Diagrammatic representation of the steps of hybridization subtraction screening using ten-day DEX-treated cells compared with control HTM cultures. The figure shows the methods employed in isolating the candidate clones, in this case showing the induction of a clone in duplicate membrane number 2 (using ten-day DEX treatment, labeled cDNA) compared with duplicate membrane number 1 (using control, labeled cDNA). As indicated, the candidate clone was lifted from the agar plate using the position located on the duplicate membrane 2. The clone obtained underwent a secondary screening after it was amplified.

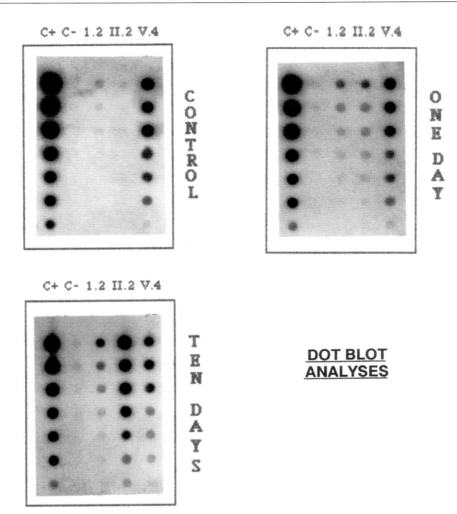

Fig. 2. Dot Blot Quantitation of cDNA Clones Selected from Library Subtraction Screening. The dot blot study conducted according to Methods demonstrates the three different clones isolated – in the which (across the top of the nitrocellulose filter) the major induction (II.2), and the major deinduction (V.4), the minor induction (1.2), are shown along with additional controls. One μg of DNA from each clone was diluted in a series of three-fold dilutions. $^{32}$P labeled cDNA of control, one-day and ten-day DEX-treated cells were used for hybridization. C$^+$ indicates a positive control using a reference clone shown to be of approximately equal amounts under the different test conditions. C– indicates a negative control using the PBR322 vector. Clone I.2 which represents $\alpha_1$-antichymotrypsin showed the expected pattern of GC inductions to maximum by day 1. The two other clones selected showed progressive changes, clone II.2 being the major DEX-induction, and clone V.4 (IGF-BP4) being the major reduction from the library subtraction procedure. From Nguyen et al. (1992), submitted.

## Comparison with other GC inductions

To evaluate the II.2 induction in comparison to other known GC regulated mRNAs, we have also quantitated the mRNA level of mouse MT, $\alpha_1$-AGP (using rat hepatoma tisue culture [HTC] cells) and human MT, $\alpha_1$-antichymotrypsin using dot blot and quantitation PCR. Densitometer scanning of ethidium bromide stained gels showed progressive inductions of II.2 mRNA, increasing approximately 30 fold in the 10-day DEX exposure, similar to the dot blot assays. Approximately five-fold inductions of TAT, MT, $\alpha_1$-AGP and $\alpha_1$-antichymotrypsin (for both mouse and human) were observed after one-day DEX exposure, with the level remaining constant in the ten-day DEX-treated samples. Actin products remained unchanged during the course of study and are shown as control. In PCR analysis, a low level of II.2 mRNA could be detected in HTM cells not exposed to DEX treat-

## STRESS RESPONSE STUDY OF II.2 CLONE
## QUANTITATION PCR OF II.2 INDUCIBLE
## RESPONSE TO VARIOUS TYPES OF STRESS

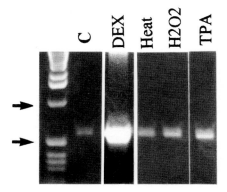

Fig. 3. PCR Quantitation of II.2 Following GC and other Potential Stress Mediators. PCR was used to quantitate changes of II.2 mRNA levels in various stress treatments to cultured HTM cells. Total RNAs were extracted using a one-step guanidinium-phenol-chloroform procedure, and 1 μg of the total RNA was used to make cDNA. Approximately $\frac{1}{20}$ of this amount (which was shown in a dilution experiment to be in the saturation range of the PCR) was used to amplify using the internal primers (e. g. II.2 SK3-II.2 KS4) of the II.2 sequences. The PCR reaction was performed according to Methods. As shown a major and specific increase in II.2 was observed in the PCR products (indicated as the 450 bp DNA bands – lower and upper DNA markers are 350 bp and 1 kb respectively) after 10-day DEX treatment with minor inductions observed 3 hours after heat, $H_2O_2$, and TPA treatments, according to Methods. A small amount of II.2 was observed in the control which was undetectable above background in the dot blot analysis. Non-stress stimulants such as growth factors (IGF, bFGF) did not induce II.2 synthesis (data not shown).

ments which was below the sensitivity of dot blot detection. This could be due to a low level of endogenous GCs in serum, but is more likely due to other factors which may affect the expression of the gene product (also see next section).

Fig. 3 emphasizes that the II.2 induction is progressive and reaches very high levels. This data may provide the first progressive GC-inducible mRNA with a clear long-term steroid regulation. The progression of II.2 mRNA levels over time was confirmed by separate mRNA isolations in three different HTM lines by PCR quantitation and in one line by dot blot studies following one, four, seven, and ten days of 500 nM DEX treatment. The high level of the ten-day DEX induction of the II.2 gene product was of considerable interest since most acute phase response

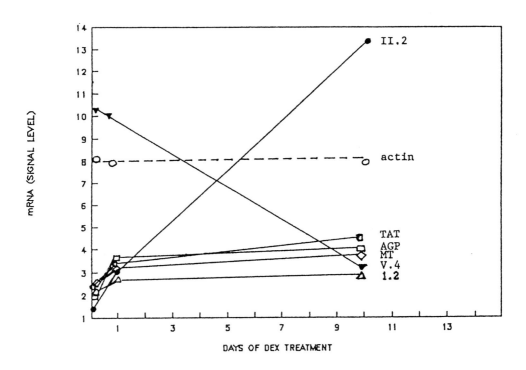

Fig. 4. Relative Inductions and Deinductions of HTM Cell mRNAs. The major, progressive induction of II.2 mRNA by DEX is shown using one-day and ten-day treatments. This induction is compared to the known GC regulated genes of metallothionein (MT) and α1-antichymotrypsin. The II.2 and MT mRNA levels were obtained from dot blot analysis and PCR quantitation, α1-antichymotrypsin mRNA was obtained for dot blot analysis. Controls for GC inductions were performed using rat hepatoma cells (HTC), PCR quantitation of other GC regulated genes such as tyrosine aminotransferase (TAT), α1-acidglycoprotein (α1-AGP) in the HTC-cells for one-day and ten-day DEX treatment show similar patterns as those of MT and α1-antichymotrypsin in HTM cells in that they were not progressive and were nearly maximal by 24 hours. II.2 mRNA is not found in HTC cells.

genes regulated by steroids are relatively low copy number, such as $\alpha_1$-antichymo-trypsin, $\alpha_1$-acid glycoprotein, tyrosine aminotransferase (TAT) and metallothio-nein (MT). These are induced to maximum levels within hours. There are reports of high copy numbers regulated (e. g. small, repeated RNA sequences of 5.4S RNA and 7SL RNA [SUN and FRANKEL 1986] both of which belong to the Alu repeat familiy); but these have not been examined for long-term progression, and none of these match the II.2 sequence. In addition, homology search by Eugene analysis did not match the II.2 sequence to any members of the heat shock family or other chaperonins including Rubisco large subunit binding protein, immunoglobulin heavy-chain binding protein (Bip), and glucose regulated proteins (GRP 78, GRP 94). In fact, the II.2 sequence does not show significant homology to any reported sequences in the Gene Bank.

## Factors influencing II.2 induction

Although structurally unrelated to the known stress proteins, we have suspected that the expression of the II.2 gene may be caused by stress stimulants. In fact, RT-PCR quantitation analysis of II.2 changes showed a minor induction following heat treatment, a larger, approximately 5 fold for 0.3 mM $H_2O_2$, and a 7 fold for 1 $\mu$M TPA treatment. Overall, sustained DEX treatment is the best inducer of II.2 with 30–50 fold induction. Whether or not the II.2 peptide has any intrinsic activity as previously defined for cellular stress response proteins (e. g. protein assembly, rena-turation and transport [ELLIS 1987]) remains to be evaluated.

Protein synthesis effects on the II.2 mRNA induction were examined by a cyclo-heximide (CH) experiment. Concentrations of 1 $\mu$g, 3 $\mu$g and 10 $\mu$g CH/ml were tested, with no effect on cell viability observed (i. e. no changes in cell morphology and a constant actin level). The expression of II.2 mRNA was totally abolished when CH was incubated for a 3 hour prior to DEX treatment, whereas DEX was able to induce, though at a lower level, the II.2 mRNA when concurrently treated with CH. In contrast, MT mRNA remained unaffected by the above treatments. These findings suggested that unstable factor(s) besides GC receptors may coordi-nately regulate the II.2 expression.

## Discussion

The current study involves the isolation of gene sequences differentially regula-ted by sustained glucocorticoid (GC) exposure to HTM cells. Our characterization of major GC-induced clone (II.2) appears to provide a correlate to the long-term

DEX-induced proteins/glycoproteins detected by 1-D and 2-D SDS gels in HTM cells (see POLANSKY et al. 1989; POLANSKY et al. 1991). Since the structural analysis of the II.2 induction indicated that it was coding for a unique, secreted molecule, there are a variety of effects such a molecule could have in the meshwork tissues, including possible direct effects on outflow facility. Whatever function(s) II.2 is eventually shown to have, our studies of this specific mRNA provide strong support for the concept of the HTM cell model, since we have clearly demonstrated the progressive induction of this gene product by sustained DEX treatment to the HTM cells.

The cDNA library subtraction procedure employed in this study was appropriate to obtain the highly-induced transcripts (usually from 0.1 % to 1 % of total mRNA) which we expected based on 2D gel protein studies and cell-free translation studies conducted earlier. The use of cDNA library subtraction is technically simpler than the subtraction hybridization method which is required to detect lower level changes (SARGENT and DAWID 1983; HEDRICK et al. 1984; TIMBERLAKE 1980). The above approach has provided us with potential molecular probes to investigate sustained DEX effects in HTM cells and meshwork tissues at the molecular level.

Importantly, the pattern of induction for the major induced clone II.2 was shown to be different from that of other known GC-regulated mRNAs including metallothionein (MT), tyrosine aminotransferase (TAT), $\alpha_1$-acid glycoprotein ($\alpha_1$-AGP), $\alpha_1$-antichymotrypsin. These mRNAs were shown to reach maximum at one day, whereas the II.2 mRNA progressively increased over 10 days of DEX tretment. This is perhaps the first progressively induced mRNA documented for a steroid regulated gene. The earlier protein/glycoprotein work could not prove this pattern of gene regulation.

Although the mechanism for this DEX induction is unknown, the inhibition of the II.2 induction (but not MT) by cycloheximide, strongly suggests the requirement ongoing protein synthesis. The partial inhibition by cycloheximide in the presence of DEX suggests the presence of unstable factor(s) coexisting with the receptor (KLEIN et al. 1987), could be playing a role in the progressive DEX induction. The recent finding that c-Fos and c-Jun act in a coordinate manner with the GC receptor to modulate gene expression (DIAMOND et al. 1990, GAUB et al. 1990, DOUCAS et al. 1991) may be relevant to these findings. In addition, the TPA induction of the II.2 provides support for the role of c-Jun and c-Fos dependent activation of this gene, but a considerable amount of work is required, including gene promoter analysis and functional studies (EVAN et al. 1988), to investigate possible transcriptional regulation mechanisms for this progressive induction. The possibility of mRNA stabilization also must be taken into consideration (BRAWERMAN 1989).

The cDNA subtraction screening methodology described in this paper has provided us with molecular probes to study sustained GC effects on HTM cells. This approach has not been applied for studies of steroid hormone action in the ocular system to our knowledge. Based on the success of this work, it should be possible to employ genetic methods for investigating certain clinical and basic aspects of the GC-induced changes. Among these are, (i) the use of II.2 probe to quantitate its level in glaucomatous HTM samples to establish possible correlations with glaucoma pathogenesis; (ii) the development of antisense mRNA for use in cultured HTM cells and meshwork tissues for functional analysis and for possible *in vitro/in vivo* correlations; (iii) the isolation of the II.2 gene and analysis of its promotor sequences to help understand the regulatory controls over GC effects on this system.

*In situ* molecular probes as well as antibody made using the II.2 sequence should help examine possible relationships with GC-induced proteins/glycoproteins. The moderate increase of clone 1.2 ($\alpha_1$-antichymotrypsin) under DEX influence might also be of interest with regard to IOP changes; the induction of this mRNA could be associated with a decreased degradation of protein in the meshwork and outflow obstruction. The significant reduction of clone V.4 which is identical to the newly described IGF-BP4, suggests a possible involvement of the IGF growth factor family in the DEX responses of HTM cells. We have recently observed various alterations of the expression levels of the IGF family members including IGF-I and II, and their receptors in response to GCs (unpublished data). Further studies of these leads could help in understanding the mechanisms for GC side-effects in the eye, and perhaps for some systemic effects and side-effects of these hormones.

## Summary

Using cDNA subtraction screening methods, three groups of mRNAs which showed differential glucocorticoid (GC) regulation were isolated from ten day dexamethasone (DEX) treated human trabecular meshwork (HTM) cells. A major induction group (30 – 50 fold, 8 clones), a major deinduction group (approximately 20 fold reduction, 3 clones), and several minor inductions (3 – 5 fold, 12 clones) were isolated. The cDNAs from the major induction group were of varying lengths from 0.8 to 2.3 Kb, which overlapped as shown by Hae III digestion, cross hybridization, and partial sequencing. This induction has been sequenced $> 95\%$, and appears to be a unique mRNA with a signal sequence and other characteristics associated with a secretory glycoprotein. The minor DEX induction showed identity with $\alpha_1$-antichymotrypsin. The major clone reduced by DEX showed homology with the IGF binding protein family, and was later found to match the sequence of the binding protein for type 4 (IGF-BP4) recently described for osteoblasts.

Kinetic analysis showed that the major GC induction in HTM cells was progressive over time and reached 2 – 4 % of the total cellular mRNA by ten days of 500 nM

DEX, from an insignificant amount in untreated cells. Other known GC-regulated species such as metallothionein (MT) showed nearly maximal inductions by one day. Stress conditions including heat, $H_2O_2$, and TPA also induced the expression of the major GC induced gene product measured using PCR quantitation and dot blot evaluations. Northern analysis showed the major GC induction to be a single class of mRNA of 2.5 Kb. Cycloheximide treatments suggested that factor(s) other then GC receptor coordinately interact and regulate the major GC-induced gene. Molecular biology approaches to provide histopathological markers and gene regulatory sequences are planned to follow up on these initial studies.

## Acknowledgements

Supported by NIH grants EY08905 (TDN), EY08973 (EB) and EY02477 (JRP), and by AHAF, National Glaucoma Research

## References

BAXTER, J. D., G. G. ROUSSEAU (1979): Glucocorticoid hormone action: An overview. In Glucocorticoid hormone action (BAXTER, J. D., G. G. ROUSSEAU [Eds.), Springer, Berlin, Heidelberg, New York) p. 1.

BAXTER, J. D., J. B. TYRELL (1981): The adrenal cortex. In: Endocrinology and metabolism (FELIG, P., J. D. BAXTER, A. E. BIOADUS, L. A. FROHMAN [Eds.]). McGraw Hill, New York, p. 385.

BAUMANN, H., W. A. HELD (1981): Biosynthesis and hormone-regulated Expression of secretory glycoproteins in rat liver and hepatoma cells. J. Biol. Chem. 256 (19): 10145–10155.

BERMAN, G., D. BURNETT, S. L. C. WOO, R. A. STOCKLEY (1988): Production of α1-antichymotrypsin by the J111 cell line. Biol. Chem. 369 (Suppl.): 23–26.

BRAWERMAN, G. (1989): mRNA decay: Finding the right targets. Cell 57: 9–10.

CROOK, R. B., M. LOUIE, T. F. DEUEL, G. M. TOMPKINS (1978): Regulation of glutamine synthetase by dexamethasone in hepatoma tissue culture cells. J. Biol. Chem. 253 (17): 6125–6131.

DIAMOND, M. T., J. N. MINER, S. K. YOSHINAGA, K. R. YAMAMOTO (1990): Transcription factor interactions: selectors of positive or negative regulation from a single DNA element. Science 249: 1266–1271.

DOUCAS, V., G. SPYROU, M. YANIV (1991): Unregulated expression of c-Jun or c-Fos proteins but not Jun D inhibits oestrogen receptor activity in human breast cancer derived cells. EMBO 10 (8): 2237–2245.

ELLIS, J. (1987): Proteins as molecular chaperones. Nature 238: 378–379.

EVANS, T., T. DeCHIARA, A. EFSTRATIADIS (1988): A promoter of the rat insulin-like growth factor II gene constists of minimal control elements. J. Mol. Biol. 199: 61–81.

GATTI, R. A., P. CONCANNON, W. SALSER (1984): Multiple use of Southern blots. BioTechniques May/June: 148–155.

GAUB, M. P., M. BELARD, I. SCHEUER, P. CHAMBON, P. SASSONE-CORSI (1990): Activation of the ovalbumin gene by the estrogen receptor involves the Fos-Jun complex. Cell 63: 1267–1276.

GUBLER, U., B. J. HOFFMAN (1983): A simple and very efficient method for generating cDNA libraries. Gene 25: 263–269.

HEDRICK, S. M., D. I. COHEN, E. A. NIELSEN, M. M. DAVIS (1984): Isolation of DNA clones encoding T cell-sepcific membrane-associate proteins. Nature 308 (8): 149–153.

KARIN, M., H. R. HERSCHMAN (1979): Dexamethasone stimulation of metallothionein synthesis in HeLa cell cultures. Science *204:* 176 – 177.

KIEFER, M. C., F. R. MASIARZ, D. M. BAUER, J. ZAPF (1991): Identification and molecular cloning of two new 30 kDa insulin-like growth factor binding proteins isolated from adult human serum. J. Biol. Chem. *266:* 9043 – 9049.

KLEIN, E. S., R. REINKE, P. FEIGELSON, G. M. RINGOLD (1987): Glucocorticoid-regulated expression from the 5'-flanking region of the rat $\alpha_1$-acid glycoprotein gene. J. Biol. Chem. *262* (2): 520 – 523.

LATOUR, D., S. MOHAN, T. A. LINKHART, D. J. BAYLINK, D. STRONG (1991): Inhibitory insulin-like growth factor-binding protein: cloning, complete sequence, and physiological regulation. Mol. End. 1806 – 1814.

LUCIBELLO, F. C., E. P. SLATER, K. U. JOOSS, M. BEATO, R. MULLER (1990): Mutual transpression of Fos and the glucocorticiod receptor: involvement of a functional domain in Fos which is absent in FosB. EMBO *9* (9): 2827 – 2834.

MCMASTER, G. K., G. G. CARMICHAEL (1977): Analysis of single and double-stranded nucleic acids on polyacrylamide and agarose gells by using glyoxal and acridine orange. Proc. Natl. Acad. Sci. *74* (11): 4835 – 4838.

NGUYEN, T. D., W. D. HUANG, A. WANG, E. BLOOM, D. FAUSS, W. SHANDS, J. R. POLANSKY (1991): Molecular biology studies of steroid-induced glaucoma model using cultures human trabecular meshwork (HTM) cells. Invest. Ophthalmol. Vis. Sci. in press.

OLSON, P. S., E. B. THOMPSON, D. K. GRANNER (1980): Regulation of hepatoma tissue culture cell tyrosine amonitransferase messenger ribonucleic acid by dexamethasone. Biochemistry *19:* 1705 – 1711.

POLANSKY, J. R., R. WEINREB (1984): Steroids as anti-inflammatory agents. In: Ocular Pharmacology. Springer-Verlag, New York and Berlin (SEARS, M., Ed.). Handbook of Exp. Pharm. *69:* 461 – 538.

POLANSKY, J. R., I. WOOD, M. MAGLIO, J. ALVARADO (1984 a): Trabecular meshwork cell culture in glaucoma research: Evaluation of biological activity and structural properties of human trabecular cells *in vitro.* Ophthalmol. *91:* 580 – 595.

POLANSKY, J. R., D. KONAMI, R. KIM, J. A. ALVARADO (1985): Glucocorticoid regulation of cultures human trabecular meshwork cells: A model system to study the effects of steroids on IOP. Invest. Ophthalmol. Vis. Sci. (Suppl) *26:* 5.

POLANSKY, J. R., R. KURTZ, J. A. ALVARADO, R. WEINREB, M. MITCHELL (1989): Eicosanoid production and glucocorticoid regulatory mechanisms in cultured human trabecular meshwork cells. Prog. Clin. Biol. Res. *312:* 113 – 138.

POLANSKY, J. R., R. M. KURTZ, T. D. NGUYEN et al. (1990): *In vitro* model for steroid effects on IOP: characterization of HTM protein/glycoprotein changes and molecular cloning approaches. Invest. Ophthalmol. Vis. Sci. (Suppl.) *31:* 377.

POLANSKY, J. R., R. M. KURTZ, D. J. FAUSS, R. Y. KIM, E. BLOOM (1991): *In vitro* correlates of glucocorticoid effects on intraocular pressure. In: Glaucoma Update. (KRIEGLSTEIN, G. K., Ed.) Springer-Verlag, Berlin, New York.

REINKE, R., P. FEIGELSON (1985): Rat $\alpha_1$-acid glycoprotein. J. Biol. Chem. *260* (7) 4397 – 4403.

SANGER, F., S. NICKLEN, A. R. COULSON (1977): DNA sequencing with chain-terminating inhibitors. Proc. Natl. Acad. Sci. *74* (12): 5463 – 5467.

SARGENT, T. D., I. B. DAWID (1983): Differential gene expression in the gastrula of Xenopus laevis. Science *222:* 135 – 139.

SCHUTZ, G., L. KILLEWICH, G. CHEN, P. FEIGELSON (1975): Control of the mRNA for hepatic tryptophan oxygenase during hormonal and substrate induction. Proc. Nat. Acad. Sci. U.S.A. *72* (3): 1017 – 1020.

SUN, L. H., F. R. FRANKEL (1986): The induction of alu-sequence transcripts by glucocorticoid in rat liver cells. J. Steroid Biochem. *25:* 2, 201 – 207.

TIMBERLAKE, W. E. (1980): Developmental gene regulation in Aspergillus nidulans. Developmental Biology *78:* 497 – 510.

WANG, A. M., M. V. DOYLE, D. F. MARK (1990): Quantitation of mRNA by the polymerase chain reaction. Proc. Natl. Acad. Sci. U.S.A. *87* (7): 2865.

*Howe Laboratory of Ophthalmology, Harvard Medical School, Massachusetts Eye & Ear Infirmary, Boston, MA, and * BioImaging Group, UMASS Medical School, Worcester, Ma.*

# The search for a sulfhydryl drug for glaucoma: From chemistry to the cytoskeleton

D. L. Epstein, A. W. de Kater, K. Erickson-Lamy, F. S. Fay, A. Schroeder and L. Hooshmand

Our interest in sulfhydryl (–SH) effects on aqueous humor outflow function emanated from early work of Bárány, who observed that the only metabolic poison he studied which affected (and increased) outflow facility in enucleated bovine eyes was iodoacetic acid (Bárány 1953). Although it was possible that this represented a nonspecific diffuse metabolic action, our studies in the crystalline lens had indicated that chemical modification of cellular sulfhydryl groups could increase tissue permeability (Epstein and Kinoshita 1970), and this was consistent with observed sulfhydryl effects in many different tissues (Sutherland, Rothstein and Weed 1967; Rothstein 1971; Mudge 1951). Such a hypothesis was further strengthened by studies involving biochemical quantifications of lactate production and enzyme activities in excised calf trabecular meshwork (TM) and correlating these findings with perfusion effects (Epstein, Hashimoto, Anderson and Grant 1981; Epstein, Patterson, Rivers and Anderson 1982; Freddo, Patterson, Scott and Epstein 1984; Chacko, Anderson and Karageuzian 1987).

In freshly enucleated calf and monkey eyes we demonstrated that several –SH reactive agents could act to increase (Epstein, Hashimoto, Anderson and Grant 1981; Epstein, Patterson, Rivers and Anderson 1982) or decrease (Freddo, Patterson, Scott and Epstein 1984) aqueous humor outflow facility. The -SH alkylating and addition agents, iodoacetamide (IA) and N-ethyl maleimide (NEM), caused an increase in outflow facility (C), wheras the mercurials, p-chloromercuribenzene sulfonate (PCMBS) and p-chloromercuribenzoate (PCMB) caused a decrease in C. Different morphological effects were observed with these different classes of –SH agents (Freddo, Patterson, Scott and Epstein 1984; Lindenmayer, Kahn, Hertzmark and Epstein 1983). NEM caused disruption of cell to cell junctions in the inner wall endothelium of Schlemm's canal (SC) (with a decrease in vacuole formation). With IA these inner wall junctions were maintained, but there was a widening of the subendothelial space, an increase in apparent vacuolar area, and apparent loss of inner wall-subendothelial cell attachments. In contrast, PCMBS caused cell swelling in the TM, particularly in the juxtacanalicular tissue (JCT), and it was hypothesized that this could then lead to a decrease in the dimensions of the extracellular outflow pathway, or alternatively, cellular swelling of the inner wall endothelium might somehow retard fluid movement into SC (FREDDO, PATTERSON, SCOTT and EPSTEIN 1984). We hypothesized that the diverse effects caused by these agents might have resulted from selective blockade of different populations of cellular –SH groups in the aqueous drainage pathway and that these -SH effects might represent perturbations of a naturally occurring mechanism for control of aqueous outflow. It seemed as if changes in cell size and shape, and cell to cell attachments and possibly contractility might underlie these different SH-effects. An additional important observation from biochemical studies of TM from enucleated calf eyes excised after perfusion, was that the effects of NEM (EPSTEIN, PATTERSON, RIVERS and ANDERSON 1982) and PCMBS (FREDDO, PATTERSON, SCOTT and EPSTEIN 1984) on facility of outflow occurred at dosages where there was little or no inhibition of TM cellular energy producing mechanisms, suggesting that cell membrane –SH groups might be directly involved in these effects.

There was obvious therapeutic implications for glaucoma from this work, but the agents used in these in vitro preparations were chemicals rather than drugs. It was soon realized, however, that the systemic drug ethacrynic acid (ECA) had specifically been developed as a –SH reactive diuretic to replace organic mercurials (SCHULTZ, CRAGOE, BICKING, BOLHOFER and SPRAGUE 1962). Ethacrynic acid had been administered to humans and was still available for clinical use (GILMAN, GOODMAN, RALL and AGURAD 1985). Although ECA was originally developed as a –SH drug, it was subsequently learned that the active site for the diuretic effect might not be the –SH reactive ligand (in fact ethacrynyl cysteine may be more potent than ECA alone (BURG and GREEN 1973; KOECHEL and CAFRUNY 1975), and ECA was subsequently replaced as a systemic diuretic by non –SH reactive drugs such as furosemide (CRAGOE, SCHULTZ, SCHNEEBERG, STOKKER, WOLTERSDORF and WATSON 1975).

We therefore next studied ECA in living monkeys and we observed that intracameral perfusion of ECA caused a dramatic increase in C, with good correlation to similar effects in enucleated calf eyes (EPSTEIN, FREDDO, BASSETT-CHU, CHUNG and KARAGEUZIAN 1987). In both systems simultaneous perfusion of ECA with cysteine seemed to block this effect, and preliminary studies with Furosemide did not indicate any C effect. Collectively, these studies indicated that the ECA-induced increase in C was a SH effect unrelated to its diuretic activity. The morphological correlate to the facility increase appeared to be cell to cell separations in the inner wall of SC and in the subendothelial tissue (EPSTEIN, FREDDO, BASSETT-CHU, CHUNG and KARAGEUZIAN 1987). Further, the monkeys were observed long term after these studies and at appropriate dosages structures of the anterior segment, i. e. the cornea and crystalline lens, did not demonstrate any clinical or pathological abnormalities.

Recent studies in organ cultured human eyes (LIANG, EPSTEIN, deKATER, SHAMSAFAEI, ERICKSON-LAMY, deKATER and EPSTEIN 1992) have demonstrated an increase in outflow facility at even lower dosages than those employed in the living monkey. Threshold anterior chamber drug levels appeared to be $10^{-5}$M. Interestingly, at these dosages no morphological change in the outflow pathway tissue was observed (LIANG et a. 1992). At higher dosages breaks in the inner wall of SC were observed and at higher dosages still, some trabecular cell swelling was seen. In addition to pointing to lower effective dosages for possible glaucoma therapy, this study suggested that there may be a truly subtle morphological correlate to the increased tissue permeability. Possibilities include enhanced trans or para-cellular flow (EPSTEIN and ROHEN 1991) across the inner wall of SC or alterations of the dimensions or composition of the extracellular outflow pathway.

The above living monkey studies were performed after two level constant pressure anterior chamber perfusion. We evaluated separately the efficacy and safety of a single 10 microliter injection of ECA into the anterior chamber of living monkeys (OZMENT, NYLEN and EPSTEIN 1988). Up to 3 mM concentrations appeared to be well tolerated and resulted in intraocular pressure lowering.

Since it is not known how long the outflow enhancing effect of such an outflow pathway drug may last (EPSTEIN 1987), it is possible that ECA might be suitable for clinical intracameral use either by itself or when the eye is already entered for other surgery, for example cataract surgery. For instance, if exfoliation glaucoma is due to the extracellular accumulation of abnormal exfoliation material proximal to the inner wall (RICHARDSON and EPSTEIN 1981; LÜTJEN-DRECOLL, FUTA and TAMM 1988), a drug which caused temporary separation of inner wall cells might allow this material to "flush out". Possibly some of the abnormal extracellular material present in primary open angle glaucoma (LÜTJEN-DRECOLL, FUTA and ROHEN 1981) might similarly be removed, yielding an unanticipated long duration of effect. This experiment needs simply to be done in the future in humans, once the ocular safety of ECA is more firmly established.

Most likely. ECA will have to be administered topically. Unfortunately, ECA alone is quite irritating to the eye when applied as an eye drop (although the IOP is reduced). Also there is the problem of potentially high levels of drug passing through the corneal endothelium, which contains –SH sensitive pumps (EDELHAUSER, VAN HORN, MILLER and PEDERSON 1976). Therefore we have begun investigations using various adducts of ECA (EPSTEIN, HOOSHMAND and EPSTEIN 1992) as potential topical antiglaucomatous agents (TINGEY, SCHROEDER, EPSTEIN and EPSTEIN 1992). The goal of these studies is to expose the cornea to minimum active drug, but to allow free ECA to be liberated in the anterior chamber and TM. Since there are known -SH sites on the corneal endothelium (EDELHAUSER, VAN HORN, MILLER and PEDERSON 1976) and lens epithelium (EPSTEIN and KINOSHITA 1970), there is potential for side effects which need to be monitored. On the other hand, similar considerations apply to all previously used systemic -SH reacting compounds such as the mercurials as well as ECA, and the apparent clinical safety of these agents must relate to the number, accessibility, and different characteristics of the cellular -SH groups in different organs as well as to their affinity, reversibility, etc. with different SH agents. Therefore, it may be possible in the future to actually develop a -SH drug for the treatment of glaucoma. Certain modifications of the ECA molecule might be fruitful.

The morphological studies in perfused tissues suggested that changes in cell shape and cell to cell attachment might underlie ECA's mechanism of action. This was studied more directly in cell culture where ECA was, in fact, observed to reversibly alter cell shape and attachment in bovine TM, human TM, and calf pulmonary artery endothelial cells (ERICKSON-LAMY, SCHROEDER and EPSTEIN 1987). The latter was used to assess general endothelial cell effects (since we have not been able to directly culture Schlemm's canal cells). Cell viability was observed to be maintained. At the time of cell shape change, various alterations in cytoskeletal protein staining were observed, e.g. with actin, vimentin, vinculin, and alpha-actinin that were also reversible (SCHROEDER, ERICKSON-LAMY and EPSTEIN 1989). However, most surprising was the observation that beta tubulin staining was altered prior to the others as well as prior to the cell shape change. In fact, the pattern of tubulin disruption appeared quite distinct (EPSTEIN, SCHROEDER, DEKATER, FAY and ERICKSON-LAMY 1991), with early loss of peripheral cellular tubulin staining and the occurrence of coiled peripheral fragments (Fig. 1).

These studies raised the question of whether cellular tubulin might normally be involved in the regulation of outflow resistance. It has been hypothesized that tubulin, which is constantly undergoing assembly and disassembly (dynamic instability) (MITCHISON and KIRSCHNER 1984), may contribute to the regulation of cell shape by constituting an opposing force to that of actin and other cytoskeletal proteins (INGBER and FOLKMAN 1989; HEIDEMANN and BUXBAUM 1990).

Such opposing force is in fact used architecturally to construct geodesic domes, as shown in the work of Buckminster Fuller (INGBER and FOLKMAN 1989; HEIDEMANN and BUXBAUM 1990.)

We wondered whether tubulin could be similarly involved in the regulation of cell shape in the outflow pathway tissue, and whether cell shape and attachments could thereby be involved in the cellular regulation of outflow resistance.

In our tissue culture studies the tubulin stabilizing drug, taxol, delayed and interfered with the ECA-induced alterations in cell shape (EPSTEIN, SCHROEDER, DEKATER, FAY and ERICKSON-LAMY 1991). In addition we have observed that pretreatment with taxol interfered with ECA's action to increase outflow facility (Table 1). Further, we have observed that taxol may diminish the magnitude of the "washout effect", the increase in outflow facility with prolonged perfusion (Table 2). In contrast, nocodazole and ouabain seemed to be without such an

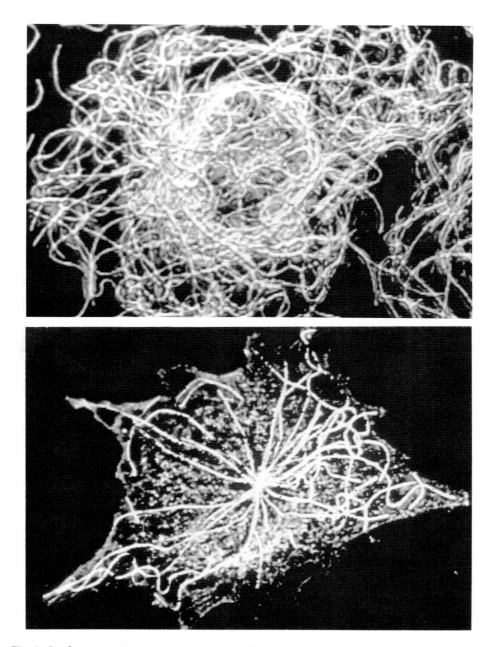

Fig. 1. Confocal scanning laser microscopy of calf trabecular meshwork cells. Images were created with digital imaging microscopy.

A) *Control.* Calf TM cell labeled with antibody to ß-tubulin. Microtubules are seen radiating outward from the microtubule organizing center.

B) *Experimental.* Calf TM cell treated with 0.1 nM ECA for 30 min. A loss of peripheral tubulin staining can be observed with an apparent retraction of tubulin from the cell membrane.

Table 1: Influence of $10^{-5}$M Taxol (T) Pretreatment on the Outflow Facility Effect of 0.06 mM Ethacrynic Acid (ECA)

| Perfusion Time (hr) | Conditions | | Facility ($\mu l$ min$^{-1}$ mmHg$^{-1}$) | |
|---|---|---|---|---|
| | Control | Experimental | Control | Experimental |
| 0 – 1 | Normal | Normal | 2.39±0.33 | 2.41±0.16 |
| 1 – 2 | Normal | Taxol | 2.75±0.30 | 2.44±0.22* |
| 2 – 3 | ECA | T + ECA | 2.86±0.27 | 2.57±0.23 |
| 3 – 4 | ECA | T + ECA | 3.57±0.25 | 3.15±0.27* |
| 4 – 5 | ECA | T + ECA | 3.93±0.38 | 3.05±0.37$^{\pm}$ |

Enucleated calf eyes were perfused by the constant pressure technique at 25°C. Results are expressed as ± S.E.M. for 10 pairs of calf eyes. Taxol was dissolved in 0.1% DMSO (final concentration), which was also added to control medium.
* $p < .05$ (paired t test)
$\pm$ $p < .025$ (paired t test)

effect. In this study, bovine eyes were subjected to an increase in perfusion pressure which is known to morphologically distend (JOHNSTONE 1979) and perhaps stretch the cells in the outflow pathway.

Thus ECA is of interest not only because of its possible use in glaucoma therapy, but because it is a possible "probe" of outflow pathway function. Further studies are clearly indicated to better delineate the role of the cytoskeleton in the cellular regulation of outflow resistance. Understanding the mechanism of action of ECA will give us a potential new tool to increase our knowledge of the aqueous outflow process. The morphological correlates to the facility effects in living monkeys might be more subtle with ECA (LIANG et al. 1992) than with cytochalasin B (SVEDBERGH, LÜTJEN-DRECOLL, OBER and KAUFMAN 1978), EDTA (BILL, LÜTJEN-DRECOLL and

Table 2: Influence of $10^{-5}$M Taxol (T), 2 X $10^{-5}$M Nocodazole (N), or $10^{-3}$M Ouabain (O) on Outflow Facility$^{\pm}$ Effects of Changing Perfusion Pressure.

| Perfusion Time (hr) | Conditions mmHg | Taxol$^{\pm}$ | | Nocodazole$^{\pm}$ | | Ouabain | |
|---|---|---|---|---|---|---|---|
| | | Control | Experimental* | Control | Experimental* | Control | Experimental* |
| 0 – 1 | 15 | 2.43±0.20 | 1.91±0.20 | 2.04±0.20 | 2.25±0.28 | 2.67±0.27 | 2.11±0.20 |
| 1 – 2 | 15 | 2.76±0.24 | 2.28±0.24 | 2.25±0.32 | 2.60±0.31 | 3.46±0.36 | 2.75±0.38 |
| 2 – 3 | 45 | 1.89±0.26 | 1.32±0.16■ | 1.51±0.20 | 1.58±0.18 | 2.25±0.31 | 2.04±0.27 |
| 3 – 4 | 15 | 4.06±0.53 | 2.47±0.41 | 2.70±0.42 | 3.03±0.33 | 3.99±0.36 | 3.28±0.44 |

Enucleated calf eyes were perfused by the constant pressure technique at 25°C at varying perfusion pressures. Results are expressed as ± S.E.M. for 6(T), 7(O), and 8(N) pairs of calf eyes.
* Experimental drugs added beginning at time 1 hr and maintained for duration of experiment.
$\pm$ Dissolved in 0.03% (N) or 0.1% (T) DMSO (final concentration) which was also added to control medium.
$\pm$ $\mu l$ min$^{-1}$ mmHg$^{-1}$
■ $p < .05$ (paired t test)

SVEDBERGH 1980; HAMANAKA and BILL 1987), or alpha chymotrypsin (HAMANAKA and BILL 1988). It is noteworthy that other perturbations of the trabecular cell - SH system involving oxidation and reduction reactions produce facility effects and morphological correlates similar to ECA (EPSTEIN, DEKATER, LOU and PATEL 1990). A better understanding of the ECA effects may give insight into the normal modulation of aqueous humor outflow by TM cells.

## Acknowledgements

Supported in part by National Glaucoma Research, a program of the American Health Assistance Foundation, and NIH grants EY01894 and EY07321.

Dr. Epstein has a proprietary interest in the development of ethacrynic acid and derivatives for the treatment of ocular hypertension and glaucoma through relevant patents and patent applications that were developed under research grant EYO 1894 from the National Eye Institute, and were assigned, according to the National Institutes of Health directives, to the Massachusetts Eye & Ear Infirmary.

## References

BÁRÁNY, E. H. (1953): In vitro studies of the resistance to flow through the angle of the anterior chamber. Acta Societatis Medicorum Upsaliensis *59:* 260 – 276.

BILL, A., E. LÜTJEN-DRECOLL, B. SVEDBERGH (1980): Effects of intracameral Na2, EDTA, and EGTA on aqueous outflow routes in the monkey eye. Invest. Ophthalmol. *19:* 492 – 504.

BURG, M., N. GREEN (1973): Effect of ethacrynic acid on the thick ascending limb of Henle's loop. Kidney Int. *4:* 301 – 308.

CHACKO, D. M., P. J. ANDERSON, L. N. KARAGEUZIAN (1987): Intraocular effects of - SH agents in calf trabecular meshwork. Invest. Ophthalmol. Vis. Sci. *28* (ARVO Suppl): 132.

CRAGOE, E. J., E. M. SCHULTZ, G. E. SCHNEEBERG, O. W. STOKKER, G. M. F. WOLTERSDORF, L. S. WATSON (1975): (1-Oxo-2-substituted-5-indanyloxy) acetic acids, a new class of potent renal agents possessing both uricosuric and saluretic activity. A re-examination of the role of sulfhydryl binding in the mode of action of acylphenoxyacetic acid saluretics. J. Med. Chem. *18:* 225.

EDELHAUSER, H. F., D. L. VAN HORN, P. MILLER, H. J. PEDERSON (1976): Effect of thiol-oxidation of glutathione with diamide on corneal endothelial function, junctional complexes and microfilaments. J. Cell Biol. *68:* 567 – 578.

EPSTEIN, D. L., J. H. KINOSHITA (1970): The effect of diamide on lens glutathione and lens membrane function. Invest. Ophthalmol. *9:* 629 – 638.

EPSTEIN, D. L., J. M. HASHIMOTO, P. J. ANDERSON, W. M. GRANT (1981): Effect of iodoacetamide perfusion on outflow facility and metabolism of the trabecular meshwork. Invest. Ophthalmol. Vis. Sci. *20:* 625.

EPSTEIN, D. L., M. M. PATTERSON, S. C. RIVERS, P. J. ANDERSON (1982): N-ethylmaleimide increases the facility of aqueous outflow of excised monkey and calf eyes. Invest. Ophthalmol. Vis. Sci. *22:* 752.

EPSTEIN, D. L. (1987): Open-angle glaucoma – why not a cure? (Editorial). Arch. Ophthalmol. *105:* 1187 – 1188.

EPSTEIN, D. L., T. F. FREDDO, S. BASSETT-CHU, M. CHUNG and L. K. KARAGEUZIAN (1987): Influence of ethacrynic acid on outflow facility in the monkey calf eye. Invest. Ophthalmol. Vis. Sci. *28:* 2067 – 2075.

EPSTEIN, D. L., A. W. DEKATER, M. LOU, J. PATEL (1990): Influences of glutathione and sulfhydryl containing compounds on aqueous humor outflow function. Exp. Eye Res. *50:* 785 – 794.

EPSTEIN, D. L., J. W. ROHEN (1991): Morphology of the trabecular meshwork and inner wall endothelium after cationized ferritin perfusion in the monkey eye. Invest. Ophthalmol. Vis. Sci. *32:* 160 – 171.

EPSTEIN, D. L., A. SCHROEDER, A. W. DEKATER, F. S. FAY, K. ERICKSON-LAMY (1991): Ethacrynic acid uniquely disrupts cellular tubulin in trabecular and other endothelial cells. Invest. Ophthalmol. Vis. Sci. *32* (ARVO Suppl): 1257.

EPSTEIN, D. L., HOOSHMAND, L. B. and EPSTEIN, M. P. M. (1991): Thiol adducts of ethacrynic acid increase outflow facility in enucleated calf eyes. Curr. Eye Res. *11:* 253 – 258, 1992.

ERICKSON-LAMY, K., A. SCHROEDER, D. L. EPSTEIN (1987): Sulfhydryl agents induce reversible shape change in cultured endothelial cells. Invest. Ophthalmol. Vis. Sci. *28* (ARVO Suppl): 283.

FREDDO, T. F., M. M. PATTERSON, D. R. SCOTT, EPSTEIN, D. L. (1984): Influence of mercurial sulfhydryl agents on aqueous humor outflow pathway in enucleated eyes. Invest. Ophthalmol. Vis. Sci. *25:* 278.

GILMAN, A. G., L. S. GOODMAN, T. W. RALL, F. AGURAD (1985): Diuretics and other agents employed in the mobilization of edema fluid. In: WEINER, I. M., G. H. MUDGE (Eds.), Goodman and Gilman's The Pharmacological Basis of Therapeutics, Seventh edition. New York, Macmillan Publishing Co., 896 – 00.

HAMANAKA, T., A. BILL (1987): Morphological and functional effects of Na$_2$ EDTA on the outflow routes for aqueous humor in monkeys. Exp. Eye Res. *44:* 171 – 190.

HAMANAKA, T., A. BILL (1988): Effects of alpha-chymotrypsin on the outflow routes for aqueous humor. Exp. Eye Res. *46:* 323 – 341.

HEIDEMANN, S. R., R. BUXBAUM (1990): Tension as a regulator and integrator of axonal growth. Cell. Motil. Cytoskeleton *17:* 6 – 10.

INGBER, D. E., J. FOLKMAN (1989): Tension and compression as basic determinants of cell form and function: utilization of a cellular tensegrity mechanism. In: Cell Shape: Determinants, Regulation, and Regulatory Role, STEIN, W. D., F. BONNER (Eds.), San Diego, Academic Press.

JOHNSTONE, M. A. (1979): Pressure-dependent changes in nuclei and the process origins of the endothelial cells lining Schlemm's canal. Invest. Ophthalmol. *18:* 44 – 51.

KOECHEL, D. A., E. J. CAFRUNY (1975): Thiol adducts of ethacrynic acid: a correlation of the rate of liberation of ethacrynic acid with the onset and magnitude of the diuretic response. J. Pharmacol. Exp. Ther. *192:* 179 – 194.

LIANG, L. L., D. L. EPSTEIN, A. W. DE KATER, SHAMSAFEI, K. A. ERICKSON-LAMY (1992): Ethacrynic acid increasis facility of outflow in the human eye in vitro. Arch. Ophthalmol. *110:* 106 – 109.

LINDENMAYER, J. M., M. G. KAHN, E. HERTZMARK, D. L. EPSTEIN (1983): Morphology and function of the aqueous outflow system in monkey eyes perfused with sulfhydryl reagents. Invest. Ophthalmol. Vis. Sci. *24:* 710.

LÜTJEN-DRECOLL, E., R. FUTA, J. W. ROHEN (1981): Ultrahistochemical studies on tangential sections of the trabecular meshwork in normal and glaucomatous eyes. Invest. Ophthalmol. Vis. Sci. *21:* 563 – 573.

LÜTJEN-DRECOLL, E., R. FUTA, E. TAMM (1988): New ultrastructural findings in exfoliation glaucoma. Invest. Ophthalmol. Vis. Sci. *29* (ARVO Suppl): 274.

MITCHISON, T., M. KIRSCHNER (1984): Dynamic instability of microtubule growth. Nature 312, 237 – 242.

MUDGE, G. M. (1951): Electrolyte and water metabolism of rabbit kidney slices. Effect of metabolic inhibitors. Am. J. Physiol. *167:* 206.

OZMENT, R. R., P. NYLEN, D. L. EPSTEIN (1988): The effect of intracameral ethacrynic acid on intraocular pressure of living monkeys. Invest. Ophthalmol. Vis. Sci. *29* (ARVO Suppl): 84.

RICHARDSON, T. M., D. L. EPSTEIN (1981): Exfoliation glaucoma: a quantitative perfusion and ultrastructural study. Ophthalmology *88:* 968 – 980.

ROTHSTEIN, A. (1971): Sulfhydryl groups in red cell membranes. Exp. Eye Res. *11:* 329.

SCHROEDER, A., K. ERICKSON-LAMY, D. L.EPSTEIN (1989): Ethacrynic acid induced changes in cytoskeletal tubulin. Invest. Ophthalmol. Vis. Sci. *30* (ARVO Suppl): 356

TINGEY, D. P., A. SCHROEDER, M. P. M. EPSTEIN, D. L. EPSTEIN (1992): Topical ethacrynic acid lowers intraocular pressure in rabbits and monkeys. Arch. Ophthalmol. *110:* 699 – 702.

SCHULTZ, E. M., E. J. CRAGOE, J. B. BICKING, W. A. BOLHOFER, J. M. SPRAGUE (1962): a,B-unsaturated ketone derivatives of aryloxyacetic acids, a new class of diuretics. J. Med. Pharm. Chem. *5:* 660 – 662.

SUTHERLAND, R. M., A. ROTHSTEIN, R. I. WEED (1967): Erythrocyte membrane sulfhydryl groups and caution permeability. J. Cell Physiol. *69:* 185.

SVEDBERGH, B., E. LÜTJEN-DRECOLL, M. OBER, P. L. KAUFMAN (1978): Cytochalasin-B induced structural changes in the anterior ocular segment of the cynomolgus monkey. Invest. Ophthalmol. *17:* 718 – 734.

*Department of Ophthalmology, University of Wisconsin*
*Medical School, Madison, Wisconsin, USA*

# Superior cervical ganglionectomy in monkeys: Pilocarpine-induced accommodation and prostaglandin $F_{2\alpha}$-induced ocular hypotension and mydriasis

J. C. ROBINSON and P. L. KAUFMAN

## *Abstract*

Following a histologically confirmed left superior cervical ganglionectomy in 6 cynomolgus monkeys, unilateral ocular sympathetic denervation was confirmed by ipsilateral ptosis, miosis, supersensitivity of pupillary dilation to topical phenylephrine and pupillary hyporesponsiveness to topical hydroxyamphetamine. Baseline intraocular pressure, refraction, accommodative responsiveness to intramuscular pilocarpine and ocular hypotensive responsiveness to topical prostaglandin $(PG)F_{2\alpha}$ were identical in the denervated and contralateral control eyes. However, the sympathetically denervated pupil dilated slightly in response to $PGF_{2\alpha}$ while the control pupil constricted slightly, so that the relative responses differed significantly.

## Introduction

Although the ciliary muscle is parasympathetically dominated, it also receives a sympathetic innervation (EHINGER 1966; RUSKELL 1973; LATIES and JACOBOWITZ 1966), and contains $\beta_2$-adrenergic receptors (WAX and MOLINOFF 1987). Electrical stimulation of the cervical sympathetics (TÖRNQVIST 1966), topical ocular application of β-adrenergic agonists and antagonists (GILMARTIN et al. 1984; HURWITZ et al. 1972; GILMARTIN and HOGAN 1985), and direct application of β-agonists and antagonists to isolated ciliary muscle strips (VAN ALPHEN et al. 1962, 1965) indicate that the adrenergic innervation and receptors mediate a relaxation of accommodation, presumably due to relaxation of the ciliary muscle. The physiologic role of this adrenergic-sympathetic mediated relaxation is not known, but it could permit the ciliary muscle to act as its own physiologic antagonist in facilitating smooth rather than tonic-clonic contraction in response to parasympathetic stimulation. The iris accomplishes this by containing within itself distinct parasympathetically dominated sphincter and sympathetically dominated dilator muscles, while the skeletal system utilizes antagonistic muscles separated by some distance.

Prostaglandin (PG)$F_{2\alpha}$ applied topically twice daily reduces intraocular pressure (IOP) substantially in all mammalian species thus far studied, including monkeys and man (CRAWFORD and KAUFMAN 1991; CRAWFORD et al. 1987; KAUFMAN and CRAWFORD 1989). At near-maximal ocular hypotensive doses in the monkey, it is also weakly miotic. Adrenergic and prostaglandin mechanisms interact in many systems (CAMRAS et al. 1987; HINMAN 1972; MIYAKE et al. 1987), and endogenously released prostaglandins or other cyclooxygenase products may in part mediate the ocular hypotensive response to epinephrine in rabbits (BHATTACHERJEE and HAMMOND 1977) and humans (CAMRAS et al. 1985).

We wished to investigate the role of the sympathetic innervation in modulating the accommodative response to pilocarpine and the ocular hypotensive and miotic responses to $PGF_{2\alpha}$. Earlier efforts to understand the role of sympathetic innervation in anterior segment physiology employed chemical approaches to create denervation and/or rabbits as the experimental animal (TREISTER and BÁRÁNY 1970; BÁRÁNY 1962; SEARS et al. 1962; SEARS and SHERK 1964; HOLLAND and MIMS 1971; GREGORY et al. 1985; GUAL et al. 1989; BRASLOW and GREGORY 1987). However, to delineate mechanisms most relevant to man, and to avoid the potentially confounding effects of ocular manipulation and administration of neurotoxic or other pharmacologic agents (TRANZER and THOENEN 1968; HANDLEY and EAKINS 1965), we studied cynomolgus monkeys in which one eye had been sympathetically denervated by unilateral superior cervical ganglionectomy.

## Materials and methods

### Animals

Six young adult female cynomolgus monkeys (Macaca fascicularis) weighing 2.0 – 2.5 kg underwent a left superior cervical ganglionectomy (SCGx) as previously described (ROBINSON and KAUFMAN, 1992). In all cases the excised tissue was examined by light microscopy and typical sympathetic neurons surrounded by an intact capsule were present. All 6 animals exhibited miosis, blepharoptosis, pupillary hyporesponsiveness to topical hydroxyamphetamine and supersensitivity to topical phenylephrine in the SCGx as compared to the contralateral eye (ROBINSON and KAUFMAN, 1992) before and after the present studies were performed.

## Physiologic measurements

Intraocular pressure (IOP) was determined non-invasively with a minified Gold-mann applanating tonometer (KAUFMAN and DAVIS 1980). Pupil diameter was measured to the nearest 0.1 mm with a vernier caliper under normal room lighting conditions (~350 lux). Refraction was determined with a Hartinger coincidence refractometer coupled to a strip chart recorder (KAUFMAN 1978; BÁRÁNY 1977). Differences between eyes and/or over time were evaluated for statistical significance by the 2-tailed paired t-test or analysis of variance for repeated measurements (ANOVA-RM).

## Drug protocols

Prostaglandin $F_{2\alpha}$-1-isopropylester ($PGF_{2\alpha}$-IE) was donated by Pharmacia Ophthalmics AB (Uppsala, Sweden) as a 0.0535% aqueous solution (in 0.5% polysorbate 80 and 0.9% NaCl) and further diluted with 0.9% NaCl to give a final concentration of 0.02%. The monkeys were trained to tolerate manual restraint supine in a net without sedation by a gloved handler. Two 5 µl drops of $PGF_{2\alpha}$-IE solution (total dose = 2 µg) were applied to the central cornea of each eye at 7:30 AM and 3:30 PM for 3 days. IOP and pupil diameter were measured in the ketamine-anesthetized prone monkey prior to beginning the study, and on treatment day 4 approximately 18 hr after the 6th bilateral 2 µg dose of $PGF_{2\alpha}$-IE, and then 0.5, 1, 1.5, 2, 3, 4, 5 and 6 hr after the 7th dose. This $PGF_{2\alpha}$-IE dose regimen is near – but-not-supra-maximal for IOP lowering and miosis in normally innervated cynomolgus eyes (CRAWFORD and KAUFMAN 1991).

Pilocarpine HCl (Sigma Chemical Co., St. Louis, MO) was dissolved in citrate/borate buffer in a concentration specific to each animal such that 3 ml provided a drug dose of 1.5 mg/kg. This was infused into the quadriceps muscle of the thigh over 10 min at a uniform rate of 0.3 ml/min, delivering a strong but submaximal dose for normally innervated cynomolgus eyes (KAUFMAN 1978). Beginning immediately before starting the infusion both eyes were refracted every 30–60 sec until the drug-induced myopia stabilized, usually about 40 min later.

The pilocarpine and $PGF_{2\alpha}$ experiments were performed 1–2 and 2–3 months respectively after SCGx. At least 2–3 weeks elapsed between successive experiments.

*Anesthesia*

Anesthesia for biomicroscopy, tonometry, pupillometry and refractometry was intramuscular (i.m.) ketamine 10 mg/kg, supplemented by 5 mg/kg every 30 – 60 min as needed. Anesthesia for SCGx was i.m ketamine 10 mg/kg + i.m. pentobarbital Na 35 mg/kg; post-surgical analgesic medication was butorphanol tartrate 0.2 – 0.3 mg/kg subcutaneously twice daily if indicated.

## Results

Under i.m. ketamine anesthesia, there was no difference between SCGx and contralateral control eyes in resting refraction (mean $\pm$ S.E.M. for OD, $-0.73 \pm 0.32$; OS, $-0.84 \pm 0.40$ diopters) or accommodative responsivesness to i.m. pilocarpine 1 – 2 months post-operatively (Fig. 1), or in resting IOP (OD, $14.6 \pm 1.2$; OS, $14.6 \pm 1.1$ mm Hg) or IOP responsiveness to topical $PGF_{2\alpha}$ 2 – 3 months post-operatively (Fig. 2). However, during topical $PGF_{2\alpha}$ treatment the SCGx and control pupils behaved differently (Fig. 3). Before the first $PGF_{2a}$ dose and 17 hr after the 6th dose, the SCGx pupil was slightly smaller than the control ($p < 0.05$ by the 2-tailed paired t-test at the -4D pretreatment baseline). Although neither pupil changed significantly over six hours following the 7th dose on treatment day 4 ($p < 0.45$ and 0.32 for normal and SCGx eyes respectively by ANOVA-RM), the SCGx pupil became significantly wider than the control ($p < 0.028$ by ANOVA-RM).

## Discussion

Under ketamine anesthesia, there was no difference between sympathetically denervated and control eyes in resting refraction (which presumably reflects tonic accommodation) (GILMARTIN and HOGAN 1985; CRAWFORD et al. 1990) or time course and amplitude of accommodation induced by a submaximum intramuscular infusion of pilocarpine. While this suggests the absence of a major sympathetic innervational role in regulating the coarse parasympathetic responses of the accommodative system, it does not rule out the fine regulatory effect postulated. To study the latter would have required a time resolution of milliseconds rather than minutes. Determining the effect of β-adrenergic agonists and antagonists on refraction and cholinomimetic drug- or central stimulation-induced accommodation in sympathectomized versus normally innervated eyes could also be relevant. We found no difference in the time course or magnitude of the ocular hypotensive response to topical $PGF_{2\alpha}$ between sympathectomized and control eyes of our

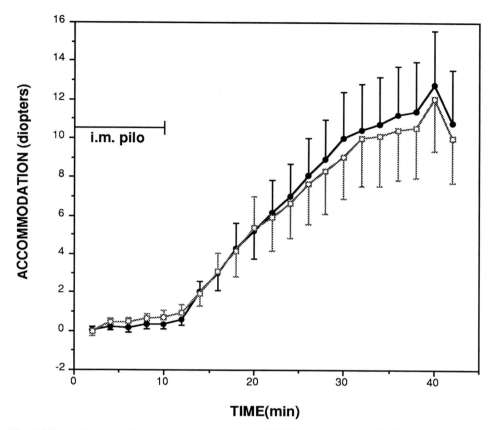

Fig. 1. Pilocarpine induced accommodation (mean ± SEM diopters) in normal (solid circles) and sympathetically denervated (open squares) eyes of 6 cynomolgus monkeys 1–2 months following unilateral SCGx. Horizontal bar indicates duration of intramuscular pilocarpine hydrochloride infusion beginning at time = 0 (total dose = 1.5 mg/kg). No statistically significant difference between treated and control eyes by the 2-tailed paired t-test or ANOVA-RM (even if the first 10 min are eliminated because the drug effect had not yet begun and/or the last 4 min are eliminated because the drug effect had plateaued).

monkeys, suggesting that the effect of exogenously administered PGs on IOP is neither mediated nor modulated by ocular sympathetic nerves. Surprisingly, the sympathetically denervated eyes exhibited a mydriatic response relative to the normally innervated contralateral controls when both were treated with $PGF_{2\alpha}$. The reasons for this are unclear. In normally innervated monkey eyes, $PGF_{2\alpha}$ usually causes a mild miosis relative to untreated contralateral controls (CRAWFORD et al. 1987). Perhaps after sympathetic denervation the pupillodilator muscle becomes supersensitive to prostaglandins, with the enhanced contractile response producing

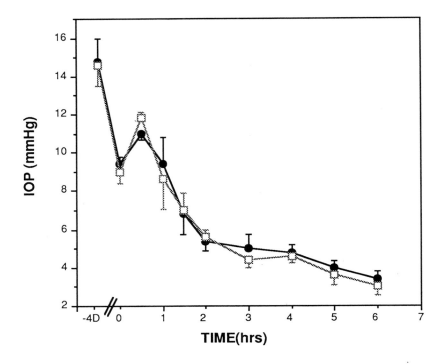

Fig. 2. Effect of prostaglandin $F_{2\alpha}$-1-isopropylester (PGF$_{2\alpha}$-IE) on intraocular pressure (IOP; mean $\pm$ SEM mm Hg), in normal (solid circles) and sympathetically denervated (open squares) eyes of 6 cynomolgus monkeys 2 – 3 months after unilateral SCGx. IOP was measured prior to beginning the study (-4D), and on treatment day 4 approximately 18 hours after the 6th bilateral 2 µg dose of PGF$_{2\alpha}$-IE (time 0) and then at 30 to 60 minute intervals beginning 30 minutes after the 7th dose. No statistically significant difference between treated and control eyes by the 2-tailed paired t-test or ANOVA-RM.

pupillary dilation even in the face of stimulation of the sphincter. This is speculation and other explanations are possible.

Studies using the unilaterally sympathectomized cynomolgus monkey to delineate the role of the ocular sympathetic innervation in maintaining normal aqueous humor physiology and its response to pharmacologic agents are underway.

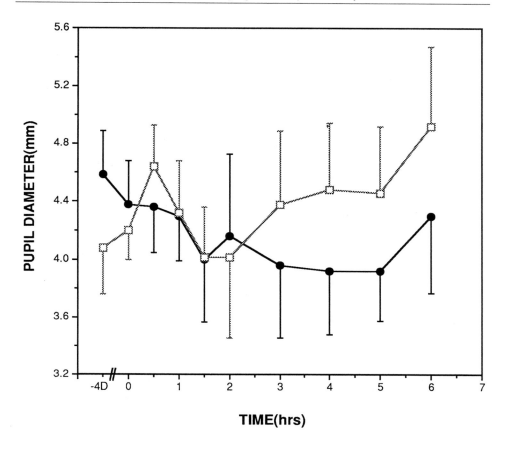

**TIME(hrs)**

Fig. 3. Effect of prostaglandin $F_{2\alpha}$-1-isopropylester (PGF$_{2\alpha}$-IE) on pupil diameter. Pupil diameter was measured prior to beginning the study (-4D), and on treatment day 4 approximately 18 hours after the 6th bilateral 2μg dose of PGF$_{2\alpha}$-IE (time 0) and then at 30 to 60 minute intervals beginning 30 minutes after the 7th dose. Data are mean ± SEM pupil diameter in normal (solid circles) and sympathetically denervated (open squares) eyes of 6 cynomolgus monkeys 2–3 months after unilateral SCGx./Significant difference between sympathetically denervated and normal eyes at -4D by the 2-tailed paired t-test ($p < 0.05$), and over time by ANOVA-RM ($p < 0.028$).

## Acknowledgements

Supported by USPHS National Eye Insitute grants EY02698 and EY06254. We thank Dr. Karl Schmidt, Department of Anatomy, University of Erlangen-Nürnberg, Germany for instruction in cervical anatomy; Dr. Ingolf Wallow (NIH grant EY01634), Department of Ophthalmology, University of Wisconsin for preparing the histologic sections of the surgical specimens; and Dr. Marion Fisher, Biostatistics Center, University of Wisconsin for statistical consultation. Expert technical assistance was provided by William Hubbard and Mary Ann Croft. The authors have no proprietary interest in any companies or compounds cited in this study.

# References

BÁRÁNY, E. H. (1962): Transient increase in outflow facility after superior cervical ganglionectomy in rabbits. Arch. Ophthalmol. *67:* 303 – 311.

BÁRÁNY, E. H. (1977): Pilocarpine-induced subsensitivity to carbachol and pilocarpine of ciliary muscle in vervet and cynomolgus monkeys. Acta Ophthalmol. *55:* 141 – 163.

BHATTACHERJEE, P., B. R. HAMMOND (1977): Effect of indomethacin on the ocular hypertensive action of adrenaline in the rabbit. Exp. Eye Res. *24:* 307 – 313.

BRASLOW, R. A., D. S. GREGORY (1987): Adrenergic decentralization modifies the circadian rhythm of intraocular pressure. Invest. Ophthalmol. Vis. Sci. *28:* 1730 – 1732.

CAMRAS, C. B., K. C. BHUYAN, S. M. PODOS, D. K. BHUYAN, R. W. P. MASTER (1987): Multiple dosing of protaglandin F$_{2\alpha}$ or epinephrine on cynomolgus monkey eyes. II. Slit-lamp biomicroscopy, aqueous humor analysis, and fluorescein angiography. Invest. Ophthalmol. Vis. Sci. *28:* 921 – 926.

CAMRAS, C. B., S. G. FELDMAN, S. M. PODOS, R. E. CHRISTENSEN, S. K. GARDNER, D. T. FAZIO (1985): Inhibition of the epinephrine-induced reduction of intraocular pressure by systemic indomethacin in humans. Am. J. Ophthalmol. *100:* 169 – 175.

CRAWFORD, K. C., B. A. T. GABELT, P. L. KAUFMAN (1990): Effects of various anesthetic and autonomic drugs on refraction in monkeys. Curr. Eye Res. *9:* 525 – 532.

CRAWFORD, K. C., P. L. KAUFMAN, B. TRUE-GABELT (1987): Effects of topical PGF$_{2\alpha}$ on aqueous humor dynamics in cynomolgus monkeys. Curr. Eye Res. *6:* 1035 – 1044.

CRAWFORD, K., P. L. KAUFMAN (1991): Dose related effects of prostaglandin F$_{2\alpha}$ isopropylester on intraocular pressure, refraction and pupil diameter in monkeys. Invest. Ophthalmol. Vis. Sci. *32:* 510 – 519.

EHINGER, B. (1966): Adrenergic nerves to the eye and to related structures in man and in the cynomolgus monkey (Macaca irus). Invest. Ophthalmol. Vis. Sci. *5:* 42 – 52.

GILMARTIN, B., R. E. HOGAN, S. M. THOMPSON (1984): The effect of timolol maleate on tonic accommodation, tonic vergence and pupil diameter. Invest. Ophthalmol. Vis. Sci. *25:* 763 – 770.

GILMARTIN, B., R. E. HOGAN (1985): The relationship between tonic accommodation and ciliary muscle innervation. Invest. Ophthalmol. Vis. Sci. *26:* 1024 – 1028.

GREGORY, D. S., O. G. AVIADO, M. L. SEARS (1985): Cervical ganglionectomy alters the circadian rhythm of intraocular pressure in New Zealand white rabbits. Curr. Eye Res. *4:* 1273 – 1279.

GUAL, A., G. M. MINTENIG, C. BELMONTE (1989): Intraocular pressure effects of water loading and venous compression tests in normal and denervated pigmented rabbits. Exp. Eye. Res. *48:* 365 – 374.

HANDLEY, E. D., K. E. EAKINS (1965): The mechanism of action of guanethidine on aqueous humor dynamics. J. Pharmacol. Exp. Ther. *150:* 393 – 397.

HINMAN, J. W. (1972): Prostaglandins. Ann. Rev. Biochem. *41:* 161 – 178.

HOLLAND, M. G., J. L. MIMS (1971): Anterior segment chemical sympathectomy by 6-hydroxydopamine. Invest. Ophthalmol. *10:* 120 – 143.

HURWITZ, B. S., J. DAVIDOWITZ, N. B. CHIN, G. M. BREININ (1972): The effect of the sympathetic nervous system on accommodation. I. Beta sympathetic nervous system. Arch. Ophthalmol. *87:* 668 – 674.

KAUFMAN, P. L. (1978): Anticholinesterase-induced cholinergic subsensitivity in primate accommodative mechanism. Am. J. Ophthalmol. *85:* 622 – 631.

KAUFMAN, P. L., G. E. DAVIS (1980): Minified Goldmann applanating prism for tonometry in monkeys and humans. Arch. Ophthalmol. *98:* 542 – 546.

KAUFMAN, P. L., K. CRAWFORD (1989): Aqueous humor dynamics. How PGF$_{2\alpha}$ lowers intraocular pressure. In: the Ocular Effects of Prostaglandins and Other Eicosanoids, BITO, L. Z., J. STJERNSCHANTZ. New York, Alan R. Liss, Inc., pp. 387 – 416.

LATIES, A. M., D. JACOBOWITZ (1966): A comparative study of the autonomic innervation of the eye in monkey, cat and rabbit. Anat. Rec. *156:* 383 – 395.

MIYAKE, K., F. KAYAZAWA, R. MANABE, Y. MIYAKE (1987): Indomethacin and the epinephrine-induced breakdown of the blood-ocular barrier in rabbits. Invest. Ophthalmol. Vis. Sci. *28:* 482 – 486.

ROBINSON, J. C., P. L. KAUFMAN (1992): Superior cervical ganglionectomy in monkeys: surgical technique. Invest. Ophthalmol. Vis. Sci. *33:* 247 – 251.

RUSKELL, G. L. (1973): Sympathetic innervation of the ciliary muscle in monkeys. Exp. Eye Res. *16:* 183 – 190.

SEARS, M. L., K. MIZUNO, C. CINTRON, A. ALTER, T. SHERK (1962): Changes in outflow facility and content of norepinephrine in iris and ciliary processes of albino rabbits after cervical ganglionectomy. Invest. Ophthalmol. *5:* 312 – 318.

SEARS, M. L., T. E. SHERK (1964): The trabecular effect of noradrenaline in the rabbit eye. Invest. Ophthalmol. *3:* 157 – 163.

TÖRNQVIST, G. (1966): Effect of cervical sympathetic stimulation on accommodation in monkeys. An example of a beta-adrenergic, inhibitory effect. Acta Physiol. Scand. *67:* 363 – 372.

TRANZER, J. P., H. THOENEN (1968): An electron microscopic study of selective, acute degeneration of sympathethic nerve terminals after administration of 6-hydroxydopamine. Experientia *24:* 155 – 156.

TREISTER, G., E. H. BÁRÁNY (1970): Degeneration mydriasis and hyperemia of the iris after superior cervical ganglionectomy in the rabbit. Invest. Ophthalmol. *9:* 873 – 887.

VAN ALPHEN, G. W. H. M., R. KERN, S. L. ROBINETTE (1965): Adrenergic receptors of the intraocular muscles: comparison to cat, rabbit and monkey. Arch. Ophthalmol. *74:* 253 – 259.

VAN ALPHEN, G. W. H. M., S. L. ROBINETTE, F. J. MACRI (1962): Drug effects on ciliary muscle and choroid preprations in vitro. Arch. Ophthalmol. *68:* 81 – 93.

WAX, M. B., P. B. MOLINOFF (1987): Distribution and properties of β-adrenergic receptors in human iris-ciliary body. Invest. Ophthalmol. Vis. Sci. *28:* 420 – 430.

*Department of Ophthalmology, Gifu University School of Medicine, Japan*

# Antiproliferative agents and ocular tissues

Y. KITAZAWA, S. JIKIHARA and T. YAMAMOTO

Wound healing and subsequent scar formation constitute the primary cause of failure of glaucoma filtering surgery (FRIEDENWALD et al. 1950). By creating a channel for the transconjunctival and subconjunctival drainage of aqueous humor, glaucoma filtration surgery reduces intraocular pressure (IOP) associated with formation of a filtering bleb (KRONFELD et al. 1952, TENG et al. 1959, ADDICKS et al. 1983). Wound healing and scar formation can disrupt the filtration channels resulting in the IOP elevation and the disappearance of the bleb. The sequence of wound healing and scar formation consists of interrelated events involving with numerous factors (TAHERY et al. 1989). However, it is the fibroblast proliferation that plays a major role in scar formation leading to the failure of the bleb (DESJARDINS et al. 1986).

The better understanding of the wound healing process has led to attempts to suppress the fibroblast proliferation and the scar formation to improve the success of glaucoma filtering surgery. In fact, a variety of antiproliferatives have been evaluated for this purpose, which include 5-flourouracil (5-FU) (GRESSEL et al. 1984), mitomycin (MMC) (CHEN et al. 1983), bleomycin (KAY et al. 1986), cytosine arabinoside (GOODWIN et al. 1990), daunorubicin (LEE et al. 1990) and doxorubicin (REN et al.1989, RADER et al. 1991).

The present paper deals with some of our clinical and experimental studies, which, we hope, will shed some lights on the future of antiproliferatives as the adjunct to glaucoma filtering surgery.

## *5-Fluorouracil*

5-FU inhibits thymidylate synthetase and this results in thymidine deficiency and drecreased DNA synthesis, leading to cell death (CHANDHURI et al. 1958, WEISS et al. 1961). 5-FU has been demonstrated to remarkably improve the success rate of filtering surgery prognosis (HEUER et al. 1984, HEUER et al. 1984, KITAZAWA et al. 1987, RUDERMAN et al. 1987, FLUOROURACIL FILTERING SURGERY STUDY 1989). The effectiveness of 5-FU estimated by life-table analysis (Kaplan-Meier) was shown in the two comparable groups of patients with primary open-angle glaucoma (TANIGUCHI et al. 1989); one group was treated with 5-Fu and the other did not receive 5-FU. Comparison of the survival curves clearly indicated a significant difference between two groups with regard to surgical prognosis. Nevertheless, 5-FU therapy has many disadvantages, including the need for repeated subconjunctival administration and ocular complications such as corneal epithelial defects which can be recalcitrant (KNAPP et al. 1987). Hence, 5-FU cannot be considered the ideal adjunct to filtering surgery.

## Mitomycin C

MMC is an antitumor antibiotic isolated from Streptomyces caespitosus in Japan (HATA et al. 1956). MMC interrupts DNA synthesis by cross-linking DNA and inhibits mitosis leading to cell death (TAHERY et al. 1989).

Recently YAMAMOTO et al. (1990) demonstrated that MMC has similar inhibitory effects to 5-FU on proliferation of cultured rabbit fibroblasts, but its antiproliferative effects is more than one hundred times as potent as that of 5-FU. Moreover, even as short as 2 days' use of a high concentration of MMC produced an adequate antiproliferative effect (88 % inhibition of growth) for as long as 14 days. Since the postoperative 2 weeks are considered to be the most crucial period for the wound healing and scar formation (SKUTA et al. 1987), their results seemed to indicate the possibility that the sufficient long-lasting antiproliferative affect is obtained when the cells are exposed to a high concentration of 5-FU or MMC. This prompted us to study the effect of MMC on ocular tissues in rabbits.

### 1. Morphological study

MMC was subconjunctivally injected under topical oxybuprocaine anesthesia in different doses (0.002 to 1.0 mg per 0.5 ml of distilled water) in one eye of 30 New Zealand albino rabbits. Five rabbits received 0.5 ml of distilled water. The contralateral fellow eye was not treated to serve as a control. The eyes were enucleated after the designated days within 1 to 28 days and were examined by biomicroscopy, dissection microscopy, light and electron microscopy. Biomicroscopy revealed conjunctival ischemia associated with mild to moderate ciliary injection in eyes that received 0.2 mg or larger amount of MMC throughout the observation period, while slight ciliary injection without conjunctival ischemia was noted in 14 and 28 days after the less amount of MMC administration. Dissection microscopic examination disclosed injection and swelling of ciliary body with 0.02 mg or higher dose of MMC administration. Not only the severity of changes but also their onset appeared to be dose-related: after 0.2 mg MMC administration the changes of ciliary body were first noted on day 3, after 0.02 mg MMC administration first on day 14.

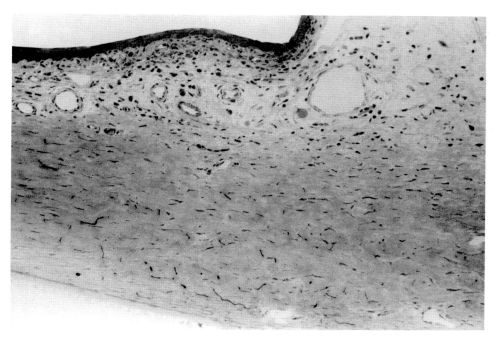

Fig. 1. Edematous, swollen conjunctiva with inflammatory cellular, mostly lymphocytic, infiltration, at the site of MMC injection. The sclera is slightly edematous with dilated spaces between collagen fibers. Fixed 3 days after subconjunctival injection of 0.01 mg MMC. Methylene blue stain. X 200.

Light microscopy revealed conjunctival edema with inflammatory cells, mainly lymphocytes following the injection of each dose of MMC and distilled water. The duration of conjuctival edema and cell infiltration to be dose-related; the changes disappeared in 7 days after the injection of 0.01 mg (Fig. 1). The changes persisted throughout the observation period after the injection of 0.02 mg or larger dose (Fig. 2). Edematous changes of sclera and ciliary body were noted after 0.002 mg and 0.02 mg MMC administration, respectively. The scleral edema appeared to correspond to the conjunctical changes with regard to dose, onset and duration (Fig. 3). On the other hand, the ciliary body edema was noted only after the administration of 0.02 mg or higher dose of MMC and the onset of changes delayed with lower doses; after the administration of 0.2 mg or 0.02 mg MMC the ciliary body edema was first noted on day 3; after 0.5 or 1.0 mg MMC injection it was present on day 1 (Fig. 4). Histological changes at the end of the oberservation period are summarized in Table 1. The dose equal to or higher than 0.02 mg seems to be needed to induce changes lasting longer than 4 weeks.

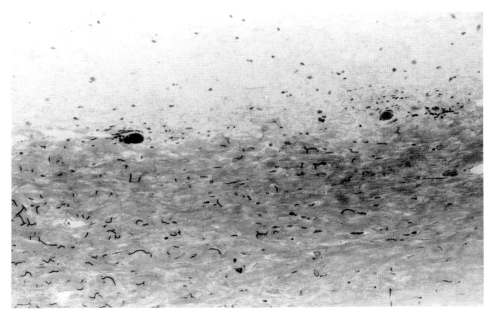

Fig. 2

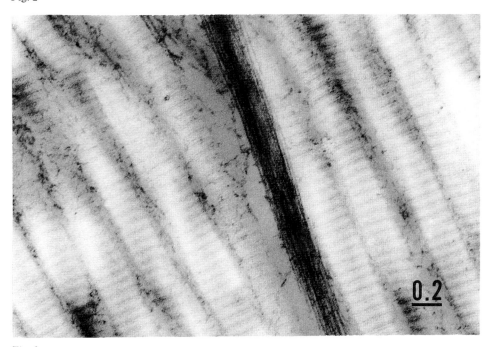

Fig. 3

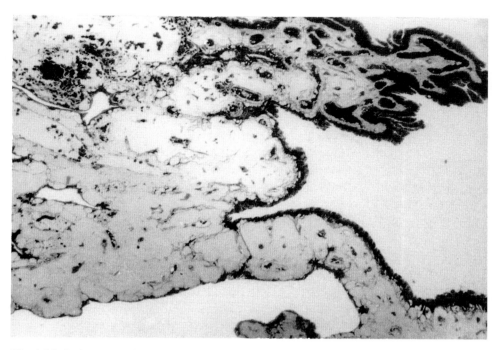

Fig. 4. Marked swelling of iridial processes at the site of MMC injection. Ciliary epithelium is distended and thinned out. Clotted erythrocytes are present in dilated capillaries. Fixed 3 days after subconjunctival injection of 0.5 mg MMC., Methylene blue stain. X 200.

◄ Fig. 2. Persisting edema of subconjunctival tissue at the site of MMC injection. Tortuosity of collagen bundles with the dilated interbundle spaces. Fixed 28 days after subconjunctival injection of 0.2 mg MMC. Methylene blue stain. X 200.

◄ Fig. 3. Electron microscopic view of the sclera in Fig. 2. Collagen fibrils retain the normal pattern of periodicity. Marker: 0.2 μm.

## 2. Clinical studies

Based on the results of histological studies in rabbits, we initiated a clinical trial in late '89. Namely, we compared MMC with 5-FU as an adjunct to trabeculectomy in eyes with poor surgical prognosis (KITAZAWA et al. 1991). We enrolled 32 patients (32 eyes). All had ocular conditions that are known to unfavorably affect the surgical outcome. The eyes were randomly allocated to either the 5-FU treatment or the MMC. One of us (YK) did all trabeculectomies.

We gave the patients allocated to the 5-FU treatment 5 mg o 5-FU by subconjunctival injection at the completion of the surgery. We injected 5-FU once a day throughout the first postoperative week and then once every other day for the second postoperative week. Thus, we gave 50 mg of 5-FU to each patient in 2 weeks. In the MMC group, we applied MMC soaked sponges to the exposed tis-

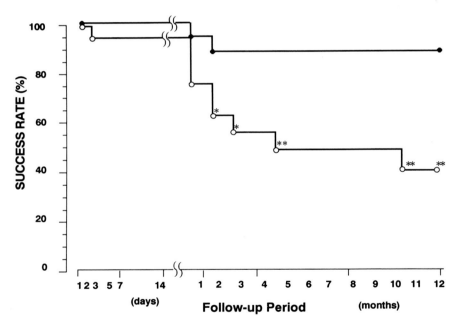

Fig. 5. Estimated cumulative rate of successful intraocular pressure control without antiglaucoma medication after trabeculectomy (category 1 success; above); with or without topical eye drops (category 2 success; top right); without medication or with topical medication and carbonic anhydrase inhibitor (category 3 success; right bottom). Closed circles represent the eyes given mitomycin; open circles , the eyes given fluorouracil; and asterisks, a significant difference between the mitomycin and the fluorouracil groups (P<0.05 by Z test). Published courtesy of American Medical Association (KITAZAWA, Y., K. KAWASE, H. MATSUSHITA, M. MINOBE: Trabeculectomy with mitomycin. Arch. Ophthalmol. (1991; *109:* 1693 – 1698, copyright American Medical Association.)

sues for 5 min. during surgery. The sponges were soaked in 0.5 ml distilled water
containing 0.2 mg MMC. This particular dose was chosen as we planned to irrigate

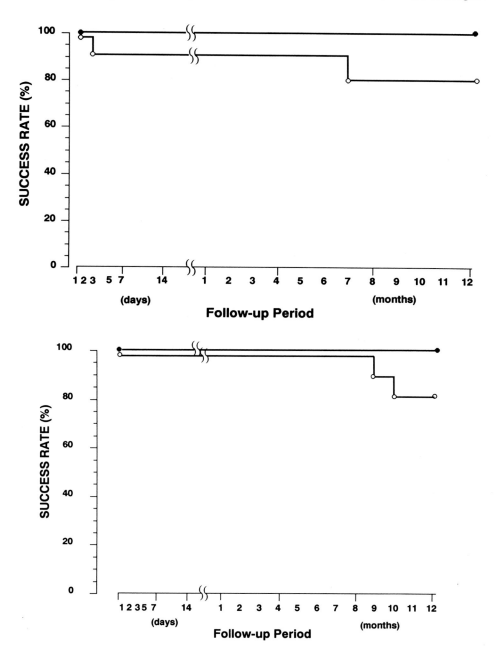

the ocular surface with a copious amount of saline to avoid the corneal complication. The irrigation was expected to reduce the tissue concentration of MMC at
least ten-to one hundredfold. After 5 minutes, we removed all the sponges and irrigated the wound and the ocular surface with 250 ml of balanced salt solution to
minimize the possible corneal damage and the intracameral penetration of MMC.
Then, we excised a block of tissue containing trabeculum,. We did not administer
MMC postoperatively.

We followed up the patients for 7 to 12 months after surgery. We estimated the
success rates of surgery by means of life-table analysis (Kaplan-Meier). We defined
the success as IOP equal to or lower than 20 mmHg. We adopted three different criteria for successful IOP control based on the use of antiglaucoma medications.
Category 1 success or the IOP control without any postoperative, antiglaucoma
medication may be referred to as the "complete" success. The "complete" success
rate was noted to be significantly different between the two groups at the sixth
postoperative month and thereafter ($P < 0.05$, Z-test) (Fig. 5). There was no significant difference in the success rates between the two groups when the eyes controlled with the topical medication were included into the successfully controlled
subset, none of the eyes in the MMC group required oral CAI for IOP control (Fig.
5). The IOPs at last examination are maintained at much lower levels in the MMC-
group (Fig. 6). The incidence of corneal complications is significantly lower in the
MMC group. Besides, the corneal epithelial defects seen in 2 eyes were minute and
cleared by themselves within 48 hours (Table 2). Even though the number of cases
was rather small and the period of observation was also limited, MMC appeared to
have promise as a better alternative to 5-FU. The above results seemed to agree
with the tissue culture study on rabbits' fibroblasts in that antiproliferative effect of
MMC lasts long enough to cover the critical phases of wound healing when the
appropriate dose(s) is administered. To determine whether or not the long-lasting
effect of MMC is due to the slow elimination from ocular tissues, we studied its
pharmacokinetics.


## 3. Pharmacokinetics


The concentration of MMC was measured in ocular tissues by means of HPLC
(KAWASE et al. 1992). MMC was administered in two different ways; one was the
subconjunctival injection and the other was to apply it with sponges to the explosed
sclera for 5 minutes, then the eye was irrigated with 250 ml of balanced salt solution
(KAWASE et al. 1992). The latter protocol was designed to simulate the use during
surgery. We found that the MMC concentration rapidly decreased within 24 hours
after the drug application in all tissues and aqueous humor. The concentration
changes in the first 3 hours could be approximated to the single exponential curve

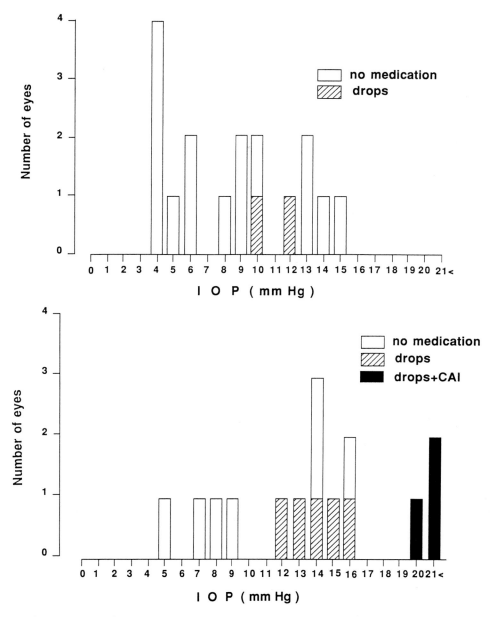

Fig. 6. Distribution of intraocular pressure measurements at the last examination in the mitomycin (top) and fluorouracil (bottom) groups. Open bars represent eyes not given antiglaucoma medication; hatched bars, eyes given topical drops only; closed bars, eyes given topical drops and oral carlonic anhydrase inhibitor. Published courtesy of American Medical Assocation (KITAZAWA, Y., K. KAWASE, H. MATSUSHITA, M. MINOBE.: Trabeculectomy with mitomycin. Arch. Opthalmol. (1991; *109:* 1693 – 1698, copyright American Medical Association).

Table 1: Doses of MMC needed to induce tissue changes of 4-week duration (28th day)

|  | MMC (mg/0.5ml) |
|---|---|
| Dissection Microscopy | |
| external segment | 0.02 |
| ciliary body | 0.02 |
| | |
| Microscopy | |
| conjunctiva | 0.02 |
| sclera | 0.2 |
| ciliary body | 0.02 |

Table 2: Complications

|  | MMC group No. % | 5–FU group No. % | P value* |
|---|---|---|---|
| Corneal erosion | 2 (12) | 8 (53) | <0.05 |
| Wound leakage | 3 (18) | 3 (20) | NS |
| surgery required | 1 (6) | 2 (13) | |
| Shallow chamber | 8 (47) | 6 (40) | NS |
| surgery required | 0 (0) | 1 (7) | |
| Choroidal detachment | 4 (24) | 7 (47) | NS |
| Hyphema | 2 (12) | 3 (20) | NS |

* : Fisher exact test
NS : not significant

Published courtesy of American Medical Association; Arch. Ophthalmol. (1991; *109:* 1693 – 1698) from KITAZAWA et al.'s "Trabeculectomy with mitomycin".

(Table 3). The estimated half-life ranged from 0.18 to 0.45 hr. in the conjunctiva, the sclera and the aqueous humor. The half-life of MMC was very similar to that of 5-FU reported by Kondo & Araie (1988). As a result of this rapid disappearance, at 72 hr the MMC concentration in ocular tissues was found to be below the minimum detectable level of $5 \times 10^{-3}$ μg/ml, which was demonstrated by YAMAMOTO and associates (1990) to induce 75% inhibition of the growth of cultured subconjunctival fibroblasts. They also reported 50% inhibition at a MMC concentration of $2 \times 10^{-3}$ μg/ml. Although their $ID_{50}$ value is lower than the minimum detectable concentration in our *in vivo* study and the tissue affinity of MMC probably varies among ocular tissues, the half-life we observed seems to strongly suggest that the MMC concentrations in the conjunctiva and the sclera are not likely to be maintained above the $ID_{50}$ value longer than a few days.

Table 3: Initial Concentration, Disappearance Time Constant, and Half–life*

| Study | Dose of MMC Applied (mg) | Conjunctiva | | | | Sclera | | | |
|---|---|---|---|---|---|---|---|---|---|
| | | Initial Concentration** (μg/g) | Time Constant (h$^{-1}$) | Half-life (h) | r | Initial Concentration** (μg/g) | Time Constant (h$^{-1}$) | Half-life (h) | r |
| Sub-conjunctival injection | 0.2 | 158.0 | 3.92 | 0.18 | -0.96 | 20.0 | 3.41 | 0.20 | -0.92 |
| | 0.02 | 5.76 | 2.33 | 0.30 | -0.90 | 0.62 | 1.82 | 0.38 | -0.81 |
| | 0.002 | 1.05 | 2.28 | 0.31 | -0.96 | 0.12 | 1.54 | 0.45 | -0.89 |
| Irrigation | 0.2 | 12.6 | 2.33 | 0.30 | -0.96 | 3.16 | 2.19 | 0.32 | -0.87 |

MMC=mitomycin C; r=correlation coefficient
* Calculated on the basis of Equation 1.
** MMC concentration at 0 hrs.

Published courtesy of Ophthalmology (1992; 99: 203 – 207) for Table 2 from Kawase et al.'s "Mitcomycin Concentration in Rabbit and Human Ocular Tissues after Topical Administration".

## Comment

Our comparative, clinical study has clearly demonstrated that MMC improves the surgical prognosis for patients at high risk for failure and that MMC seems to facilitate filtering bleb formation more favorably than does 5-FU. Our results seem to support the notion that the single application of MMC during trabeculectomy could be more effective in improving surgical prognosis than standard 5-FU therapy in which 5-FU is repeatedly administered for 2 weeks. Our results of MMC trabeculectomy are consistent with those reported by CHEN et al. (1983) and PALMER (1991). The major complication specific to 5-FU therapy is the corneal epithelial defect which is seen in 40 to 60% of cases (RADER and PARRISH 1991). By contrast, the single administration of MMC induced minor corneal erosion in 2 out of 17 eyes (12%). MMC inhibits the epithelial wound healing of the rabbits' cornea and the inhibitory effect has been found approximately one hundred times as potent as that of 5-FU (ANDO et al. 1992). Hence the striking difference in the incidence and the severity of corneal problems seems to be attributable to the frequency of administration (only once during surgery) and irrigation of the ocular surface with a copious amount of balanced salt solution immediately after removing sponges soaked in MMC. In fact, irrigating the ocular surface reduced the MMC concentration to one fifteenth or one tenth in the conjunctiva and the sclera in rabbits. The MMC concentration in the trabeculectomy specimen was demonstrated to be quite similar to that in rabbits' sclera obtained in the experiment designed to simulate the clinical application of MMC (KAWASE et al. 1992). It was demonstrated that 0.02 mg/0.5 ml of subconjunctivally injected MMC achieved almost identical MMC concentration in the sclera to that after the administration of 0.2 mg followed by irrigation and brought about the edematous changes of the subconjunctival and the scleral tissue lasting at least for 28 days. The findings provide further evidence that a single administration of MMC in clinically applied dose can bring about changes in the tissues where the postoperative scarring processes take place. Also the duration of the changes is long enough to cover the critical period of fibroblast proliferation following surgical intervention. However, the disappearance rate of MMC from the ocular tissues is almost identical to that of 5-FU and there is little possibility that the longer-lasting antiproliferative effect of MMC as compared with that of 5-FU is attributable to the difference in the elimination rate of the two compounds. Rather, we need to elucidate the effect of MMC and 5-FU on the cellular level. It is known that cell death caused by 5-FU is followed by cellular proliferation in some tissues. By contrast, little if any cellular proliferation takes place after the same tissue is exposed to MMC. If this is the case with the conjunctiva and the sclera, the clinically observed difference in the duration of antiproliferative effects between 5-FU and MMC may be, at least in part, plausible based on the difference in cellular reaction after the tissue is exposed to antiproliferatives.

Further studies are needed to clarify the interrelated cellular response to different antiproliferatives in the process of wound healing and scar formation, which will enable physicians to make the best of antiproliferative agents in glaucoma filtering surgery.

# References

ADDICKS, E. M., H. A. QUIGLEY, W. R. GREEN et al. (1983): Histologic characteristics of filtering blebs in glaucomatous eyes. Arch. Ophthalhmol. *101:* 795.

ANDO, H., Y. KAWAI, Y. KITAZAWA et al. (1992): Effect of mitomycin C and 5-fluorouracil on the healing process of corneal epithelial defect in rabbits. Ophthalmology *99:* 1809.

CHAUDHURI, N. K., B. J. MONTAG, C. HEIDELBERGER (1958): Studies on fluorinated pyrimidines. III. The metabolism of 5-fluorouracil-2-C$^{14}$ and 5-fluoroorotic-2-C$^{14}$ acid in vivo. Cancer Res. *18:* 318.

CHEN, C. W. (1983): Enhanced intraocular pressure controlling effectiveness of trabeculectomy by local application of mitomycin-C. Trans. Asia-Pacif. Acad. Ophthalmol. *9:* 172.

DESJARDINS, D. C., R. K. II. PARRISH, R. FOLBERG et al. (1986): Wound healing after filtering surgery in owl monkeys. Arch. Ophthalmol. *104:* 1835.

FLUOROURACIL FILTERING SURGERY GROUP (1989): Fluorouracil filtering surgery study one-year follow-up. Am. J. Ophthalmol. *108:* 625.

FRIEDENWALD, J. S. (1950): Some problems in the diagnosis and treatment of Glaucoma. Am. J. Ophthalmol. *33:* 1523.

GOODWIN, L. T., K. W. LEONG, D. A. LEE et al. (1990): The effects of cytosine arabinoside impregnated bioerodible polymers on glaucoma filtration surgery in rabbits. ARVO Abstracts. Invest. Ophthalmol. Vis. Sci. *31* (suppl): 86.

GRESSEL, M. G., R. K. II. PARRISH, R. FOLBERG (1984): 5-fluorouracil and glaucoma filtering surgery. I. An animal model. Ophthalmology *91:* 378.

HATA, T., R. SUGAWARA, A. MATSUME et al. (1956): Mitomycin, a new antibliotic from streptomyces. J. Antibiotic (Tokyo) Ser. A, *9:* 141.

HEUER, D. K., M. G. GRESSEL, R. K. II. PARRISH et al. (1984): Trabeculectomy in aphatkic eyes. Ophthalmology *91:* 1045.

HEUER, D. K., R. K. II. PARRISH, M. G. GRESSEL et al. (1984): 5-fluorouracil and glaucoma filtering surgery. II. A pilot study. Ophthalmology *91:* 384.

KAWASE, K., H. MATSUSHITA, T. YAMAMOTO et al. (1992): Mitomycin concentration in rabbit and human ocular tissues after topical administration Ophthalmology. *99:* 203 – 207.

KAY, J. S., B. S. LITIN, M. A. JONES et al. (1986): Delivery of antifibroblast agents as adjuncts to filtration surgery. Part II: Delivery of 5-fluorouracil and belomycin in a collagen implant: Pilot study in the rabbit. Ophthalmic. Surg. *17:* 796.

KITAZAWA, Y., T. TANIGUCHI, T., Y. NAKANO et al. (1987): 5-fluorouracil for trabeculectomy in glaucoma. Graefes Arch. Clin. Exp. Ophthalmol. *225:* 403.

KITAZAWA, Y., K. KAWASE, H. MATSUSHITA et al. (1991): Trabeculectomy with mitomycin a comparative study with fluorouracil. Arch. Ophthalmol. *109:* 1693.

KNAPP, A., D. K. HEUER, G. A. STERN et al. (1987): Serious corneal complications of glaucoma filtering surgery with postoperative 5-fluorouracil Am. J. Ophthalmol. *103:* 183.

KONDO, M., M. ARAIE (1988): Concentration changes of fluorouracil in the external segment of the eye after subconjunctival injection. Arch. Ophthalmol. *106:* 1718.

KRONFELD, P. C. (1952): The chemical demonstration of transconjunctival passage of aqueous after antiglaucomatous operations. Am. J. Ophthalmol. *35:* (5 pt 2): 38.

LEE, D. A., LEE, T. C., A. E. CORTES et al. (1990): Effects of mithramycin, mitomycin, daunorubicin, and bleomycin on human subconjunctival fibroblast attachment and proliferation. Invest. Ophthalmol. Vis. Sci. *31:* 2136.

PALMER, S. S. (1991): Mitomycin as adjunct chemotherapy with trabeculectomy. Ophthalmology *98:* 317.

RADER, J. E., R. K. II. PARRISH (1991): Update on adjunctive antimetabolites in Glaucoma surgery. Ophthalmol. Clin. North Am. *4:* 861.

REN, J., H. WEI, S. ZENG et al. (1989): Doxorubicin inhibition of subconjunctival fibroblast proliferation and its pharamacokinetics in rabbit eyes. Glaucoma *11:* 152.

RUDERMAN, J. M., D. B. WELCH, M. F. SMITH et al. (1987): A randomized study of 5-fluorouracil and filtration surgery. Am. J. Ophthalmol. *104:* 218.

SKUTA, G. L., R. K. II. PARRISH (1987): Wound healing in glaucoma filtering surgery. Surv. Ophthalmol. *32:* 149.

TAHERY, M. M., D. A. LEE (1989): Review: Pharmacologic control of wound healing in glaucoma filtration surgery. J. Ocular. Pharmacol. *5:* 155.

TANIGUCHI, T., Y. KITAZAWA, U. SHIMIZU (1989): Long-term results of 5-fluorouracil trabeculectomy for primary open-angle glaucoma. Int. Ophthalmol. *13:* 145.

TENG, C. C., H. H. CHI, H. M. KATZIN (1959): Histology and mechanism of filtering operations. Am. J. Ophthalmol. *47:* 16.

WEISS, A. J., L. G. JACKSON, R. CARABASI (1961): An evaluation of 5-fluorouracil in malignant disease. Ann. Intern. Med. *55:* 731.

YAMAMOTO, T., J. VARANI, H. SOONG et al. (1990): Effects of 5-fluorouracil and mitomycin C on cultured rabbit subconjunctival fibroblasts. Ophthalmology *97:* 1204.